NELSON·GCSE
MATHS

INTERMEDIATE 1

BARBARA BALL·DEREK BALL – SERIES EDITORS
CHRISTINE ATKINSON·WENDY FISHER·MARGARET POSTON
JEREMY RICHARDSON·ADRIAN SMITH

Thomas Nelson & Sons Ltd
Nelson House
Mayfield Road
Walton-on-Thames
Surrey KT12 5PL
United Kingdom

First published by Thomas Nelson & Sons Ltd 1998
ISBN   0-17-431483-3
9 8 7 6 5 4 3 2
02 01 00 99

Printed in China by L Rex Printing Co. Ltd

Acquisition: Jean Carnall
Editorial: Jenny Lawson, First Class Publishing
Production: Alison Ealden, Liz Carr
Design: Sharon Rudd
Cover design: R&B Creative Services

The authors and publishers are grateful to the following schools involved in trials of material
from this series:

Worle School, Avon; Holte School, Birmingham; The Woodrush School, Birmingham;
Hayle Community College, Cornwall; Ash Green School, Coventry; Stainburn School, Cumbria;
The Deanes School, Essex; Pontllanfraith High School, Gwent; The Hayling School, Hants;
Swakeleys School, Hillingdon; Crown Hills Community College, Leicester; Hampstead School,
London; St Martin's in the Fields High School, London; Kenton School, Newcastle upon Tyne;
Walbottle High School, Newcastle upon Tyne; Belfast Royal Academy, Northern Ireland;
The Bluecoat School, Nottingham; Bretton Woods School, Peterborough; Eccles C of E School,
Salford; Our Lady of Mount Carmel High School, Salford; Ludlow C of E School, Salop;
St Richard Gwyn R.C. High School, South Glam; Headlands School, Wilts.

Some of the revision questions on pages 271–291 have been reproduced from past examination
papers, as cited in the text. Copyright in these questions is held by the examination boards, and the
publishers would like to thank the Midland Examining Group (MEG), Northern Examinations and
Assessment Board (NEAB), Northern Ireland Council for the Curriculum, Examinations and
Assessment (CCEA), Southern Examining Group (SEG) and Edexcel (formerly University of London
Examinations and Assessment Council, ULEAC) for permission to reproduce this material.
The answers supplied to these questions are, however, the responsibility of the authors.

Map p 148 ©Crown copyright License No. MC87815M0001.
Maps pages 149, 150 from *Good Walks Guide* ©1990 Which? Books.

While every effort has been made to trace copyright holders, if any acknowlegements have been
inadvertently omitted, the publishers will be pleased to make the necessary arrangements at the
earliest opportunity.

CONTENTS

1

NUMBERS

- place value in whole numbers and decimals

- multiples, factors and primes

- ordering decimals

- mental methods of calculating with decimals

- equivalence between decimals, fractions and percentages

- calculating fractional and percentage parts

- rounding whole numbers and decimals using decimal places and significant figures

- expressing numbers in standard form.

Place value in whole numbers

DISCUSSION POINT
- These are all correct calculations.
- How do they work?
- How can you tell that the . is not always being used as a decimal marker?
- What do the symbols stand for?
- Where do you still see numbers like X and V, and MCMLXXIV nowadays? What do they mean?
- What did the Romans mean by LX and XL?

III + ᴄI = ᴄIIII

X + L = LX

L – X = XL

5.3 + 2.11 = 8.2

4.3 + 6.6 = 11.2

6.80 + 7.95 = 14.75

⌣ + ⌣ + ⌣ = 1

βⁱ + βⁱ = α or one

Gradually all of Europe adopted what had developed in India and Arabia – a number system where only the digits 1, 2, 3, 4, 5, 6, 7, 8, 9 and 0 are used and *position* matters.

For example, 2134 and 2314 are *different,* although the *same* digits are used.

1 Use the digits 2, 5 and 9 to make 3-digit numbers.

Use each of them once.

(**a**) Write all the numbers you can make.

(**b**) List them in order of size, starting with the smallest.

2 Use the digits 2 and 6 to make 3-digit numbers.

One number you can make is 262.

Another is 222.

(**a**) Write down all the numbers you can make.

(**b**) List them in order of size, starting with the smallest.

3 (**a**) In each of these, replace each star by one of the digits 3, 5 or 8.
You can only use each digit once in each part.
Try to make your answers as *large* as possible.

(**i**) * * + *   (**ii**) ** – *   (**iii**) ** × *

(**iv**) * × * + *   (**v**) * × * – *

(**b**) This time, try to make your answers as *small* as possible (but still positive).

4 (**a**) In each of these, replace each star by one of the digits 2, 4, 5 or 9.
You can only use each digit once in each part.
Try to make your answers as *large* as possible.

(**i**) * * * + *   (**ii**) * * + * *   (**iii**) * * + * + *

(**iv**) * * * – *   (**v**) * * – * *   (**vi**) * * – * – *

(**vii**) * × * + * + *   (**viii**) * × * – * *   (**ix**) * * × * *

(**b**) This time, try to make your answers as *small* as possible.

5 In this sum, four 3s and two + signs are used to make 39.

33 + 3 + 3 = 39

(**a**) Use five 2s and + signs to make 28.

(**b**) Use eight 8s and + signs to make 1000.

6 Use five 1s and a – sign to make 100.

7 Use each of 1, 2, 3, 4, 5, 6, 7, 8 and 9 once, and + and – signs to make 100.

222

Choose any three different digits (e.g. 2, 4 and 7).

♦ Write down all the 3-digit numbers you can make from them, e.g. 247, 742. Do not repeat any digit.

♦ Add up all your numbers and divide by the sum of your digits, 13.
  2 + 4 + 7 = 13

♦ Repeat this for several sets of three different digits. What do you notice? Can you explain why this happens?

You can extend your work in various ways. Here are some of them.

♦ What happens if two of your digits are the same, or if *all* your digits are the same, e.g. if you choose 4, 4 and 7 or 4, 4 and 4?

♦ What happens if you make numbers from *two* digits instead of from *three*, e.g. from 4 and 7?

♦ What happens if you choose more than three digits?

Multiples, factors and primes

> If you multiply a whole number by 6, the answer is a **multiple** of 6.
> 12, 24, 42 and 60 are all multiples of 6.
> 5, 15, 40, 50 and 100 are all multiples of 5.
> 7, 14, 28, 42, 63 and 77 are all multiples of 7.

EXERCISE 2

1 Here are the beginnings of lists of multiples of 4 and 8.

4, 8, 12, ...
8, 16, 24, ...

(a) What is the 8th number in the list of multiples of 4?

(b) What is the 9th number in the list of multiples of 8?

(c) What is the 13th multiple of 4?

(d) What is the 37th multiple of 8?

(e) The third multiple of 8 is the same as the 6th multiple of 4.

  (i)   Which multiple of 4 is the same as the 5th multiple of 8?

  (ii) Which multiple of 8 is the same as the 14th multiple of 4?

  (iii) Which multiple of 4 is the same as the 42nd multiple of 8?

2 (a) Write down the first 12 multiples of 9.

(b) What is the 23rd multiple of 9?

(c) Which multiple of 6 is the same as the 4th multiple of 9?

(d) Which multiple of 9 is the same as the 12th multiple of 6?

(e) Which multiple of 6 is the same as the 20th multiple of 9?

3 (a) Write down *all* the multiples of 4 which are less than 100.

(b) Write down what you notice about the last digit of each of the numbers in part (a).

(c) Look at numbers in part (a) where the last digit is 0, 4 or 8. Write down what you notice about the other digit.

(d) Look at the numbers in part (a) where the last digit is 2 or 6. Write down what you notice about the other digit.

(e) Which of these numbers is a multiple of 4?

> A number is a multiple of 4 if the last two digits are a multiple of 4.

1789   312   207   552   414   120   276   3788

4 (a) Write down *all* the multiples of 9 which are less than 100.

(b) Add up the digits of each of the numbers in part (a). What do you notice?

(c) Which of these numbers are multiples of 9?

900   666   1341   234   180   511   345   8388

5 (a) Write down *all* the multiples of 3 which are less than 40.

(b) Add up the digits of each of the numbers in part (a). What do you notice?

(c) Which of these numbers are multiples of 3?

72   69   555   83   358   274   642   144

6 (a) Write down all the multiples of 7 which are less than 40.

(b) There is no easy way of finding whether a number is a multiple of 7. Divide by 7 to find out which of these numbers is a multiple of 7.

91   445   728   154   1001   243   882   343

7 (a) Write down some multiples of 6. Find a rule to help you to decide whether a number is a multiple of 6.

(b) What rule can help you to decide whether a number is a multiple of 100?

(c) Find a rule to help you to decide whether a number is a multiple of these numbers.

(i) 50   (ii) 40   (iii) 15

8 Each of these lists is part of the list of the multiples of a number. (Some of the digits have been replaced by stars.)

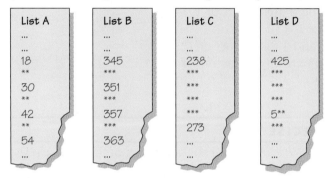

List A	List B	List C	List D
...	...	...	...
...	...	...	...
18	345	238	425
**	***	***	***
30	351	***	***
**	***	***	***
42	357	***	5**
**	***	***	***
54	363	273	...
...	...	...	...

Copy each list and complete them by replacing the stars in each list.

9 Each of these lists is part of the list of the multiples of a number bigger than 1. Some of the digits have been replaced by stars.

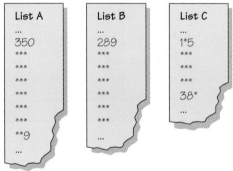

List A	List B	List C
...	...	...
350	289	1*5
***	***	***
***	***	***
***	***	***
***	***	38*
***	***	...
***	***	
**9	...	
...		

Copy each list and complete them by replacing the stars in each list.

10 This list is part of the list of multiples of a number bigger than 1.

Copy this list and complete it by replacing the stars in the list.
There is more than one possible answer – find them all.

```
...
***
***
***
667
***

...
```

Factors

These are *all* the different rectangles that can be made from 12 squares.

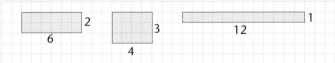

$6 \times 2 = 12$
6 and 2 are called **factors** of 12.
$4 \times 3 = 12$
4 and 3 are factors of 12.
$12 \times 1 = 12$
12 and 1 are factors of 12.
Here are *all* the factors of 12: 1, 2, 3, 4, 6, 12.

 ## EXERCISE 3

1 Here is part of a table to show the factors of all numbers from 1 to 30.
Only the first few, and the last few, rows are shown here.

Number	Factors	Number of factors
1	1	1
2		
3		
4	1, 2, 4	3
5	1, 5	2
...	...	...
29		
30		

(a) The last column shows how many factors each number has.
The rows for 1, 4 and 5 have been completed for you.
Copy and complete the table.

(b) List all the numbers which have exactly two factors.

(c) Which numbers between 1 and 30 have an *odd* number of factors?

(d) What type of numbers are the numbers you listed in part (c)?

(e) Write down the numbers between 30 and 99 which have an odd
number of factors.

2 Find all the factors of each of these numbers.
(a) 50   (b) 53   (c) 66   (d) 100   (e) 72   (f) 1001

EXERCISE 4

The method used in
Question 1 is called
the **sieve of
Eratosthenes**. It is
a method for finding
prime numbers. A
prime number is a
number which has
only two factors:
itself and 1. All the
numbers you did not
cross out in
Question 1 are prime
numbers.

1 Look at this diagram. It shows the numbers from 1 to 100 in a square grid.

(a) On your copy of Resource Sheet C: *Hundred Square*, cross out the square with number 1.

(b) Put a circle round the number 2 on your 100 square.

(c) Now cross out all the multiples of 2 except 2.

(d) Put a circle round the next number after 2 *which is not crossed out*. This is 3.

(e) Now cross out all the multiples of 3 except 3.

1	2	3	4	5	6	7	8	9	10
11	12	13	14	15	16	17	18	19	20
21	22	23	24	25	26	27	28	29	30
31	32	33	34	35	36	37	38	39	40
41	42	43	44	45	46	47	48	49	50
51	52	53	54	55	56	57	58	59	60
61	62	63	64	65	66	67	68	69	70
71	72	73	74	75	76	77	78	79	80
81	82	83	84	85	86	87	88	89	90
91	92	93	94	95	96	97	98	99	100

(f) Put a circle round the next number *which is not crossed out*.

(g) Now cross out all the multiples of this number except itself.

(h) Keep repeating instructions (f) and (g) until you have finished and all numbers are either circled or crossed out.

2 (a) Write down all the prime numbers which are less than 100.

(b) How many prime numbers are there, which are less than 100?

3 Look again at your answer to Question 1.
Almost all the prime numbers are in just four columns.

(a) Which prime numbers are not in any of these four columns?

(b) Why do four columns have no prime numbers in them?

(c) Why do two columns have only one prime number in each of them?

Making general
statements

4 (a) Copy and complete this way of writing the numbers up to 50 in four columns.

1	2	3	4
5	6	7	8
9	10	11	12
13	14	...	...

(b) Put a circle round each of the prime numbers.

(c) Explain why, except for one number, there are no prime numbers in two of the columns.

(d) If you continued with numbers beyond 50, where would the prime numbers be?

Nelson GCSE Maths   NUMBERS (INTERMEDIATE)

5 (a) Copy and complete this way of writing the numbers up to 50 in six columns.

$$\begin{array}{cccccc} 1 & 2 & 3 & 4 & 5 & 6 \\ 7 & 8 & 9 & 10 & 11 & 12 \\ 13 & 14 & \dots & \dots & \dots & \dots \end{array}$$

(b) Put a circle round each of the prime numbers.

(c) Explain why, except for two numbers, there are no prime numbers in four of the columns.

(d) If you continued with numbers beyond 50, where would the prime numbers be?

6 Explain why each of these numbers is a *not* a prime number.

(a) 300	**(b)** 590	**(c)** 166	**(d)** 235
(e) 87	**(f)** 49	**(g)** 11121	**(h)** 2000 001

DISCUSSION POINT

Discuss how you could find out if a number *is* a prime number.
You have to make sure that no other prime number is a factor of it.
Use a calculator to find out which of these numbers *are* prime numbers.

119   179   139   169   149

Prime factors

The number 24 has eight factors. These are 1, 2, 3, 4, 6, 8, 12 and 24.
24 can be written as the product of some of its factors in many different ways. For example:

$24 = 4 \times 6$
$24 = 8 \times 3$
$24 = 4 \times 2 \times 3$
$24 = 12 \times 2 \times 1 \times 1$

Two of the factors of 24 are **prime factors** (factors which are prime numbers). These are 2 and 3.

24 can be written as the **product of prime factors** in only one way (apart from order).

$24 = 2 \times 2 \times 2 \times 3.$

This can be shortened using index notation.
$24 = 2^3 \times 3$

Do as much of this
exercise as you
can without a
calculator.

EXERCISE 5

1 Write each of these numbers as a product of prime factors, using index
notation where you need to.

   (a) 12   (b) 50   (c) 9   (d) 8

   (e) 75   (f) 35   (g) 32   (h) 53

   (i) 144   (j) 1001   (k) 1111   (l) 111 111

2 (a) Write the numbers 72 and 126 as a product of their prime factors.

   (b) Use your answer to part (a) to find the *largest* number which is a factor
   of both 72 and 126. This is called their **highest common factor**.

   (c) Use your answer to part (a) to find the *smallest* number which both 72
   and 126 will divide into. This is called their **lowest common multiple**.

3 (a) Write the numbers 375 and 600 as the product of prime factors.

   (b) Find the highest common factor of 375 and 600.

   (c) Find the lowest common multiple of 375 and 600.

Decimals

This scale has two numbers marked on it.
The space between these numbers is divided
into five sections.

So, the other division marks can be labelled
like this.

DISCUSSION POINT
What numbers are needed to mark the divisions on these number lines?

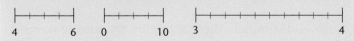

EXERCISE 6

1 Copy these diagrams. Put numbers on all the division marks.

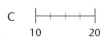

2 Copy these diagrams. Put numbers on all the division marks.

A |————————————————|
   6   7

B |————————————————|
   22   23

C |————————|
   5   6

D |————————————————|
   10   12

E |————————|
   2   4

F |————————————————|
   0   1

G |————————————————|
   0   4

H |————————|
   4   5

DISCUSSION POINT

What numbers are needed to mark the divisions on this number line?

4.3   4.4

Squared paper may be useful for this exercise.

EXERCISE 7

1 Copy and complete these diagrams, by putting numbers on all the division marks.

A |————————————————|
   6.2   6.3

B |————————————————|
   7   7.1

C |————————————————|
   29.9   30

D |————————————————|
   0.3   0.4

2 Copy and complete these diagrams, by putting numbers on all the division marks.

A   4.2   4.3

B   3   3.1   C   4.9   5

D   0   0.1

3 Copy and complete these diagrams, by putting numbers on all the division marks.

A   2.4   2.6

B   1.8   2

C   12   12.2

D   4.4   4.6

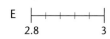
E   2.8   3

F   3.2   3.6

Nelson GCSE Maths   NUMBERS (INTERMEDIATE)

4 Copy and complete these diagrams, by putting numbers on all the division marks.

A
0   0.2

B
4.4   4.6

C
2.4   2.5

D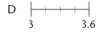
3   3.6

5 Copy and complete these diagrams, by putting numbers on all the division marks.

A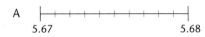
5.67   5.68

B
3.1   3.11

C
2.99   3

D
10   10.01

6 Copy and complete these diagrams, by putting numbers on all the division marks.

A
0   0.02

B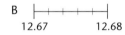
12.67   12.68

C
3.34   3.36

D
0.98   1

7 Copy and complete these diagrams, by putting numbers on all the division marks.

A
−1   0

B
−2   0

C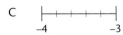
−4   −3

D
−1   1

EXERCISE 8

1 Arrange these numbers in order of size, starting with the smallest.

3.2   3.09   31.0   0.31   3.1   3.16   31.1   0.319   0.33   3.301

2 Arrange these numbers in order of size, starting with the smallest.

10   10.11   0.11   10.01   11.01   11.1   11.11   0.111   1.11   1.01

3 Arrange these numbers in order of size, starting with the smallest.

0.4   0.8   0.12   0.16   0.2   0.24   0.28   0.32   0.36   0.44

4 Arrange these numbers in order of size, starting with the smallest.

2.5   2.65   2.45   20.5   20   2.255   2.05   20.225   2.525   2.25

5 What does the digit 3 stand for in each of these numbers?

(a) 5.3   (b) 53.2   (c) 0.53   (d) 0.0532   (e) 0.000 532

DISCUSSION POINT
Discuss how you would work out these sums.

$35 \times 10 = 350$ $6.14 \times 10 = 61.4$

$24 \times 100 = 2400$ $5.1732 \times 100 = 517.32$

$50 \times 1000 = 50\,000$ $6.14 \times 1000 = 6140$

$6.004 \times 10 = 60.04$ $3460 \div 100 = 34.6$

$550 \div 10 = 55$ $48.3 \div 1000 = 0.0483$

 ## EXERCISE 9

1 Write down answers for these multiplications.

(a) 16×10 (b) 5.12×10 (c) 16.02×10 (d) 0.0403×10

2 Write down answers for these multiplications.

(a) 78×100 (b) 7.8×100 (c) $0.034\,21 \times 100$

3 Write down answers for these multiplications.

(a) 15.73×1000 (b) $0.106\,32 \times 1000$

4 Write down answers for these divisions.

(a) $150 \div 10$ (b) $63 \div 10$ (c) $2432 \div 10$

(d) $14.1 \div 10$ (e) $0.043 \div 10$

5 Write down answers for these divisions.

    (a) 6000 ÷ 100   (b) 420 ÷ 1000   (c) 6.3 ÷ 100

    (d) 0.0762 ÷ 100   (e) 0.603 ÷ 1000

6 Write down the next four numbers in each of these sequences.

    (a) 7000, 700, 70, ...   (b) 15 000, 1500, 150, ...

    (c) 5200, 520, 52, ...   (d) 30 400, 3040, 304, ...

7 Write down the numbers that are 100 times the size of each of these numbers.

    (a) 5   (b) 0.2   (c) 1.6

    (d) 0.34   (e) 0.02   (f) 0.034

8 Copy and complete these, replacing the **?** by a number.

    (a) 3.2 × 10 = ?   (b) 0.4 × 100 = ?   (c) ? × 10 = 6.7

    (d) ? × 100 = 53   (e) 8 ÷ 10 = ?   (f) 0.17 ÷ 10 = ?

    (g) ? ÷ 10 = 0.69   (h) ? ÷ 10 = 4.7   (i) 3.6 ÷ ? = 0.036

    (j) 8.8 × ? = 8800

DISCUSSION POINT

Discuss these sums.

7 × 8 = 56   0.7 of 8 = 5.6   0.7 of 0.8 = 0.56

3 × 4 = 12   0.3 × 4 = 1.2   0.3 × 0.04 = 0.012

 ## EXERCISE **10**

1 Write down the answer for each of these multiplications.

    (a) 0.1 × 60   (b) 0.2 × 60   (c) 0.1 × 11   (d) 0.2 × 11

    (e) 0.1 × 3.2   (f) 0.2 × 3.2   (g) 0.1 × 7.4   (h) 0.2 × 7.4

2 Write down the answer for each of these multiplications.

    (a) 0.1 × 0.2   (b) 0.3 × 0.2   (c) 0.1 × 0.3   (d) 0.3 × 0.3

    (e) 0.1 × 0.9   (f) 0.3 × 0.9   (g) 0.1 × 0.8   (h) 0.3 × 0.8

3 Write down the answer for each of these multiplications.

    (a) 5 × 9   (b) 0.5 × 9   (c) 0.5 × 0.9   (d) 9 × 6

    (e) 0.9 × 6   (f) 0.9 × 0.6   (g) 0.09 × 0.6   (h) 0.09 × 0.06

4 $7 \times 13 = 91$. Write down the answer for each of these multiplications.

(a) 0.7×13 (b) 0.7×1.3 (c) 0.07×1.3

5 $6 \times 54 = 324$. Write down the answer for each of these multiplications.

(a) 0.6×54 (b) 0.6×5.4 (c) 0.06×5.4

Rounding

DISCUSSION POINT

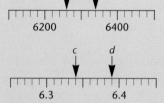

What does *a* point to?
What does *b* point to?

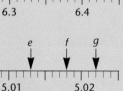

What does *c* point to?
What does *d* point to?

What is each sub-division?
What does *e* point to?
What do *f* and *g* point to?

Decimal places

This number line shows that 6.34 is nearer to 6.3 than to 6.4, but that 6.39 is nearer to 6.4 than to 6.3.

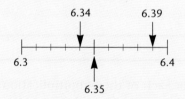

6.34 = 6.3 to the nearest 0.1
6.39 = 6.4 to the nearest 0.1

This is called 'rounding to the nearest 0.1 or **1 decimal place**'.

6.35 is midway between 6.3 and 6.4. Usually 6.35 is rounded up to 6.4 to the nearest 0.1.

This number line shows that 5.013 is nearer to 5.01 than to 5.02, but that 5.018 is nearer to 5.02 than to 5.01.

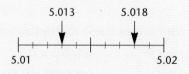

5.013 = 5.01 to the nearest 0.01
or 2 decimal places
5.018 = 5.02 to the nearest 0.01
or 2 decimal places

EXERCISE 11

1 What numbers do these arrows point to?

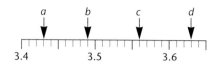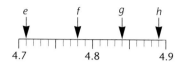

Use the scales in Question 1 to help you to answer Question 2.

2 (a) Is 3.48 nearer to 3.4 or to 3.5?   **(b)** Is 3.53 nearer to 3.5 or to 3.6?

(c) Is 4.76 nearer to 4.7 or to 4.8?   **(d)** Is 13.04 nearer to 13.0 or to 13.1?

The scales in Question 1 may help you in Question 3.

3 In each of these sequences, the numbers go up or down by the same amount each time. Find the next four terms of each sequence.

(a) 3.41, 3.43, 3.45, ...   **(b)** 3.41, 3.44, 3.47, ...

(c) 4.71, 4.76, 4.81, ...   **(d)** 4.91, 4.88, 4.85,4.82, ...

4 Round each of these numbers to the nearest 0.1.

(a) 3.46   **(b)** 3.52   **(c)** 3.58   **(d)** 4.84   **(e)** 13.08

5 What numbers come halfway between these pairs of numbers?

(a) 3.4, 3.5   **(b)** 4.7, 4.8   **(c)** 4.8, 4.9   **(d)** 13.0, 13.1

6 Round each of these numbers to 1 decimal place.

(a) 4.36   **(b)** 5.78   **(c)** 6.72   **(d)** 9.04   **(e)** 0.62

7 (a) A number was written down as '3.5 to the nearest 0.1'. Write down four different numbers that would have rounded to this value.

(b) Write down four different numbers that would have rounded to '4.8 to the nearest 0.1'.

8 (a) What numbers do these arrows point to?

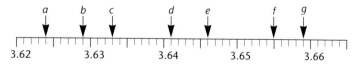

(b) Round these numbers to 2 decimal places.

(i) 3.624   **(ii)** 3.629   **(iii)** 3.637   **(iv)** 3.651   **(v)** 3.678

(c) What numbers come halfway between these pairs of numbers?

(i) 3.62, 3.63   **(ii)** 3.65, 3.66   **(iii)** 4.75, 4.76

9 Round each of these numbers to the nearest 0.01.

(a) 4.732   **(b)** 14.657   **(c)** 3.048   **(d)** 15.725

10 Round each of these numbers to 1 decimal place.

(a) 2.048327   (b) 0.07312   (c) 0.0406   (d) 3.197

11 Round each of these numbers to 2 decimal places.

(a) 2.048327   (b) 0.07312   (c) 0.04061   (d) 3.197

Significant figures

Large numbers like 6129807 also need to be rounded sometimes.
6129807 is 'about 6 million'. That is 'correct to the nearest million' and the approximation uses the most important or **significant** figure.

Significant figures (s.f.) are counted from the left to right starting at the first non-zero digit.

39123 is 40000 to 1 s.f.   0.00234567 is 0.002 to 1 s.f.
39123 is 39000 to 2 s.f.   0.00234567 is 0.00235 corrected to 3 s.f.
39123 is 39100 corrected to 3 s.f.

DISCUSSION POINT

What is the value of these numbers?

0.00345 corrected to 2 d.p.   4.992 corrected to 2 d.p
0.00345 corrected to 2 s.f.   4.992 corrected to 1 d.p.
0.00345 corrected to 1 s.f.   4.992 corrected to 3 s.f.
3964 corrected to 2 s.f.   4.992 corrected to 2 s.f.

EXERCISE 12

1 Round each of these numbers to the nearest thousand.

(a) 28613   (b) 471481   (c) 4036317   (d) 5741   (e) 931

2 Round each of these numbers to the nearest million.

(a) 1524431   (b) 2341650   (c) 2510206   (d) 3496000   (e) 752140

3 Round each of these numbers to 2 significant figures.

(a) 28613   (b) 5741   (c) 56.1471   (d) 0.04061   (e) 0.07995

4 Round each number in Question 3 to 3 significant figures.

5 Which of these numbers would *not* round to 4.62 to 3 significant figures?

(a) 4.6153   (b) 4.62234   (c) 4.614972   (d) 4.624972   (e) 4.6253

6 Which of these numbers would *not* round to 0.40 to 2 significant figures?

(a) 0.3963   (b) 0.3949   (c) 0.395   (d) 0.4032

Fractions

The early users of fractions seem to have used fractions which always had a 1 on the top, e.g.

$\frac{1}{2}$ $\frac{1}{3}$ $\frac{1}{5}$ $\frac{1}{10}$

⏜ was a third in Egyptian hieroglyphic.

β' was a half in Ancient Greek.

They would have come into use when there were things to be *shared out*: money, for example.

Writings show that early users of fractions understood things like $\frac{1}{3}$ of means the same as ÷ 3.

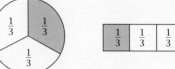

In other words, the whole is divided into 3 equal parts.

DISCUSSION POINT

How do you work out $\frac{2}{3}$ of 60?

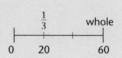

EXERCISE 13

1 Copy and complete each of these diagrams, replacing each ? by a number.

2 Copy and complete each of these diagrams, replacing each ? by a number.

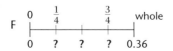

3 What is $\frac{2}{4}$ the same as?

4 Copy and complete each of these diagrams, replacing each **?** by a number.

5 How are $\frac{2}{5}$ and $\frac{4}{5}$ of an amount related?

6 Calculate these amounts.

(a) $\frac{1}{10}$ of 500 and $\frac{7}{10}$ of 500   (b) $\frac{1}{10}$ of 70 and $\frac{3}{10}$ of 70

(c) $\frac{1}{10}$ of 35 and $\frac{4}{10}$ of 35   (d) $\frac{1}{10}$ of 3.4 and $\frac{8}{10}$ of 3.4

(e) $\frac{1}{10}$ of 0.24 and $\frac{5}{10}$ of 0.24   (f) $\frac{1}{10}$ of 0.036 and $\frac{3}{10}$ of 0.036

7 (a) Work out $\frac{2}{5}$ of 45 and $\frac{4}{10}$ of 45. What do you notice?

     (b) Work out $\frac{2}{5}$ of 75 and $\frac{4}{10}$ of 75. What happens?

8 Calculate $\frac{1}{100}$ and $\frac{7}{100}$ of these amounts.

(a) 800   (b) 130   (c) 42   (d) 6.3   (e) 0.74

9 Calculate these amounts.

(a) $\frac{2}{3}$ of 1500   (b) $\frac{3}{4}$ of 240   (c) $\frac{2}{7}$ of 21   (d) $\frac{3}{4}$ of 4500

(e) $\frac{3}{100}$ of 200   (f) $\frac{9}{10}$ of 32   (g) $\frac{2}{3}$ of 4.8   (h) $\frac{3}{4}$ of 0.44

(i) $\frac{2}{5}$ of 0.15   (j) $\frac{3}{100}$ of 12   (k) $\frac{3}{8}$ of 7.2   (l) $\frac{7}{10}$ of 4.8

10 What fraction of 400 are these numbers?

(a) 200   (b) 100   (c) 40   (d) 80

(e) 160   (f) 300   (g) 50   (h) 350

The fractions $\frac{3}{6}$ and $\frac{1}{2}$ are equivalent.

The fractions $\frac{2}{5}$ and $\frac{4}{10}$ are also equivalent.

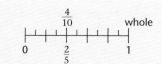

DISCUSSION POINT

Explain how you know that

$\frac{1}{2} = \frac{2}{4}$ $\qquad$ $\frac{1}{3} = \frac{2}{6}$ $\qquad$ $\frac{3}{5} = \frac{6}{10}$

$\frac{4}{12} = \frac{1}{3}$ $\qquad$ $\frac{12}{16} = \frac{3}{4}$ $\qquad$ $\frac{10}{50} = \frac{1}{5}$

Find several fractions which are equivalent to $\frac{1}{2}$.

Find several fractions which are equivalent to these fractions.

$\frac{1}{4}$ $\qquad$ $\frac{2}{3}$ $\qquad$ $\frac{1}{5}$ $\qquad$ $\frac{5}{6}$

EXERCISE 14

1 Copy and complete these equivalent fraction pairs, replacing the ? by a number.

(a) $\frac{1}{2} = \frac{3}{?}$ $\qquad$ (b) $\frac{1}{2} = \frac{?}{8}$ $\qquad$ (c) $\frac{1}{2} = \frac{12}{?}$ $\qquad$ (d) $\frac{1}{3} = \frac{?}{12}$

(e) $\frac{1}{3} = \frac{?}{15}$ $\qquad$ (f) $\frac{1}{3} = \frac{10}{?}$ $\qquad$ (g) $\frac{1}{3} = \frac{?}{42}$ $\qquad$ (h) $\frac{3}{4} = \frac{?}{12}$

(i) $\frac{3}{4} = \frac{?}{20}$ $\qquad$ (j) $\frac{3}{4} = \frac{?}{100}$ $\qquad$ (k) $\frac{3}{4} = \frac{150}{?}$ $\qquad$ (l) $\frac{3}{4} = \frac{330}{?}$

(m) $\frac{4}{5} = \frac{?}{20}$ $\qquad$ (n) $\frac{4}{5} = \frac{80}{?}$ $\qquad$ (o) $\frac{4}{5} = \frac{36}{?}$ $\qquad$ (p) $\frac{4}{5} = \frac{?}{50}$

2 In this group of fractions, there are three families of equivalent fractions and one odd one out. Find each family and the odd one out.

$\frac{2}{3}$ $\quad$ $\frac{1}{4}$ $\quad$ $\frac{24}{36}$ $\quad$ $\frac{10}{35}$ $\quad$ $\frac{24}{84}$ $\quad$ $\frac{5}{20}$ $\quad$ $\frac{16}{24}$

$\frac{6}{9}$ $\quad$ $\frac{3}{12}$ $\quad$ $\frac{2}{7}$ $\quad$ $\frac{4}{6}$ $\quad$ $\frac{9}{12}$ $\quad$ $\frac{10}{15}$ $\quad$ $\frac{4}{14}$

$\frac{16}{56}$ $\quad$ $\frac{25}{100}$

Fractions and decimals

The relationship between fractions and decimals can be shown using a number line.

Fractions can be converted to decimals by using division.

$\frac{5}{16} = 5 \div 16 = 0.3125$ $\qquad$ $\frac{4}{7} = 4 \div 7 = 0.571$ to three decimal places

Decimals can be converted to fractions by using place value.

$0.45 = \frac{45}{100} = \frac{9}{20}$ $\qquad$ $0.636 = \frac{636}{1000} = \frac{59}{250}$

EXERCISE 15

1 (a) Copy and complete these diagrams, by marking all the divisions of both diagrams with fractions and decimals.

(b) Write $\frac{3}{10}$ as a decimal. **(c)** Write $\frac{4}{5}$ as a decimal.

(d) Write 0.7 as a fraction. **(e)** Write 0.4 as a fraction.

2 (a) Copy and complete these diagrams, by marking all the divisions of both diagrams with fractions and decimals.

(b) Write $\frac{1}{2}$ as a decimal. **(c)** Write $\frac{3}{8}$ as a decimal.

(d) Write 0.25 as a fraction. **(e)** Write 0.875 as a fraction.

3 Copy and complete these diagrams, by marking all the divisions of each diagram with both fractions and decimals.

4 (a) Copy and complete these diagrams, by marking all the divisions of each diagram with both fractions and decimals.

(b) Write these numbers as decimals.

  (i) $2\frac{3}{8}$ **(ii)** $3\frac{1}{4}$ **(iii)** $12\frac{3}{5}$ **(iv)** $1\frac{1}{5}$

(c) Write these numbers as fractions.

  (i) 3.75 **(ii)** 12.4 **(iii)** 0.4 **(iv)** 2.625

  (v) 1.6 **(vi)** 2.875 **(vii)** 12.8 **(viii)** 0.8

5 Write these fractions as decimals.

(a) $\frac{1}{8}$ (b) $\frac{7}{20}$ (c) $\frac{7}{16}$ (d) $\frac{9}{25}$

(e) $3\frac{5}{8}$ (f) $7\frac{11}{40}$ (g) $16\frac{13}{16}$ (h) $9\frac{73}{80}$

6 Write each of these fractions as a decimal, correct to three decimal places.

(a) $\frac{2}{3}$ (b) $\frac{5}{11}$ (c) $\frac{4}{7}$ (d) $\frac{11}{13}$

(e) $\frac{27}{29}$ (f) $4\frac{1}{3}$ (g) $7\frac{1}{7}$ (h) $99\frac{16}{17}$

7 Write these decimals as fractions.

(a) 0.37 (b) 0.84 (c) 0.25 (d) 0.999

(e) 0.002 (f) 0.255 (g) 0.625 (h) 0.0007

Percentages, decimals and fractions

Percentages of amounts

Per cent means 'out of 100' or 'for every 100'. So, 3% means $\frac{3}{100}$.

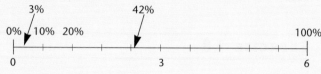

3% of 6 means $\frac{3}{100}$ of 6 = 0.18.   42% of 6 means $\frac{42}{100}$ of 6 = 2.56.

DISCUSSION POINT

How would you work these out? Without a calculator? With a calculator?

15% of 6   8% of 6   32% of 6   47.6% of 6

EXERCISE 16

1 Write these percentages as decimals.

(a) 13% (b) 63% (c) 7% (d) 1% (e) 0.2%

2 Calculate these amounts.

(a) 4% of 200 (b) 7% of 800 (c) 11% of 300

(d) 3% of 140 (e) 5% of 320 (f) 8% of 450

3 Copy and complete these calculations, replacing each ? by a number.

(a) ?% of 400 = 12 (b) ?% of 800 = 72 (c) ?% of 230 = 6.9

EXERCISE 17

Calculate these amounts.

1 (a) 18% of 30   (b) 35% of 600   (c) 87% of 4   (d) 40% of 850

2 (a) 7% of 4340   (b) 3.5% of 80   (c) 15% of 430   (d) 27% of 4300

3 (a) 17.5% of 40   (b) 17.5% of 6.5   (c) 20% of 80   (d) 25% of 44

DISCUSSION POINT

Explain how you know that

$50\% = \frac{1}{2}$ $25\% = \frac{1}{4}$ $20\% = \frac{1}{5}$

$\frac{3}{4} = 75\%$ $\frac{2}{5} = 40\%$ $\frac{1}{3} = 33\frac{1}{3}\%$

EXERCISE 18

1 Convert these percentages to fractions, in their simplest form.

(a) 25%   (b) 40%   (c) 10%   (d) 5%   (e) 8%

2 Convert these fractions to percentages.

(a) $\frac{15}{25}$ (b) $\frac{32}{50}$ (c) $\frac{9}{10}$ (d) $\frac{18}{20}$

3 Some of the fractions, decimals and percentages shown below are equivalent. Find them.

0.3 $\frac{4}{5}$ 35%   5%   0.28   28% $\frac{7}{20}$ 0.8 $\frac{1}{5}$ 8%   80%
20% $\frac{3}{10}$ 0.35 $\frac{7}{25}$ 3% $\frac{1}{20}$ 70%

4 Copy and complete this table.

Amount	Fraction	Decimal	Percentage	Answer
35	$\frac{2}{5}$	0.4	40%	14
84		0.75		
150			70%	
60	$\frac{2}{3}$			
	$\frac{1}{4}$			55
200				120
			15%	45

Some fractions convert to exact percentages. Some do not.

$\frac{1}{4} = 25\%$ So $\frac{1}{4}$ does convert exactly.

$\frac{2}{3} = 66.66...\%$ So $\frac{2}{3}$ does not convert exactly.

How can you tell in advance which fractions will convert to exact percentages?

Standard form: a shorthand for long numbers

During the twentieth century, science has involved working with numbers like these.

2900 000 000 – the distance in kilometres of planet Uranus from the sun 0.000 000 0157 – the diameter in centimetres of a sodium atom.

These two numbers, written in ordinary form, need many digits because the distance to Uranus is very large and the diameter of a sodium atom is very small.

No one wants to write these numbers out in full every time they need to work with them. So, a shorthand way has been internationally adopted, called **standard form** or **standard index form**.

2900000000 could be written as

$2.9 \times 10 \times 10 \times 10 \times 10 \times 10 \times 10 \times 10 \times 10 \times 10$

which shortens to

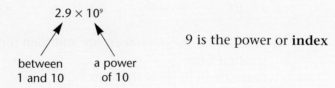

9 is the power or **index**

Small numbers *could* be written using dividing by powers of 10.

$1.57 \div 10^8$ means

$1.57 \div 10 \div 10 \div 10 \div 10 \div 10 \div 10 \div 10 \div 10 = 0.000 000 0157$

But, in standard form, you write

$0.000 000 0157 = 1.57 \times 10^{-8}$

EXERCISE 19

1 Rewrite these numbers so they are *not* in standard form.

(a) 3×10^4 (b) 4.6×10^2 (c) 7.3×10^5 (d) 5.36×10^1

(e) 6.92×10^5 (f) 9.8031×10^6 (g) 4×10^{-2} (h) 3.7×10^{-4}

(i) 5.03×10^{-5} (j) 6.427×10^{-3} (k) 3.104×10^{-6} (l) 8.4621×10^{-1}

2 Convert these numbers to standard form.

(a) 450   (b) 36 000   (c) 6 000 000   (d) 502 000

(e) 4 360 000   (f) 456 030 000   (g) 0.03   (h) 0.000 45

(i) 0.000 4078   (j) 0.020 305   (k) 0.000 004 72   (l) 0.000 000 005 389

3 Think what these numbers are, then put them in order of size with the smallest first.
Leave them in standard form.

3×10^5 5×10^2 2×10^7 8×10^5 6×10^3

4 Think what these numbers are and then put them in order of size with the smallest first.
Leave them in standard form.

4×10^{-5} 6×10^{-2} 3×10^{-7} 9×10^{-5} 7×10^{-3}

5 Write these numbers in order of size with the smallest first.
Leave them in standard form.

5×10^{-4} 6×10^{-7} 3×10^4 2×10^8 9×10^5 7×10^{-5}

6 Write these numbers in order of size with the smallest first.
Leave them in standard form.

3.2×10^6 7.5×10^{-4} 6.8×10^{-3} 9.3×10^4 8.3×10^6

7 Here is some data about planets.

	Earth	Saturn	Mercury	Neptune	Venus	Uranus
Volume (km³)	1.083×10^{12}	9.05×10^{14}	6.02×10^{10}	6.33×10^{13}	9.29×10^{11}	7.46×10^{13}
Mass (tonnes)	5.98×10^{21}	5.69×10^{23}	3.34×10^{20}	1.02×10^{23}	4.9×10^{21}	8.67×10^{22}

(a) Put the planets in order of their size by volume with the smallest first.

(b) Put the planets in order of size by mass with the smallest first.

(c) Which planet has a mass that is about:

    (i) 100 times as big as the Earth's?   (ii) the same as the Earth's?

8 Here is some information about sub-atomic particles.

Name	muon	lambda	positive pion	positive kaon
Life (seconds)	2.20×10^{-6}	2.63×10^{-10}	2.60×10^{-8}	1.24×10^{-8}

(a) Put them in order of life length, with the longest first.

(b) Which particle has a life about a hundred times that of a positive pion?

(c) Which particle has a life about twice that of a positive kaon?

CHAPTER SUMMARY

Types of numbers

Multiples: If you multiply a whole number by 8, the answer is a multiple of 8.
16, 40, 64 and 160 are all multiples of 8.
7, 14, 21, 28, 35 and 42 are the first six multiples of 7.

Factors of a number are those numbers that divide into it exactly.
For example:

- the factors of 6 are 1, 2, 3, 6
- the factors of 20 are 1, 2, 4, 5, 10, 20

Square numbers are 1, 4, 9, 16, 25, ...

A **prime number** does not have any factors except 1 and the number itself.
These are the prime numbers less than 100: 2, 3, 5, 7, 11, 13, 17, 19, 23, 29, 31, 37, 41, 43, 47, 53, 59, 61, 67, 71, 73, 79, 83, 89, 97.

Prime factors are factors which are prime numbers.
Numbers can be written as the product of prime factors. For example:

$$30 = 2 \times 3 \times 5$$
$$36 = 6 \times 6$$
$$ = 2 \times 3 \times 2 \times 3$$
$$ = 2^2 \times 3^2$$

Rounding

Decimal places (d.p.) are counted from the decimal point to the right.

5.674 722 is 5.6747 correct to 4 d.p.

5.674 722 is 5.675 correct to 3 d.p.

5.674 722 is 5.67 correct to 2 d.p.

Significant figures (s.f.) are counted from the left to right, starting at the first non-zero digit.

0.007 754 33 is 0.00775 corrected to 3 s.f.   563 422 is 563 000 corrected to 3 s.f.

0.007 754 33 is 0.008 to 1 s.f.   563 422 is 560 000 to 2 s.f.

563 422 is 600 000 to 1 s.f.

Equivalence between fractions and decimals

These are worth remembering.

Remember that $\frac{a}{b}$ is the same as $a \div b$. So $\frac{7}{8} = 7 \div 8 = 0.875$.

To convert a decimal to a fraction, use place value, and then simplify.

$0.6 = \frac{6}{10} = \frac{3}{5}$

$0.07 = \frac{7}{100}$

$0.375 = \frac{375}{1000} = \frac{3}{8}$

Percentages: 37% is the same as $\frac{37}{100}$ or 0.37.

Standard form

$1.083 \times 10^5 = 1.083 \times 10 \times 10 \times 10 \times 10 \times 10 = 108\,300$

$2.2 \times 10^{-4} \quad = 2.2 \div 10^4 = 2.2 \div 10\,000 = 0.000\,22$

2 GEOMETRICAL PATTERNS

This chapter is about:

- angles between parallel lines and intersecting lines
- triangles and quadrilaterals
- regular polygons
- symmetry
- making and justifying generalisations.

Angles round a point

When there are several angles round a point, the sum of these angles is 360°.

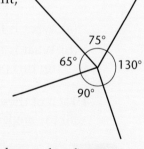

$130° + 90° + 65° + 75° = 360°$

You can use this fact to find the angles in shapes that fit together to form a tessellation. For example:

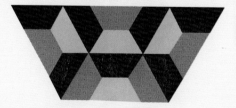

At some points, three angles of the trapezium meet.

All these angles are the same size. So, each of these angles is 120°.

At other points, six angles of the trapezium meet.

All these angles are the same size. So, each of these angles is 60°.

Do not use a protractor for this exercise. All the questions can be answered by using the fact that angles around a point add up to 360°.

EXERCISE 1

1 In this tessellation, all the angles are equal.

(a) What is the size of these equal angles?

(b) What is the name of the shapes making up this pattern?

2 In this tessellation of triangles, all the angles are equal.

(a) What is the size of these equal angles?

(b) These triangles are given a special name. Write down this name and explain what it means.

3 In this tessellation, all the angles are equal.

(a) What is the size of these equal angles?

(b) What is the name of the shapes making up this pattern?

4 Each of these designs is made using just one shape. For each design, find all the angles in the shape.

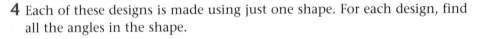

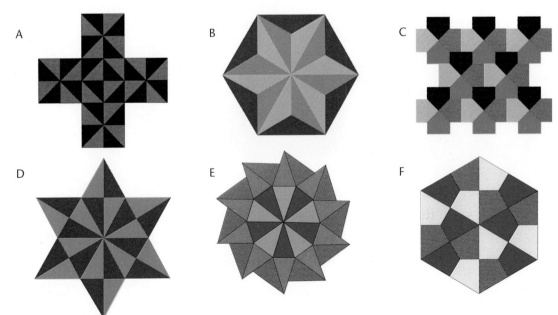

A   B   C

D   E   F

5 Each of these designs is made using two different shapes. In each design, one of the shapes is either a square or an equilateral triangle or a regular hexagon. For each design, find all the angles in each of the two shapes.

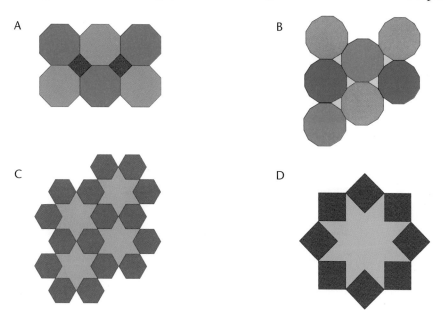

A

B

C

D

Symmetry

These shapes and patterns have **line symmetry**. The **line of symmetry** is shown by a dotted line.

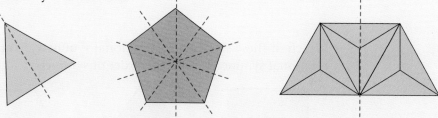

These shapes and patterns have **rotational symmetry**. The **order** of rotational symmetry of a shape is the number of ways it can be fitted into its outline by rotating it.

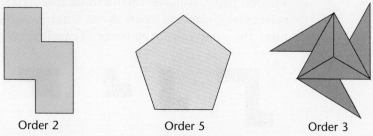

Order 2   Order 5   Order 3

▷ Scissors
▷ Resource Sheet A:
  Isometric dot

1 Which of these shapes have line symmetry?

    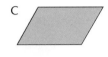

A   B   C   D

2 Each of these designs is made by shading squares. Copy each design on to squared paper. Add *one* square to each design so that the new design has line symmetry. Draw the line of symmetry. For some, there is more than one possible answer. Try to find *all* possible answers.

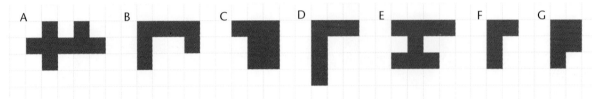

A   B   C   D   E   F   G

3 Copy each of these designs on to isometric paper. Add *one* triangle to each design so that the new design has line symmetry. Draw the line of symmetry on each design. Try to find *all* the answers.

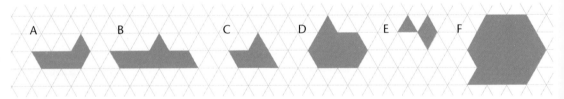

A   B   C   D   E   F

4 Which of these shapes have rotational symmetry? For each shape with rotational symmetry, state the order of symmetry.

A   B   C   D

5 Each of these designs is made by shading squares. Copy each design on to squared paper. Add *one* square to each design so that the new design has rotational symmetry. Write down what the order is. For some, there is more than one possible answer. Try to find *all* possible answers.

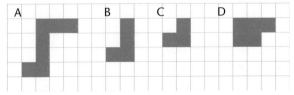

A   B   C   D

6 Copy each of these designs on to isometric paper. Add *one* triangle to each design so that the new design has rotational symmetry. Try to find *all* possible answers.

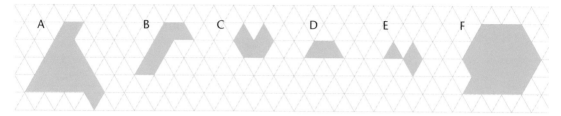

7 Look at these coloured designs.

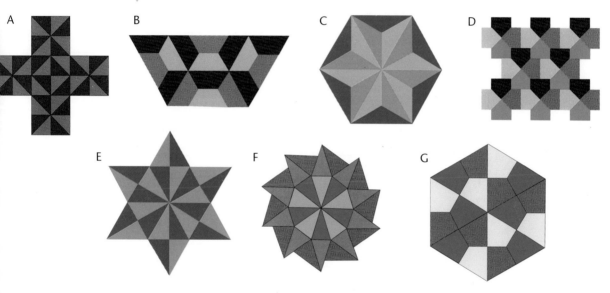

(a) (i) Which of these designs have line symmetry?

(ii) Which of them have line symmetry, if colour is ignored?

(b) (i) Which of these designs have rotational symmetry?
State the order of symmetry.

(ii) Which of these designs have rotational symmetry, if colour is ignored?
State the order of symmetry.

8 Draw a sketch of each of these triangles (*if it is possible*) and mark the lines of symmetry in each of your drawings.

(a) A triangle with no lines of symmetry

(b) A triangle with one line of symmetry

(c) A triangle with two lines of symmetry

(d) A triangle with three lines of symmetry

(e) A triangle with more than three lines of symmetry.

Angles and lines

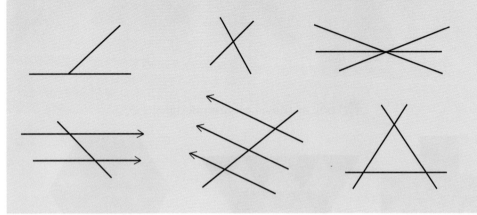

EXERCISE 3

1 Find the size of the angle marked *x* in each of these diagrams.

A

B

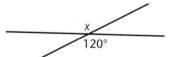

C

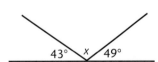

D

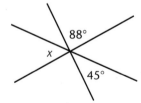

E

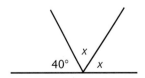

F

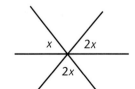

2 Find the size of the angle marked *x* in each of these diagrams.

A
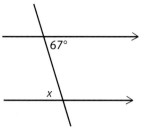
67°

x

B
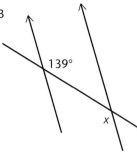
139°

x

C
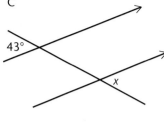
43°

x

D
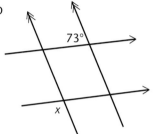
73°

x

E
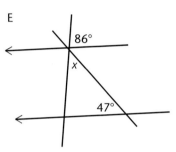
86°

x

47°

F
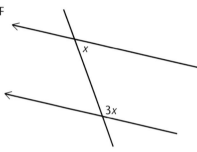
x

3*x*

3 Find the size of the angle marked *x* in each of these diagrams.

A
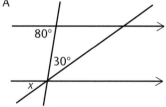
80°

30°

x

B
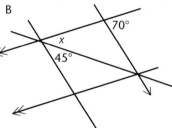
70°

x

45°

C
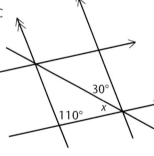
30°

x

110°

D
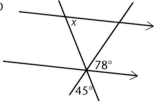
x

78°

45°

E
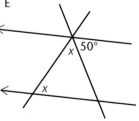
50°

x

x

F
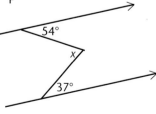
54°

x

37°

Some pairs of angles have special names.

Adjacent angles add up to 180°.

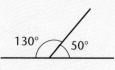

Vertically opposite angles are equal.

Corresponding angles are equal.

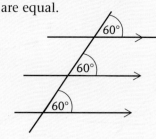

Alternate angles are equal.

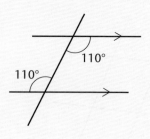

Triangles

▷ Resource Sheet E: *Triangles tessellation*

DISCUSSION POINT

You need a copy of Resource Sheet E: *Triangles tessellation,* which looks like this.

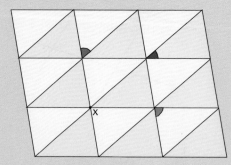

- Mark with red all the angles on the diagram which are the same size as the red angle.

- Mark with blue all the angles on the diagram, the same size as the blue angle. Do the same for the green angles.

- Look at the angles which touch the point marked X. Explain how this shows that the red, blue and green angles add up to 180°.

- Explain how this shows that the sum of the angles of the triangle is 180°.

EXERCISE 4

1 Calculate the size of each angle labelled *x* in these triangles.

A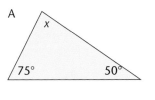

B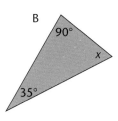

C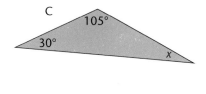

D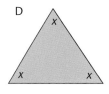

2 Calculate the size of each angle labelled *x* in these isoceles triangles.

In an isosceles triangle, two of the angles are equal.

A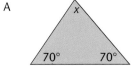

B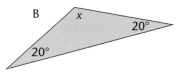

C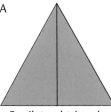

D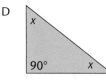

3 Find all the angles of all the triangles in each of these diagrams.

A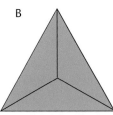

B

C

Equilateral triangle cut in half

Equilateral triangle divided into three equal pieces

Equilateral triangle divided by lines at right angles to sides

Each angle of a regular hexagon is 120°.

D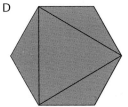

E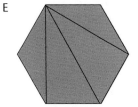

Regular hexagon divided into four triangles

Regular hexagon divided into four triangles

4 This diagram shows a square divided into four triangles. One of the angles in the blue triangle is 30°. The red triangle is isosceles.

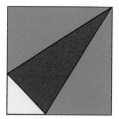

Copy this diagram and work out the sizes of all the angles.

5 A triangle has one line of symmetry. One of its angles is 80°. Find the sizes of the other two angles. (There are two possible answers.)

6 Each of these diagrams consists of four identical isosceles triangles. Calculate the angles in one of the triangles in each diagram.

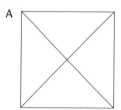

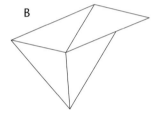

Quadrilaterals

It may be helpful to look at the larger drawings on Resource Sheet D: Special quadrilaterals.

DISCUSSION POINT

A quadrilateral is a polygon with four sides. Several special types of quadrilateral have special names. For each type of quadrilateral, write down what is true for *all* quadrilaterals of this type.

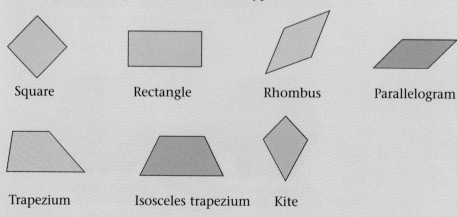

EXERCISE 5

1 A parallelogram has two pairs of parallel sides. How many pairs of parallel sides does each of these shapes have?

(a) Square   (b) Rectangle   (c) Rhombus

(d) Kite   (e) Trapezium

2 Here is a rectangle. Letters have been used to show which sides are equal.

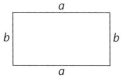

Draw sketches of these shapes, using letters to show which sides are equal.

(a) Square   (b) Parallelogram   (c) Rhombus

(d) Kite   (e) Isosceles trapezium

3 The four angles of a square add up to 360°. Work out what the four angles of each of these shapes add up to.

(a) Rectangle   (b) Parallelogram   (c) Isosceles trapezium

4 (a) Make approximate copies of these three quadrilaterals.

A    B    C

(b) Divide each quadrilateral you have drawn into two triangles.

(c) What is the sum of the angles of each triangle?

(d) What does this tell you about the sum of the angles of any quadrilateral?

5 Here is a parallelogram. Letters have been used to show which angles are equal.

Draw sketches of these shapes, using letters to show which angles are equal.

(a) Rhombus   (b) Kite   (c) Isosceles trapezium

6 A rectangle has two lines of symmetry and rotational symmetry of order 2. This diagram shows the lines of symmetry of a rectangle.

Describe the symmetry of each of these shapes as clearly as you can.

(**a**) Square   (**b**) Rhombus   (**c**) Parallelogram

(**d**) Kite   (**e**) Trapezium   (**f**) Isosceles trapezium

It may be helpful to draw the diagonals on your copy of Resource Sheet D: Special quadrilaterals.

7 Here is a rectangle and its diagonals. Letters have been used to show which angles are equal.

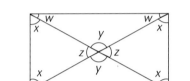

Draw sketches of these shapes and their diagonals, using letters to show which angles are equal.

(**a**) Square   (**b**) Rhombus   (**c**) Parallelogram

(**d**) Kite   (**e**) Trapezium   (**f**) Isosceles trapezium

8 The diagonals of a square are the same length. They cross each other at right-angles and cross at their mid-points.

Copy and complete this table about the diagonals of various quadrilaterals.

	Diagonals		
	same length	cross at right-angles	cross at mid-points
Square	YES	YES	YES
Rectangle			
Rhombus			
Parallelogram			
Kite			
Trapezium			
Isosceles trapezium			

1 Find *x* and *y* for each of these shapes.

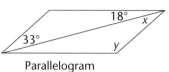

Parallelogram

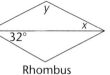

Kite

Rhombus

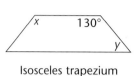

Isosceles trapezium

2 Find the size of the two unmarked angles in this kite.

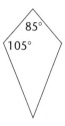

3 ABCD is a rectangle. ∠BCA is 65°. Draw a rough sketch of the diagram and fill in the sizes of the other angles.

4 PQRS is a rhombus. ∠QPR is 30°. Draw a rough sketch of the diagram and fill in the sizes of the missing angles.

5 ABCD is a rhombus. ∠BAC is 37°. Draw a sketch and find the four angles of the rhombus.

6 ABCD is a parallelogram. Find *x*, *y* and *z*.

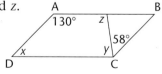

7 ABCD is an isosceles trapezium. ∠BAD is three times the size of ∠ADC. Find the angles of the trapezium.

Polygons

DISCUSSION POINT

Use these drawings to explain what is meant by:

- a regular polygon
- an equilateral polygon
- an equiangular polygon.

Regular hexagon   Equilateral hexagon   Equilangular hexagon

Find out what these words mean.

- Pentagon
- Heptagon
- Octagon
- Nonagon
- Decagon
- Dodecagon

EXERCISE 7

1 Look at these shapes.

A   B   C   D

E   F   G   H

I   J   K   L

Match each shape to this list of names and write down whether the shape is regular.

TRIANGLE   QUADRILATERAL   PENTAGON   HEXAGON

HEPTAGON   OCTAGON   NONAGON   DECAGON

2 If a triangle has all its angles equal, does it have to be a regular polygon?

3 If a quadrilateral has all its angles equal, does it have to be a regular polygon?

4 Which of these words describe a shape which *has to be* a regular polygon?

(**a**) Rectangle   (**b**) Equilateral triangle   (**c**) Hexagon

(**d**) Isosceles triangle   (**e**) Rhombus   (**f**) Square

(**g**) Pentagon

Angles in polygons

Vertex is the name usually used for the corner of a polygon. When there is more than one vertex, they are called **vertices**.

At each vertex of a polygon, there is an **interior angle** and an **exterior angle**.

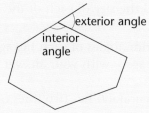

interior angle + exterior angle = 180°

In a regular polygon, all the interior angles are equal to one another, and all the exterior angles are equal to one another.

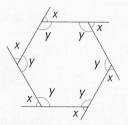

EXERCISE 8

1 Check that you agree with this statement.

Any pentagon can be divided into three triangles.

What is the sum of the interior angles of a pentagon?

2 This design is made using just one shape: a pentagon with line symmetry.

(**a**) Find the size of each of the interior angles of the pentagon.

(**b**) Add up the interior angles of the pentagon. Compare your answer with the answer to Question 1.

3 Divide an irregular hexagon into four triangles.
What is the sum of the interior angles of a hexagon?

4 Each of these diagrams includes a hexagon as one of the shapes used to
make the tessellation.
(The other shapes are squares and equilateral triangles.)

A 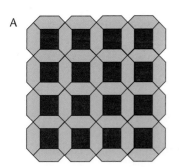   B 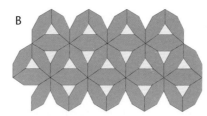   C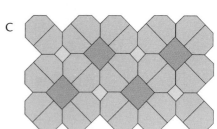

(a) For each tessellation, find the size of each of the interior angles of the
hexagon.

(b) Find the sum of the interior angles of each hexagon.
Check that your answers agree with your answer to Question 3.

5 This hexagon (not drawn accurately) has two lines of symmetry.

One of its interior angles is 140°.
Find the sizes of the other interior angles.

6 Find the sum of the interior angles of these shapes by dividing them into
triangles.

(a) Heptagon   (b) Octagon   (c) Nonagon   (d) Decagon

7 (a) Predict the sum of the interior angles of a dodecagon.

(b) Check your answer to part (a) by dividing the dodecagon into triangles.

8 (a) State a rule which gives the number of triangles into which a polygon
with any number of sides can be divided.

(b) State a rule which gives the sum of the interior angles of any polygon.

*Making and justifying
a generalisation*

DISCUSSION POINT

In a regular polygon, *all* the interior angles are equal. Copy this table, and use your results from Exercise 8 to complete the table.

Shape	No. of sides	Sum of angles	Interior angle	Exterior angle
Equilateral triangle				
Square	4	360°	90°	90°
Regular pentagon				
Regular hexagon	6	720°	120°	60°
Regular heptagon				
Regular octagon				
Regular nonagon				
Regular decagon				

This exercise is about two other ways of finding the interior and exterior angles of a regular polygon.

EXERCISE 9

1 This diagram shows a regular pentagon divided into triangles by joining the vertices to the centre.

(a) Into what type of triangles has the pentagon been divided?

(b) Find the size of one of the angles at the centre.

(c) Work out the size of the other angles in each of the triangles.

(d) Use your answer to part (c) to find the size of an interior angle of a regular pentagon.
Check that your answer agrees with your answer in the discussion point.

2 (a) Use the method of Question 1 to find the size of an interior angle of a regular:

(i) hexagon   (ii) octagon   (iii) nonagon

(b) Check that your answers agree with your answers in the discussion point.

3 Here is another way of finding the size of an interior angle in a regular pentagon.

Imagine a very large regular pentagon and imagine walking round it.

At each vertex, you turn through the same amount (the exterior angle).

By the time you are back at the start, you will have turned through 360° altogether.

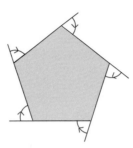

(a) Given that there are five vertices, find the size of the exterior angle at one vertex.

(b) Subtract your answer to (a) from 180° to find the size of an interior angle of a regular pentagon.

4 Use the method of Question 3 to find the size of an interior angle of a regular:

(a) nonagon   (b) decagon   (c) heptagon

5 Imagine a regular polygon with 20 sides.

(a) Imagine that you join each vertex up to the centre of the polygon.

     (i)   How many triangles are there?

     (ii) What are the sizes of the angles in each triangle?

     (iii) What is the interior angle of a regular 20-sided polygon?

     (iv) What is the exterior angle of a regular 20-sided polygon?

(b) Now imagine that you walk round the 20-sided polygon.

     (i)   How many times will you turn?

     (ii) What is your angle of turn each time?

     (iii) What is the exterior angle of a regular 20-sided polygon?

     (iv) What is the interior angle of a regular 20-sided polygon?

6 Repeat Question 5 for a regular polygon with 30 sides.

7 A regular polygon has n sides.
What is the size of each *exterior* angle?
What is the size of each *interior* angle?

Nelson GCSE Maths · GEOMETRICAL PATTERNS (INTERMEDIATE)

1 This diagram shows part of a regular polygon.
O is the centre of the polygon.

(a) How many sides does the polygon have?

(b) What are the interior angles of the polygon?

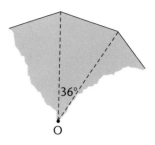

2 ABCDE is a regular pentagon.

(a) Calculate the size of ∠ABE.

(b) Calculate the size of ∠BEC.

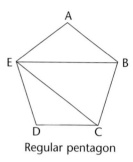

Regular pentagon

3 PQRSTU is a regular hexagon.

(a) Name the shape PRST.

(b) Work out the size of each of the four angles in this shape.

4 Triangle ABC is drawn inside a regular octagon.

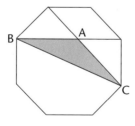

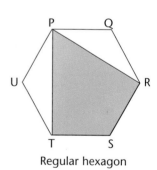

Regular hexagon

Work out the size of each of the angles in triangle ABC.

5 This diagram shows part of a ring of regular pentagons.
The hole in the middle of the ring
is a regular polygon.

(a) Calculate p and q.

(b) How many pentagons are there in the ring?

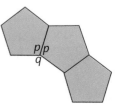

6 The exterior angle of a regular polygon is 24°.
How many sides does the polygon have?

7 The exterior angle of a regular polygon is $2x°$ and the interior angle is $10x°$.

(a) Calculate x.

(b) Find how many sides the polygon has.

8 In an irregular pentagon ABCDE, $\angle B = \angle E = 144°$ and $\angle C = \angle D = 108°$.

(a) Calculate the size of $\angle A$.

(b) Prove that AB is parallel to ED.

(c) Sketch the pentagon ABCDE, given that it has one line of symmetry.
Indicate clearly the pairs of sides of the pentagon which are parallel.

COURSEWORK OPPORTUNITY

Star-shaped tessellations

This diagram shows a tessellation using two different shapes: a regular nonagon and a star shape.

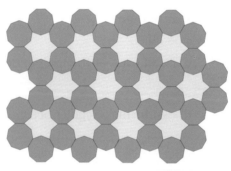

There are several ways in which you could work with this tessellation.

♦ You could make a copy of it using a plastic or cardboard nonagon or using a computer.

♦ You could colour the tessellation systematically.

♦ You could describe the symmetry of the shapes and of the tessellation.

♦ You could find the angles of the shapes and prove that they obey the rules you have discovered in this chapter.

You could also investigate what other tessellations you could make using regular polygons which leave star-shaped holes.

♦ There are other tessellations you can make with regular nonagons and different star-shaped holes.

♦ You can decide what other regular polygons are appropriate to use for this activity. Some work much better than others.

Symmetry

Line symmetry: The dotted lines are lines of symmetry.

 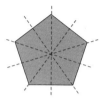 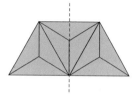

Rotational symmetry: the **order** of rotational symmetry of a shape is the number of ways it can be fitted into its outline by rotating it.

Order 2   Order 5   Order 3

Angles and lines

The sum of the **angles round a point** is 360°.

The sum of **adjacent angles on a straight line** is 180°.

Vertically opposite angles are equal.

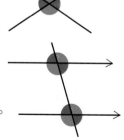

For **parallel lines**:
* all the red angles are equal
* all the blue angles are equal
* the sum of a red angle and a blue angle is 180°

Corresponding angles are equal.

Alternate angles are equal.

Quadrilaterals

Shape	Diagonals			
	same length	cross at right angles	cross at mid-points	bisect angles of quad
Square Regular quadrilateral; all angles right-angles and all sides equal	YES	YES	YES	YES
Rectangle All angles right-angles	YES	NO	YES	NO
Rhombus All sides equal	NO	YES	YES	YES
Parallelogram Opposite sides parallel	NO	NO	YES	NO
Kite Two pairs of adjacent sides equal	NO	YES	NO	NO
Trapezium One pair of opposite sides parallel	NO	NO	NO	NO
Isosceles trapezium Trapezium with non-parallel sides equal	YES	NO	NO	NO

Polygons

A polygon is a shape whose boundary is made up of a number of straight sides.

A **regular polygon** has all its sides equal *and* all its angles equal.

Interior and exterior angles

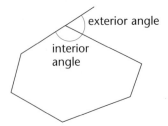

exterior angle

interior angle

At a **vertex**:
interior angle + exterior angle = 180°

Polygon names	Number of sides
Triangle	3
Quadrilateral	4
Pentagon	5
Hexagon	6
Heptagon	7
Octagon	8
Nonagon	9
Decagon	10
Dodecagon	12

In a **regular polygon** with n sides all the **exterior angles** are equal, and are found by dividing 360° by n.

The **sum of the angles of a polygon** can be found by dividing the polygon up into triangles.

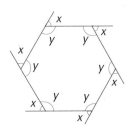

3 FUNCTIONS AND FORMULAE

This chapter is about:

- functions
- inverse operations
- arithmetic without a calculator
- negative numbers
- order of operations
- simplifying algebraic expressions
- substituting into formulae
- developing skills with applying algebra to contexts where it is useful
- making and justifying generalisations.

Using rules with numbers

In a game, one person, whose turn it is, thinks of a rule.

The other people playing the game think of numbers and the person uses the rule on their numbers.

The others have to guess what the rule is.

For the rule 'add 17', the game can be recorded like this.

$30 \rightarrow 47$
$53 \rightarrow 70$

The arrow represents the rule being used in the game.

For this exercise, you will need to be able to do calculations like these, without a calculator.

$36 + 47$
$354 + 278$
$75 - 46$
$472 - 255$

EXERCISE 1

1 In this question, the arrow represents the rule 'add 17'. Copy these, replacing the question mark with a number so that each one follows the rule.

(a) $7 \rightarrow ?$ (b) $285 \rightarrow ?$ (c) $? \rightarrow 100$ (d) $? \rightarrow 17$

2 Make these follow the rule 'add 58'.

(a) $20 \rightarrow ?$ (b) $? \rightarrow 257$ (c) $365 \rightarrow ?$ (d) $? \rightarrow 100$

3 Make these follow the rule 'add 376'.

(a) 87 → ?   (b) 424 → ?   (c) ? → 1000   (d) ? → 904

4 Make these follow the rule 'subtract 38'.

(a) 100 → ?   (b) 1000 → ?   (c) ? → 100   (d) ? → 77

5 Make these follow the rule 'subtract 49'.

(a) 100 → ?   (b) ? → 951   (c) 48 → ?   (d) 0 → ?

6 Make these follow the rule 'subtract 66'.

(a) ? → 34   (b) 1000 → ?   (c) ? → 66   (d) 732 → ?

7 Make these follow the rule 'subtract 347'.

(a) 1000 → ?   (b) ? → 400   (c) 247 → ?   (d) 0 → ?

8 Make these follow the rule 'add 36 and then add 60'.

(a) 100 → ?   (b) 53 → ?   (c) 36 → ?   (d) 60 → ?

9 Make these follow the rule 'add 66 and then subtract 116'.

(a) 73 → ?   (b) 50 → ?   (c) 200 → ?   (d) 449 → ?

10 Make these follow the rule 'subtract 33 and then add 72'.

(a) 17 → ?   (b) 33 → ?   (c) 65 → ?   (d) 361 → ?

EXERCISE 2

For this exercise, you will need to be able to do calculations like these, without a calculator.

7 × 43
29 × 37
96 ÷ 6
989 ÷ 23

1 In this question, the arrow represents the rule 'multiply by 4'.
Copy these, replacing the question mark with a number so that each one follows the rule.

(a) 10 → ?   (b) 99 → ?   (c) ? → 24   (d) ? → 10

2 Make these follow the rule 'multiply by 7'.

(a) 10 → ?   (b) ? → 700   (c) 80 → ?   (d) ? → 630

3 Make these follow the rule 'multiply by 16'.

(a) 100 → ?   (b) ? → 320   (c) 37 → ?   (d) ? → 44

4 Make these follow the rule 'multiply by 37'.

(a) 20 → ?   (b) ? → 3737   (c) 13 → ?   (d) ? → 999

5 Make these follow the rule 'multiply by 120'.

(a) 20 → ?   (b) ? → 3600   (c) ? → 1440   (d) ? → 40

6 Make these follow the rule 'multiply by 243'.

(a) 3 → ?   (b) 60 → ?   (c) ? → 4860   (d) ? → 121.5

7 Make these follow the rule 'divide by 5'.

(a) 35 → ?   (b) ? → 12   (c) 0 → ?   (d) 9 → ?

8 Make these follow the rule 'divide by 6 and then multiply by 3'.

(a) 18 → ?   (b) 42 → ?   (c) 15 → ?   (d) 10 → ?

9 Make these follow the rule 'multiply by 3 and then add 1'.

(a) 3 → ?   (b) 33 → ?   (c) 17 → ?   (d) 300 → ?

10 Make these follow the rule 'multiply by 4 and then subtract 3'.

(a) 7 → ?   (b) 1 → ?   (c) 19 → ?   (d) 200 → ?

DISCUSSION POINT

In a game, the person whose turn it is changes the numbers like this.

4 → 10	1 → 1	10 → 28
9 → 25	100 → 298	12 → 34

What rule is being used?
Make these follow the same rule.

? → 4
? → 22
? → 100
? → 43

Using flowcharts can help when rules involve two operations.
Here, the rule is 'multiply by 2 and add 3'.

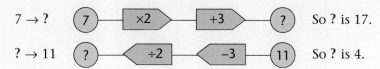

7 → ?   So ? is 17.

? → 11   So ? is 4.

EXERCISE 3

1 In this question, the arrow represents the rule 'multiply by 2 and add 5'. Copy these, replacing the question mark with a number so that each one follows the rule.

(a) $6 \to ?$ (b) $28 \to ?$ (c) $? \to 13$

(d) $? \to 79$ (e) $377 \to ?$ (f) $? \to 95$

2 Make these follow the rule 'multiply by 5 and subtract 2'.

(a) $8 \to ?$ (b) $27 \to ?$ (c) $? \to 3$

(d) $? \to 33$ (e) $60 \to ?$ (f) $? \to 98$

3 Make these follow the rule 'divide by 3 and add 4'.

(a) $9 \to ?$ (b) $42 \to ?$ (c) $? \to 11$

(d) $? \to 24$ (e) $153 \to ?$ (f) $? \to 4$

4 The goes in one game are shown in this box.

$43 \to 134$
$165 \to 256$
$217 \to 308$
$7 \to ?$
$449 \to ?$
$? \to 300$

The arrows represent the rule used in the game.

(a) Decide what the rule is for this game. Write down your rule.

(b) Copy and complete the box, replacing the question mark with a number so that each one follows your rule.

5 Decide what the rule is for these games. For each game, write down your rule. Then, copy and complete the box.

Game A	Game B	Game C	Game D
$6 \to 2$	$7 \to 49$	$4 \to 9$	$20 \to 80$
$60 \to 20$	$10 \to 100$	$1 \to 3$	$1 \to 99$
$99 \to 33$	$4 \to ?$	$100 \to 201$	$5 \to 95$
$21 \to ?$	$1 \to ?$	$17 \to ?$	$7 \to ?$
$96 \to ?$	$? \to 64$	$? \to 17$	$100 \to ?$
$? \to 17$	$? \to 1000000$	$? \to 1$	$? \to 50$

6 Make up your own rules. Write down some number patterns using your rules. Challenge someone else to discover your rules.

Calculating with negative numbers

Adding negative numbers

Example

$(-8) + (-5) = (-13)$

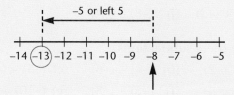

Example

$(-8) + (+12) = (+4)$

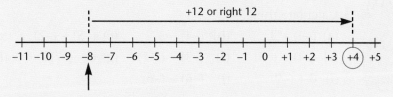

Subtracting negative numbers

Example

$(+63) - (+56) = (+7)$

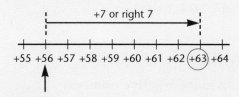

Example

$(-2) - (-8) = (+6)$

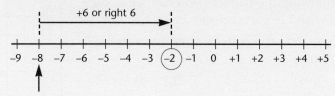

Example

$(-5) - (+3) = (-8)$

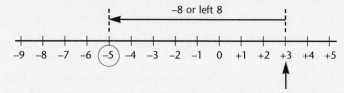

EXERCISE 4

1 Calculate these additions.

(a) (−3) + (+2)   (b) (−4) + (+6)   (c) (−5) + (−1)   (d) (−5) + (+1)

(e) (+6) + (−4)   (f) (+5) + (−8)   (g) (−10) + (+ 7)   (h) (−7) + (+ 10)

(i) (−12) + (−3)   (j) (−8) + (−4)

2 Calculate these subtractions.

(a) (−3) − (+2)   (b) (−4) − (−6)   (c) (−5) − (−1)   (d) (−5) − (+1)

(e) (+6) − (−4)   (f) (+5) − (−8)   (g) (−10) − (− 7)   (h) (−7) − (− 10)

(i) (−12) − (−3)   (j) (−8) − (−4)

3 Calculate these.

(a) (−4) + 3   (b) (−4) − 3   (c) (−5) − (−2)   (d) 6 + (−8)

(e) (−4) + (−5)   (f) (−3) − (− 7)   (g) 6 − (−7)   (h) 0 − (−5)

(i) 0 + (−9)   (j) (−6) − (−6)

> Positive numbers are usually written without the + sign. +3 is written as 3.

4 Calculate these.

(a) 3 − 5   (b) −6 + 3   (c) −5 − 7   (d) 3 − (−5)

(e) −8 − 0   (f) −7 − (−4)   (g) −9 + 12   (h) 3 − 5 − 2

(i) −4 − 5 + 7   (j) −6 + 3 + (−5)

> Negative numbers are often written without brackets. (−5) is written as −5.

DISCUSSION POINT

Multiplying and dividing negative numbers

What numbers are needed to complete this multiplication chart? Make sure you keep following the patterns you can see in each row and in each column.

To extend the pattern, these answers are needed.

$(−3) × (+2) = −6$ $(−4) × (−3) = +12$

$(+3) × (−5) = −15$

x	−4	−3	−2	−1	0	1	2	3	4
−4									
−3									
−2									
−1									
0					0	0	0	0	0
1					0	1	2	3	4
2					0	2	4	6	8
3					0	3	6	9	12
4					0	4	8	16	20

What is the rule for multiplying a positive number by a negative number?

What is the rule for multiplying two negative numbers?

How can you use the chart to answer these questions?

$(+9) ÷ (+3)$ $(−8) ÷ (+4)$ $(−16) ÷ (−4)$ $(+12) ÷ (−3)$

What is the rule for dividing a positive number by a negative number?

What is the rule for dividing two negative numbers?

EXERCISE 5

1 Calculate these multiplications.

(a) $(-3) \times (+2)$　　(b) $(-4) \times (+6)$　　(c) $(-5) \times (-1)$　　(d) $(-5) \times (+1)$

(e) $(+6) \times (-4)$　　(f) $+5 \times -8$　　(g) $-10 \times +7$　　(h) $-7 \times +10$

(i) -12×-3　　(j) -8×-4

Remember, for both multiplication and division:
* if one sign is negative, the answer is negative
* if both signs are negative, the answer is positive.

2 Calculate these divisions.

(a) $(-6) \div (+2)$　　(b) $(-12) \div (-6)$　　(c) $(-5) \div (-1)$　　(d) $(-5) \div (+1)$

(e) $(+16) \div (-4)$　　(f) $+40 \div -8$　　(g) $-21 \div -7$　　(h) $-21 \div -3$

(i) $-12 \div +3$　　(j) $-8 \div -4$

3 Calculate these.

(a) $(-4) \times 3$　　(b) $(-15) \div 3$　　(c) $(-16) \div (-2)$　　(d) $6 \times (-8)$

(e) $(-4) \times (-5)$　　(f) $-28 \div -7$　　(g) 6×-7

(h) $5 \div -5$　　(i) 1×-9　　(j) $-6 \div -6$

Using algebra for functions

In this game, the rule is 'add 17'

$7 \to 24$
$285 \to 302$
$83 \to 100$
$0 \to 17$

This rule can be written as
$n \to n + 17$

Rules like these are sometimes called **functions**.
Now look at this game.

$3 \to 12$
$7 \to 28$
$25 \to 100$
$10 \to 40$

This time the function is 'multiply by 4'. This function can be written as $n \to n \times 4$
But $n \times 4$ is usually shortened to $4n$, so the function is usually written as $n \to 4n$

Now look at this game.

$3 \to 9$
$5 \to 25$
$10 \to 100$
$21 \to 441$

This time the function is 'square the number'.
This function can be written as
$n \to n \times n$
or
$n \to n^2$

EXERCISE 6

1 The function is 'add 58'. Write this function using *n*.

2 Write these functions using *n*.

(a) Subtract 17   (b) Add 6 and then subtract 8

(c) Multiply by 4   (d) Divide by 2

3 The function is 'multiply by 4 and then divide by 2'. Write this function using *n*.

4 Write these functions using *n*.

(a) Multiply by 2 and then add 3   (b) Multiply by 5 and then subtract 4

(c) Divide by 3 and then add 2   (d) Square and then add 1

EXERCISE 7

1 The function is $n \rightarrow 3n + 1$. Copy and complete this box.

$$n \rightarrow 3n + 1$$
$$6 \rightarrow ?$$
$$23 \rightarrow ?$$
$$? \rightarrow 100$$
$$? \rightarrow 1$$

$3n^2$ means $3 \times n^2$. Square the number and then multiply by 3.

2 Copy and complete these boxes.

$$n \rightarrow 4n - 3$$
$$4 \rightarrow ?$$
$$7 \rightarrow ?$$
$$? \rightarrow 17$$
$$? \rightarrow 97$$

$$n \rightarrow \tfrac{1}{2}n + 1$$
$$12 \rightarrow ?$$
$$50 \rightarrow ?$$
$$? \rightarrow 50$$
$$? \rightarrow 1$$

$$n \rightarrow 3n^2$$
$$5 \rightarrow ?$$
$$12 \rightarrow ?$$
$$? \rightarrow 300$$
$$? \rightarrow 507$$

3 Copy and complete these boxes.

$$n \rightarrow n^2 - 1$$
$$3 \rightarrow ?$$
$$20 \rightarrow ?$$
$$? \rightarrow 80$$
$$? \rightarrow 440$$

$$n \rightarrow n^2 + n$$
$$6 \rightarrow ?$$
$$23 \rightarrow ?$$
$$? \rightarrow 30$$
$$? \rightarrow 110$$

$$n \rightarrow n^2 - 3n$$
$$5 \rightarrow ?$$
$$2 \rightarrow ?$$
$$? \rightarrow 18$$
$$? \rightarrow 0$$

4 Copy and complete these boxes.

$n \to n^2 - 2n + 1$	$n \to n^2 + n + 5$	$n \to 4n^2 + 4n$
$3 \to ?$	$3 \to ?$	$10 \to ?$
$10 \to ?$	$7 \to ?$	$7 \to ?$
$? \to 25$	$? \to 25$	$? \to 80$
$? \to 100$	$? \to 137$	$? \to 120$

This exercise is about writing functions more simply.

EXERCISE 8

1 The function for this box is $n \to 3n + 2 + 4$.

    (a) Copy and complete the box.

    (b) What is a simpler way of writing this function?

$n \to 3n + 2 + 4$
$8 \to ?$
$23 \to ?$
$0 \to ?$

2 Copy and complete these boxes, and write each function in a simpler way.

$n \to 5n + 2 - 3$	$n \to 5n - 3n$	$n \to 4n - 5n + 3n$
$8 \to ?$	$6 \to ?$	$10 \to ?$
$20 \to ?$	$10 \to ?$	$32 \to ?$
$1 \to ?$	$13 \to ?$	$1 \to ?$
$n \to$	$n \to$	$n \to$

3 Copy and complete these boxes, and write each function in a simpler way.

$n \to 2n - 5n$	$n \to n^2 + 2n + n$	$n \to 2n^2 - n^2 - 1$
$10 \to ?$	$10 \to ?$	$3 \to ?$
$15 \to ?$	$20 \to ?$	$5 \to ?$
$1 \to ?$	$0 \to ?$	$10 \to ?$
$n \to$		$n \to$

4 Copy and complete these boxes, and write each function in a simpler way.

$n \to 3n \times 2$	$n \to 8n \div 2$
$4 \to ?$	$6 \to ?$
$7 \to ?$	$9 \to ?$
$20 \to ?$	$100 \to ?$
$n \to$	$n \to$

5 Write these functions in simpler ways. You can try them out on some numbers if you want to.

(a) $n \to 2n + 1 + n + 1$

(b) $n \to 3n - 2n + 4$

(c) $n \to n + 100 - 2n$

(d) $n \to 2n - 4 - n + 2$

(e) $n \to 3n - 3 - 4n + 5 + 3n$

(f) $n \to n^2 + n + 2n^2$

(g) $n \to n^2 + n - 2n$

(h) $n \to n^2 + 2 + 2n^2$

(i) $n \to 3n^2 + n + 2n^2 - 3n$

(j) $n \to 4n \times 3$

(k) $n \to 12n \div 6$

(l) $n \to 4n \div 8$

Using algebra to solve problems

DISCUSSION POINT

Here is a grid containing the numbers 1 to 100. Look at the grid through the 3-by-2 window.

What is the smallest number in the window?

What is the biggest number?

1	2	3	4	5	6	7	8	9	10
11	12	13	14	15	16	17	18	19	20
21	22	23	24	25	26	27	28	29	30
31	32	33	34	35	36	37	38	39	40
41	42	43	44	45	46	47	48	49	50
51	52	53	54	55	56	57	58	59	60
61	62	63	64	65	66	67	68	69	70
71	72	73	74	75	76	77	78	79	80
81	82	83	84	85	86	87	88	89	90
91	92	93	94	95	96	97	98	99	100

Imagine moving the window, so that the smallest number in the window is 23.

What is the biggest number now?

Imaging moving the window, so that the smallest number in the window is 88.

What is the biggest number now?

Without looking at the grid, can you write down what the biggest number is, if the smallest number is 34?

What is the biggest number in the window, if the smallest number is n?
What is the smallest number in the window, if the biggest number is 93?
What is the smallest number in the window, if the biggest number is p?

Suppose you call the smallest number in a 3-by-2 window n, and call the biggest number p.

p can be written in terms of n.

$$p = n + 12$$

Look at the window on the grid and explain *why* $p = n + 12$.

EXERCISE 9

1 Look at the grid through this 4-by-3 window.

(a) What is the smallest number in the window?
What is the biggest number?

(b) The window is moved.
Now the smallest number in the window is 43.
What is the biggest number?

(c) Suppose the smallest number in the window is n and the biggest number is p.
Write p in terms of n.

1	2	3	4	5	6	7	8	9	10
11	12	13	14	15	16	17	18	19	20
21	22	23	24	25	26	27	28	29	30
31	32	33	34	35	36	37	38	39	40
41	42	43	44	45	46	47	48	49	50
51	52	53	54	55	56	57	58	59	60
61	62	63	64	65	66	67	68	69	70
71	72	73	74	75	76	77	78	79	80
81	82	83	84	85	86	87	88	89	90
91	92	93	94	95	96	97	98	99	100

(d) Look at the window on the grid and explain *why* your formula is correct.

2 Now look at the same grid through a 3-by-5 window. The smallest number in the window is n and the biggest number is p.

(a) Write p in terms of n.

(b) Look at the window on the grid and explain *why* your formula is correct.

3 Look at the same grid through this 2-by-1 window.
The smallest number in the window is 73.
The sum of the numbers in the window is 147.

(a) The window is moved. The smallest number in the window is now 45.
What is the sum of the numbers in the window now?

(b) The window is moved again.
The smallest number is now 58.
What is the sum of the numbers in the window now?

1	2	3	4	5	6	7	8	9	10
11	12	13	14	15	16	17	18	19	20
21	22	23	24	25	26	27	28	29	30
31	32	33	34	35	36	37	38	39	40
41	42	43	44	45	46	47	48	49	50
51	52	53	54	55	56	57	58	59	60
61	62	63	64	65	66	67	68	69	70
71	72	73	74	75	76	77	78	79	80
81	82	83	84	85	86	87	88	89	90
91	92	93	94	95	96	97	98	99	100

(c) The window is moved again.
The sum of the numbers in the window is now 27.
What is the smallest number in the window now?

(d) The smallest number in the window is n.
What is the other number?

(e) The sum of the numbers in the window is s.
Write s in terms of n.

4 Now look at the same grid through this 2-by-2 window.

1	2	3	4	5	6	7	8	9	10
11	12	13	14	15	16	17	18	19	20
21	22	23	24	25	26	27	28	29	30
31	32	33	34	35	36	37	38	39	40
41	42	43	44	45	46	47	48	49	50
51	52	53	54	55	56	57	58	59	60
61	62	63	64	65	66	67	68	69	70
71	72	73	74	75	76	77	78	79	80
81	82	83	84	85	86	87	88	89	90
91	92	93	94	95	96	97	98	99	100

(a) What is the smallest number in the window?
What is the sum of the numbers in the window?

(b) The window is moved so that the smallest number is now 35.
What is the sum of the numbers in the window now?

(c) The window is moved so that the sum of the numbers in the window is now 186.
What is the smallest number in the window now?

(d) The smallest number in the window is n.
What are the other numbers?

(e) The sum of the numbers in the window is s.
Write s in terms of n.

5 Now look at the same grid through a 2-by-3 window.

(a) The window is placed so that the smallest number is 25.
What is the sum of the numbers in the window?

(b) The window is moved so that the smallest number is 51.
What is the sum of the numbers in the window now?

(c) The window is moved so that the sum of the numbers in the window is 135. What is the smallest number in the window now?

(d) The smallest number in the window is n.
What are the other numbers?

(e) The sum of the numbers in the window is s.
Write s in terms of n.

6 Look at the same grid through this window.

(a) The window is placed on the grid so that the smallest number in the window is 32.
Find the sum of the numbers in the window.

(b) The smallest number in the window is n.
What are the other numbers?

(c) The sum of the numbers in the window is s.
Write s in terms of n.

7 Answer Question 6 for this window.

8 Answer Question 6 for this window.

9 Find a suitably shaped window for each of these formulae.

    (a) $s = 3n + 21$ **(b)** $s = 4n + 31$ **(c)** $s = 5n + 51$

▶ Resource Sheet C:
Hundred square

COURSEWORK OPPORTUNITY

Windows

Look at the 100-square grid through different shaped windows.

♦ Call the smallest number in the window n.

♦ Call the sum of the numbers in the window s.

♦ Find the formula for s in terms of n.

You could explore patterns in your formulae for some of the following ideas, or you could use other ideas of your own.

♦ Use rectangular windows of different shapes.

♦ Use non-rectangular windows consisting of a given number of squares.

♦ Use windows of different sizes but of a particular type, e.g. L-shaped windows.

♦ Call the largest number in the window p. Compare the formula for s in terms of p with the formula for s in terms of n.

Simplifying algebraic expressions

When an algebraic expression is simplified, terms with *exactly* the same letters can be collected together.

For example

    $n + n = 2n$

    $3n + 5n = 8n$

    $4n + 6 + 3 = 4n + 9$

    $a + a + a = 3a$

    $2a + 3b + 5a = 7a + 3b$

(The $2a$ and $5a$ can be collected together.)

    $5x - 4y - 3x = 2x - 4y$

(The $5x$ and $3x$ can be collected together.)

    $4xy + 2x - 3y - 2xy = 2xy + 2x - 3y$

(The $4xy$ and $2xy$ can be collected together.)

    $x^2 + x^2 + x^2 = 3x^2$

But $3x^2 + 4x$ cannot be simplified (the x^2 is *not* exactly the same as the x).

Note that:

$4a - 3a = a$

You do not usually write $1a$.

1 Simplify these expressions, where possible.

(a) $n + n + n + n$

(b) $3n + 4n - 5$

(c) $6n - 2n + 3$

(d) $4a + 2b + 6a$

2 Simplify these expressions, where possible.

(a) $3x + 2y + 4x + 3y$

(b) $5p + 6q + 7 + p + 2q + 3$

(c) $5c + 4d - 2c$

(d) $5a + 4b - 2b + 2a$

3 Simplify these expressions, where possible.

(a) $6x + 8y - 3x + 2y$

(b) $4c - 2d + 6c + 7d$

(c) $5a + 3b - 5$

(d) $6x - 8y - 4x - 2y$

4 Simplify these expressions, where possible.

(a) $3x + 5y - 7$

(b) $-2x + 5x - 10$

(c) $5x - y + 3x - 2y$

(d) $a - 2b + 7b - 4a$

5 Simplify these expressions, where possible.

(a) $-2x + w - 3p - w - p + 6x$

(b) $7a - 5 - 3b - 2 + 6b - 2a$

(c) $14f - 7g - 2f + 9h - 9f + 5g - 11h$

(d) $7ab + 3ab$

6 Simplify these expressions, where possible.

(a) $4p^2 + 5p^2$

(b) $3x^2 + 2x + 5x^2$

7 Simplify these expressions, where possible.

(a) $4x^2 + 3y^2 + 2x^2 + 5y^2$

(b) $6a^2 - 8b^2 + 4a^2 - 3b^2$

(c) $3a^2 - 5 - a^2 + 3$

8 Simplify these expressions, where possible.

(a) $3a^2 + 4ab + 5b^2 + 6ab$

(b) $a - b + 2a - 3c + 4a^2$

(c) $4x^2 - 6x + 8 - 3x$

9 Simplify these expressions, where possible.

(a) $3p^2 - 4pq + 2q^2 + 3pq$

(b) $3x^2 + 3x - 7x^2 - x$

Here are some more examples.

$2b$ means $2 \times b$

ab means $a \times b$

a^2 means $a \times a$

a^3 means $a \times a \times a$

$2ab$ means $2 \times a \times b$

$2a^3$ means $2 \times a \times a \times a$

$2a \times 3b$ means $2 \times a \times 3 \times b = 2 \times 3 \times a \times b = 6ab$

$\dfrac{6b^2}{3b}$ means $\dfrac{6 \times b \times b}{3 \times b} = 2b$

EXERCISE 11

1 Simplify these expressions.

(a) $a \times a$ (b) $3a \times a$ (c) $3a \times 4c$

2 Simplify these expressions.

(a) $7b^2 \times 2b$ (b) $5 \times a^2 \times a \times b$ (c) $6 \times a^2 \times b \times b^2$

3 Simplify these expressions.

(a) $a \times a \times b^2$ (b) $a^2 \times a \times 5b$ (c) $3 \times a \times b \times c$

4 Simplify these expressions.

(a) $2a \times 3b \times 4c$ (b) $3x \times 4x \times 5y$

5 Simplify these expressions.

(a) $\dfrac{4x^2}{2x}$ (b) $\dfrac{9y^3}{3y}$ (c) $\dfrac{6a^3}{2a^2}$

6 Simplify these expressions.

(a) $\dfrac{20b^5}{4b^3}$ (b) $\dfrac{36a^2b^3}{9ab}$ (c) $\dfrac{4abc}{2ab}$

7 Simplify these expressions.

(a) $\dfrac{18x^3y}{2xy}$ (b) $\dfrac{6abc^2}{8a^2bc}$ (c) $\dfrac{15xy^2}{20x^3}$

Order of operations

EXERCISE 12

1 The function is $n \rightarrow 2(n + 1)$. Copy and complete these.

    (a) $4 \rightarrow ?$ **(b)** $7 \rightarrow ?$ **(c)** $? \rightarrow 20$ **(d)** $? \rightarrow 100$

2 The function is $n \rightarrow 3(n - 2)$. Copy and complete these.

    (a) $6 \rightarrow ?$ **(b)** $11 \rightarrow ?$ **(c)** $? \rightarrow 27$ **(d)** $? \rightarrow 60$

3 The function is $n \rightarrow 4(n + 3)$. Copy and complete these.

    (a) $2 \rightarrow ?$ **(b)** $10 \rightarrow ?$ **(c)** $17 \rightarrow ?$ **(d)** $25 \rightarrow ?$

4 The function is $n \rightarrow 4n + 3$. Copy and complete these.

    (a) $2 \rightarrow ?$ **(b)** $10 \rightarrow ?$ **(c)** $17 \rightarrow ?$ **(d)** $25 \rightarrow ?$

5 Write these functions using n.

    (a) Add 2 and multiply by 5   **(b)** Multiply by 5 and add 2

6 Write these functions using n.

    (a) Subtract 2 and multiply by 3   **(b)** Multiply by 3 and subtract 2

7 Write these functions using n.

    (a) Multiply by 3 and subtract 4   **(b)** Subtract 4 and multiply by 3

8 Write these functions using n.

    (a) Divide by 2 and add 6   **(b)** Add 6 and divide by 2

9 Describe these functions in words.

    (a) $n \rightarrow 2n - 1$ **(b)** $n \rightarrow 2(n - 1)$

10 Describe these functions in words.

    (a) $n \rightarrow n^2 + 3$ **(b)** $n \rightarrow (n + 3)^2$

Unlike reading English, you don't start at the left and do the operations as you move across to the right.

There is a particular order for doing operations.

B   brackets ( )
I   indices (x^2, x^3, etc.)
D   division
M   multiplication
A   addition
S   subtraction

When you have a calculation with a fraction, like this

do this

$$\frac{3.7 + 5.2}{1.9 \times 1.8} = \frac{8.9}{3.42} = 2.6 \text{ to 2 significant figures}$$

then do this

you work out the top number followed by the bottom number, and *then* you do the division.

DISCUSSION POINT

In how many different ways can you put in brackets and replace the '?' with a number to complete this equation?

$8 = 24 \div 4 + 2 \times ?$

EXERCISE 13

1 Work out these.

(a) $3 \times 6 - 4$ (b) $5 + 4 \times 3$ (c) $4 \times 8 - 3 \times 6$

2 Work out these.

(a) $5 \times (7 - 3) + 6$ (b) $5 \times 7 - 3 + 6$ (c) $5 \times 7 - (3 + 6)$

3 Work out these.

(a) $30 + 15 \div 3$ (b) $40 - 3 \times 8$ (c) $12 - 36 \div 6$

(d) $13 + 7 \div 7$ (e) $15 - 2 \times 6$ (f) $3 + 20 \div 5$

4 Work out these.

(a) $2 \times 7 + 3 \times 5$ (b) $6 \times 4 - 3 \times 5$ (c) $2 \times 8 + 3 \times 3$

(d) $3 \times 5 - 24 \div 4$ (e) $27 \div 3 + 5 \times 4$ (f) $21 \div 3 - 3 \times 2$

5 Work out these.

(a) $\dfrac{3 \times 6 - 4}{7 \times 2}$ (b) $\dfrac{13 - 12 \div 4}{4 + 3 \times 2}$

You will need to find out the order in which your calculator does operations. It may be helpful to find out how to use the memory and brackets on your calculator.

EXERCISE 14

1 Use the minimum number of key presses on your calculator to work out these.

(a) $\dfrac{8.3 + 2.86}{3.4}$ (b) $\dfrac{12.3 + 20.4}{0.765}$

Give your answers correct to 3 significant figures.

2 Use the minimum number of key presses on your calculator to work out these.

(a) $2.4 + 9.7 \times 0.63$ (b) $8.7^2 - 23$
(c) $3.79^2 + 12.24$ (d) $3.95^3 - 2.73$

Give your answers correct to 3 significant figures.

3 Use the minimum number of key presses on your calculator to work out these.

(a) $\dfrac{7.9^2 - 4.5}{7.36}$ (b) $(5.7 - 4.32)^2$

(c) $\dfrac{7.6 \times 5.1}{3.6 - 2.8}$ (d) $\dfrac{18.7}{31.6 - 7.8}$

Give your answers correct to 3 significant figures.

4 Use the minimum number of key presses on your calculator to work out these.

(a) $\dfrac{9.76 - 8.35}{4.29 - 3.07}$ (b) $115.8 - 5.36^2$ (c) $\dfrac{4.89^2}{8.6^2 - 39.2}$

Give your answers correct to 3 significant figures.

5 Use the minimum number of key presses on your calculator to work out these.

(a) $\left(\dfrac{103.6}{110} + \dfrac{4.15}{3.7} \right)^2$ (b) $\left(\dfrac{1}{2.37} - \dfrac{1}{8.4} \right)^3$

Give your answers correct to 3 significant figures.

Substitution

EXERCISE 15

1 If $x = 5$, $y = 4$ and $z = 2$, find the value of a in each of these equations.

(a) $a = x + y + z$ (b) $a = 3x + z$ (c) $a = 5x + y - 3z$

(d) $a = 5(y - z)$ (e) $a = 3(4x - 3z)$ (f) $a = x(y - z)$

(g) $a = \dfrac{x}{5} + \dfrac{y}{2}$ (h) $a = \dfrac{2x + y}{7}$ (i) $a = \dfrac{2(2x + z)}{y}$

2 If $a = 6$, $b = 4$ and $c = 1$, find the value of x in each of these equations.

(a) $x = a^2 + b^2$ (b) $x = (a + b)^2$ (c) $x = 2b^2$

(d) $x = (2b)^2$ (e) $x = \dfrac{a^2}{3}$ (f) $x = \left(\dfrac{a}{3}\right)^2$

3 If $f = -8$, $g = 2$ and $h = 3$, find the value of y in each of these equations.

(a) $y = f^2 - h^2$ (b) $y = (f - h)^2$ (c) $y = \left(\dfrac{f}{2g}\right)^2 - h$

4 If $a = \frac{1}{2}$, $b = 4$ and $c = -3$, find the value of t in each of these equations.

(a) $t = b - c$ (b) $t = a + b + c$ (c) $t = c - a$

(d) $t = abc^2$ (e) $t = a(bc)^2$ (f) $t = \dfrac{a^2b}{c}$

In this exercise, give
your answers
correct to 3
significant figures.

EXERCISE 16

1 Using the formula $V = IR$, find V if $I = 4.2$ and $R = 60$.

2 Using the formula $E = mgh$, find E if $g = 9.8$, $h = 3.6$ and $m = 8.2$.

3 Using the formula $v = u + at$, find v if $a = 14.6$, $t = 7.2$ and $u = 3$.

4 Using the formula
$$p = \frac{F}{A}$$
find p if $A = 19.6$ and $F = 123$.

5 Using the formula $P = I^2R$, find P if $I = 15.7$ and $R = 3.8$.

6 Using the formula $s = ut + \frac{1}{2}at^2$, find s if $a = 2.9$, $t = 5.3$, and $u = 7$.

7 Using the formula

$$P = \frac{Fs}{t}$$

find P if $F = 17.4$, $s = 8.3$ and $t = 1.8$.

8 Using the formula

$$C = \frac{5(F - 32)}{9}$$

find C if $F = 46$.

9 Using the formula $v^2 = u^2 + 2as$, find v if $a = 7$, $s = 12.9$ and $u = 15$.

CHAPTER SUMMARY

Adding negative numbers

$(-6) + (-3) = -9$

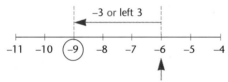

$(-6) + 8 = 2$

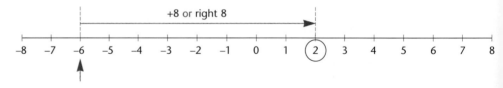

Subtracting negative numbers

$33 - 27 = 6$ $\qquad\qquad\qquad\qquad (-3) - (-5) = 2$

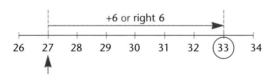 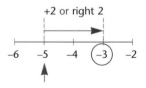

$(-6) - (+2) = -8$

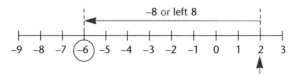

Multiplying and dividing negative numbers

If *one* sign is negative the answer is *negative*.
If *both* signs are negative the answer is *positive*.

$(-3) \times (+2) = -6$ $(-6) \div (+3) = -2$

$(-4) \times (-3) = +12$ $(-20) \div (-4) = +5$

$(+3) \times (-5) = -15$ $(+16) \div (-2) = -8$

Functions

Functions are often described using algebra.

The function *add 2* can be written as $n \to n + 2$.

The function *square the number* can be written as $n \to n^2$.

The function *multiply by 3 and add 2* can be written as $n \to 3n + 2$.

The function *add 2 and multiply by 3* can be written as $n \to 3(n + 2)$.

Simplifying

$a + a + a = 3a$ $a \times a \times a = a^3$

$2a + 5a = 7a$ $2a \times 5a = 2 \times a \times 5 \times a = 10a^2$

$3a - 4b + 2a = 5a - 4b$ $3a \times 4b \times 2a = 24a^2b$

$3ab + 4ab = 7ab$ $3ab \times 4ab = 12a^2b^2$

$x^2 + 5x$ $x^2 \times 5x = 5x^3$

$6x^2y - 2x$ $6x^2y \div 2x = \dfrac{6x^2y}{2x} = 3xy$

Order of operations

B   brackets ( )
I   indices (x^2, x^3, etc.)
D   division
M   multiplication
A   addition
S   subtraction

WORKING WITH DATA

- different types of data
- the collection and organisation of data
- interpreting and representing data by means of bar charts, histograms, frequency polygons and pie charts
- calculating mean, median and mode, and range
- constructing and using grouped frequency distributions
- finding the modal class and mean of grouped frequency distributions
- hypothesis testing
- drawing conclusions based on graphs and simple statistics
- comparing two distributions
- evaluating results critically.

Statistics and why we need them

When you open a newspaper or watch the news headlines on television, the centre of the argument is often some numbers, a chart or a graph. The information might be published by an organisation interested in convincing us of a particular opinion that they hold, or it may be prepared by a research team for that particular story.

It is important that you understand the information and do not rely too heavily on the opinions of others.

EXERCISE 1

1 Look at these three newspaper cuttings.

Teenagers fail to kick their habit

THE RISE IN DRUG USE

15 and 16 year olds who have used illicit drugs	GIRLS		BOYS	
	1996	1989	1996	1989
Cannabis	38.0%	15%	43.6%	22%
Glues and solvents	21.0%	2%	19.7%	4%
Amphetamines	12.3%	1%	14.5%	4%
Ecstasy	7.3%	2%	9.2%	3%
Tranquillisers/sedatives	9.5%	1%	6.9%	1%
Cocaine	2.4%	1%	2.8%	1%
Heroin	1.5%	0.5%	1.7%	0.5%

Nearly half of 15- and 16-year-olds admit that they have tried illegal drugs, the survey says, with 38 per cent of the girls and 43.6 per cent of the boys saying they have used cannabis.

The 1989 survey of 7,000 young people in England by the Health Education Authority found that 15 per cent of girls and 22 per cent of boys had used cannabis.

Three times as many boys and girls now use ecstasy, perhaps the most widespread hard drug in currency among young people, than admitted using it before.

They found that there had been a trebling of teenage experimentation with heroin: 1.5 per cent of girls and 1.7 per cent of boys, compared with 0.5 per cent of 16-year-olds who told researchers seven years ago that they had tried heroin.

(a) What percentage of girls admitted to the use of cannabis in

   (i) 1989?   (ii) 1996?

   Discuss this statement.

   The proportion of girls admitting to the use of cannabis doubled between 1989 and 1996.

(b) Discuss this statement.

   A higher proportion of girls admitted to the use of sedatives than boys.

   Would you change the statement?

(c) Which illicit drugs have a higher proportion of boys admitting to their use than girls in 1989?

(d) Which illicit drugs have a higher proportion of boys admitting to their use than girls in 1996?

2 Look at this newspaper cutting.

Rail passengers appear to be dissatisfied with most things. Complete this sentence.

Customer relations have shown an improvement in the area of ...

Rail complaints at new high after privatisation

RAIL passengers are making more complaints than ever, the national rail watchdog said yesterday.

Complaints in 1995–96 were up 15 per cent on the previous year and have increased five-fold since 1982, the Central Rail Users' Consultative Committee said in its annual report.

Most of the record 11,640 complaints made to the committee in 1995–96 were about punctuality, refunds, information at stations, policy on fares and marketing, and cancellations.

YEAR OF MOANS

1995–96

Complaint	Total	Change
Punctuality	2,024	+33.3
Refunds	1,839	+20.6
Information	1,143	–0.5
Fares	940	+16.0
Cancellations	710	–5.5
Station facilities	684	+8.9
Timetable	627	–9.5
On-Train facilities	592	+78.9
Staff conduct	523	+8.5
Overcrowding	485	+48.3
Correspondence	366	–12.2
Telephone inquiries	252	+42.4
Passenger's charter	244	+32.6
Information on board	228	+6.0
Connection failures	215	+13.8
Reservations	146	+22.7
On-train catering	138	+46.8
Safety, security	128	+2.4
Road rail co-ordination	109	+28.2
Conveyance of cycles	39	+30.0
Smoking policy	31	+3.3
Total	11,640	+14.5

3 Look at this cutting from a newspaper.

The holiday destination chart shows that approximately three times more people travelled to the Greek Islands than to Cyprus. Write three more statements about the holiday data.

Holiday destinations

Top 10 destinations for British holiday makers, 1995.

Balearic Islands	1,877,000
Greek Islands	1,311,000
Mainland Spain	1,074,000
Canaries	951,000
Turkey	624,000
US	473,000
France	465,000
Cyprus	416,000
Portugal	413,000
Italy	314,000

Different types of data

DISCUSSION POINT

Discuss what this diagram means.

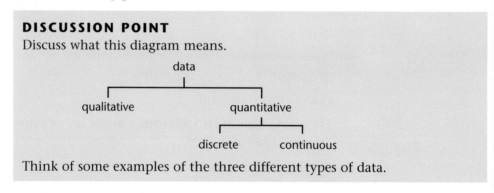

Think of some examples of the three different types of data.

EXERCISE 2

1 Look at this list of questions.

A: Do you wear glasses?

B: How many brothers and sisters do you have?

C: How much do you weigh?

D: What colour eyes do you have?

E: How many televisions are there in your house?

F: What is your hand span?

G: What did you have for lunch yesterday?

H: How much money did you spend last week?

I: What is your shoe size?

J: How old are you?

(a) Which questions involve qualitative data?

(b) Which questions involve discrete data?

(c) Which questions involve continuous data?

Answering questions using data

A statement that is made about a data set is called a **hypothesis**.

A **statistical investigation** may be undertaken, or an experiment carried out, to find out whether a hypothesis might be true. It is often useful to think of a statistical investigation or an experiment as having four stages.

- A **question** is asked about the hypothesis.
- Information is **collected**. This information is called a **data set**.
- The data is **analysed**. It may be sorted and may be used to form a table, chart or graph.
- The data is **interpreted** to decide what it is telling us.

DISCUSSION POINT

A hypothesis is made that:

'*Coronation Street* is more popular than *EastEnders*.'

An investigation produces this information.

What the nation watched

BBC1	Millions	BBC2	Millions	ITV	Millions	C4	Millions
Eastenders (Thu/Sun)	17.17	Have I Got News for You (Fri/Sat)	6.74	Coronation St (Mon/Wed)	17.19	Brookside (Fri/Sat)	5.80
The National Lottery Live	15.32	Doing Rude Things	4.93	Stars in Their Eyes	11.81	The Politician's Wife	4.91
Neighbours (Tue)	12.68	Steptoe and Son	4.38	Emmerdale (Tue/Thu)	11.43	GoodFellas	3.54
Fawlty Towers	10.91	Gardeners' World	3.77	The Bill (Fri)	10.61	Drop the Dead Donkey	3.46
Bugs	10.08	More Rhodes around Britain	3.68	Home and Away (Thu)	10.59	ER	3.24
Next of Kin	9.77	Star Trek: the Next Generation	3.25	The Governor	10.26	The World of Lee Evans	3.01
Birds of a Feather	9.44	Rab C Nesbitt	3.23	Bramwell	9.54	Eurotrash	3.00
The Vet	9.13	Absolute Strangers	3.18	Heartbeat	9.42	Roseanne	2.82
Men Behaving Badly	8.80	Screen Two: Black Easter	2.92	Heartbreak Ridge	9.39	The Crystal Maze	2.49
The Hanging Gale	8.73	Ready, Steady, Cook (Tue)	2.86	Dangerous Lady	9.33	Fifteen-to One	2.36

BBC1	Millions	BBC2	Millions	ITV	Millions	C4	Millions
EastEnders (Thu/Sun)	17.11	Have I Got News for You	8.02	Coronation Street (Mon/Wed)	17.22	Brookside (Fri/Sat)	5.97
Neighbours (Tue)	11.90	World Tour of Billy Connolly	5.93	Emmerdale (Tue/Thu)	12.64	Cutting Edge	4.69
The National Lottery Live	10.85	Secrets of Lost Empires	5.44	The Bill (Tue)	11.53	ER	4.38
Antiques Roadshow	9.25	Spanish Grand Prix	4.81	Home and Away (Tue)	11.21	Encounters	2.92
Doctor Who	9.08	Billy Connolly's World Tour of TV	4.46	The Knock	9.92	NYPD Blue	2.78
Airport	8.79	Home Front	4.38	Police, Camera, Action!	9.29	Friends	2.75
News/Weather (Sun 8.50pm)	8.42	Murder Most Horrid	4.05	Bramwell	9.04	Fifteen-to-One	2.68
Birds of a Feather	8.35	Gardeners' World	3.92	Take Your Pick	8.46	GoodFellas	2.55
No Bananas	8.27	Ready, Steady, Cook	3.76	A Touch of Frost	8.43	Death in Small Doses	2.45
Shirley Valentine	8.24	Postcards from the Country	3.73	SAS – the Soldiers' Story	8.24	Roseanne	2.28

- How many viewers watched *Coronation Street* in the week of 1st July to 7th July 1995?
- How many viewers watched *EastEnders* in the week of 1st July to 7th July 1995?
- Is there much difference in these numbers?
- Would it be reasonable to make a decision about which programme was most popular using these figures?
- Consider the figures for the week of 29th June to 5th July 1996. Does this information support the hypothesis: '*Coronation Street* is more popular than *EastEnders*'?
- What other conclusions might you draw from the information provided? You could produce a poster to display your conclusions.

Representing data

DISCUSSION POINT

What can you find out from each of these diagrams?

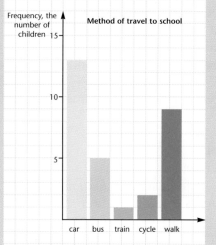

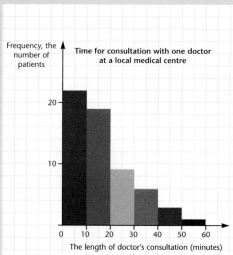

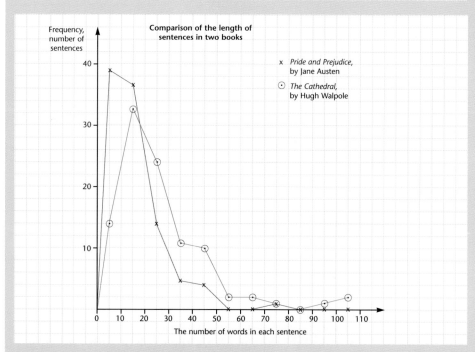

The names of these diagrams are **histogram**, **frequency polygon** and **bar chart**. Which is which?

Which type of diagram would you use for qualitative data?

Which would you use for continuous data?

Which would you use for discrete data?

1 This pictogram shows six of the seven most popular pets in the UK in 1994 according to estimates by the Pet Food Manufacturers Association.
Fish have been excluded from the pictogram.

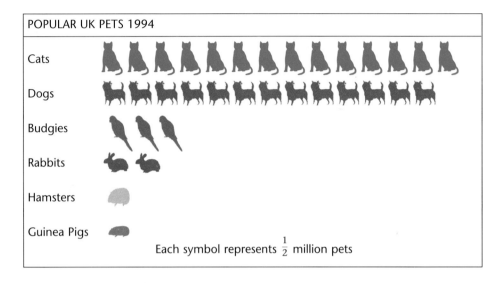

POPULAR UK PETS 1994

Cats

Dogs

Budgies

Rabbits

Hamsters

Guinea Pigs

Each symbol represents $\frac{1}{2}$ million pets

(a) Write down an estimate of the number of pets there were of each type.

(b) It was estimated that there were 24 million fish. How many symbols would be needed to show the fish in the pictogram?

(c) How many pets were there estimated to be altogether?

2 A sample of the films shown at the local cinema is displayed in this bar chart.

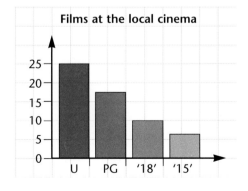

Films at the local cinema

(a) How many PG films were shown?

(b) How many films were in the sample?

3 This line graph shows the average monthly temperatures in London over the last forty years.

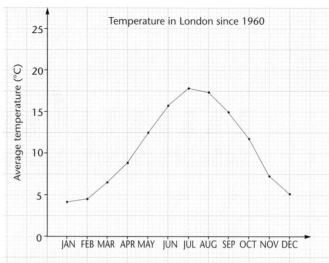

(a) Write down the average temperature for May.

(b) What is the hottest month on average?

(c) What is the coldest month on average?

(d) Write down the difference in temperature between the hottest and coldest months.

4 Look at this data.

Sales (millions) of LPs and CDs (1984–1994)											
	1984	1985	1986	1987	1988	1989	1990	1991	1992	1993	1994
LPs	54	53	52	52	50	39	25	20	7	5	4
CDs	1	5	8	18	29	42	51	58	71	93	116

> Think carefully about the vertical scale.

(a) Draw two line graphs on the same set of axes to illustrate the data.

(b) What do your line graphs show?

5 This frequency polygon shows the time a group of children take to travel to school.

(a) How many children travel to school in less than 10 minutes?

(b) How many children take longer than half an hour to travel to school?

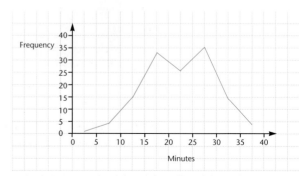

6 The number of trains leaving a railway station was surveyed.

Here are the results.

Draw a frequency polygon to show this information.

Time	Frequency
8–9am	25
9–10am	12
10–11am	5
11–12 noon	5
12–1pm	3
1–2pm	3
2–3pm	3
3–4pm	12
4–5pm	10
5–6pm	24

DISCUSSION POINT

This table shows how a group of 30 children travel to school each morning.

Car	Bus	Train	Cycle	Walk
13	5	1	2	9

This pie chart shows the same information.

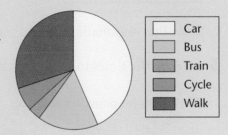

Discuss how you could draw this pie chart accurately, using a protractor.

EXERCISE 4

1 Some students were asked to name one favourite sport. The results are shown in this pie chart.

Football was the favourite of five students.

(**a**) Estimate how many students preferred tennis.

(**b**) Estimate how many students chose cricket.

(**c**) Estimate how many students were asked about their favourite sport.

Favourite sports of students

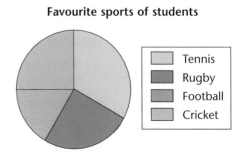

2 A survey of the colour of 60 cars was carried out in a car park.

Here are the results.

Use a protractor to draw a pie chart showing the colours of the cars.

Red	10	Blue	5
Black	12	Green	7
White	8	Other	18

3 A sample of cars were categorised as saloon, hatchback and estate.

Saloon	12
Hatchback	24
Estate	4

Draw a pie chart to show the numbers in each category.

4 These are the flavours of crisps sold from a vending machine.

Plain	67
Cheese and Onion	23
Salt and Vinegar	35
Other	55

Show this information using a pie chart.

5 Here are the times for a popular music CD and a classical music CD.

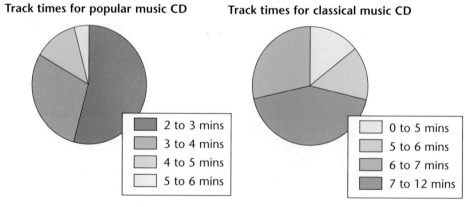

Track times for popular music CD

- 2 to 3 mins
- 3 to 4 mins
- 4 to 5 mins
- 5 to 6 mins

Track times for classical music CD

- 0 to 5 mins
- 5 to 6 mins
- 6 to 7 mins
- 7 to 12 mins

(a) What is the modal track time for the popular music CD?

(b) What is the modal track time for the classical music CD?

(c) There are 24 tracks altogether on the popular music CD. How many tracks are there for each time interval?

(d) There are 7 tracks altogether on the classical music CD. How many tracks are there for each time interval?

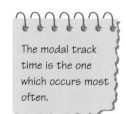

The modal track time is the one which occurs most often.

Analysing data: median, mean and range

DISCUSSION POINT

These are the marks out of 10 for a mental arithmetic test.

Girls	7	2	5	9	8	4	4	9	2	3	8	9	3		
Boys	5	5	6	10	7	3	8	9	7	5	7	10	4	6	8

Who did better in this test, the girls or the boys?

One way of answering this question is to find the **mean.**

Find the mean mark for the boys, for the girls *and* for the whole class.

What do these mean marks tell you?

> To find the **mean**, add all the items together, and then divide by the number of items.

Another way of answering the question is to find the **median.**

> To find the **median**, list all the items in order of size, and then pick the item in the middle of·the list.

Find the median mark for the boys, for the girls *and* for the whole class.

What do these median marks tell you?

Whose marks varied the most – boys or girls?

One way of answering this question is to find the **range.**

Find the range for the boys, for the girls *and* for the whole class.

What do these ranges tell you?

> The **range** is the difference between the largest and the smallest item.

EXERCISE 5

1 A group of 27 students took part in a mental arithmetic test and the scores were recorded out of ten. Here are their scores.

4 4 5 6 7 8 6 10 9 5 4 4 5 6

7 8 10 4 9 9 6 7 7 5 5 7 8

(a) Calculate the mean mark of the group.

(b) Calculate the range in the group.

2 Ten children are selected from a year group at school. Here are their weights, recorded in kilograms.

53 51 61 48 59 57 50 71 45 63

(a) Calculate the mean weight of the children in the sample.

(b) Calculate the range of the weights in the sample.

3 Find the median and the range of these sets of numbers.

A

4	5	5	6	6
7	7	7	7	8
8	9	10	10	10

B

13	14	15	34	23
56	76	23	45	18
19	11	13	24	25

C

3	4	2	6	8	9	11	2	5	7
7	6	8	5	4	7	6	10	2	4
6	5	5	7	8	2	9	4		

4 Sileby United had a goal average of exactly 3 after they had played eight games.

They played two more games without scoring another goal.

What was their new goal average?

5 A set of six numbers has a mean of 12.

Five of these numbers are 8, 15, 19, 7 and 14.

What is the sixth number?

6 A team scored 2, 4, 0, 12, 8, 5, 3 in seven netball matches.

(a) How many goals did they score altogether?

(b) What is the mean number of goals per match?

(c) What do they need to score in the next match, if they are to improve their mean to exactly 5 goals per match?

7 Write down a set of six numbers that has a median of 7 and a mode of 5.

8 Write down a set of five numbers that has a median of 10 and a mean of 20.

9 A group of musicians needed to find out how many songs to write for their first release in the CD market.

A small sample of CDs issued by groups was carried out.
Here are the results.

Number of tracks on CDs:	12 12 12 18 11 15 15 11 10 15

(a) Calculate the mean number of tracks.

(b) Find the median number of tracks.

(c) How many songs should they write?

10 A survey was taken of the numbers of tracks on a wider range of CDs. The CDs were categorised according to the style of music.

Country	15	10	14	10	14	15	11	12	13	13
Folk	12	12	10	12	13	12	15	12	14	12
Jazz and blues	20	10	9	14	25	7	8	10	12	12
Films and shows	65	16	25	17	16	28	17	24	15	16
Bands	20	20	14	14	19	24	20	20	14	17

(a) Calculate the median for each category.

(b) Calculate the mean for each category.

(c) Which category has the largest median?

(d) Which category has the largest mean?

(e) Calculate the range for each category.

(f) Which category has the widest range?

(g) Write one or two sentences comparing the numbers of tracks on CDs for the five different styles of music.

Means of frequency distributions

▷ Resource Sheet F: *Y10 data*

This table shows the shoe sizes for the male students on Resource Sheet F: *Y10 data*.

Shoe size	6	7	8	9	10	11	12	13	14
Frequency	3	6	7	15	10	4	3	0	1

The Y10 data was collected from Y10 students in a school in Cornwall.

One way of measuring the average shoe size for these students would be to work out the mean. To do this, you need to add up all the shoes sizes and divide by the number of students, 49.

It is helpful to put all the calculations into a table like this.

Shoe size	Frequency	Frequency × shoe size
6	3	3 × 6 = 18
7	6	6 × 7 = 42
8	7	7 × 8 = 56
9	15	15 × 9 = 135
10	10	10 × 10 = 100
11	4	4 × 11 = 44
12	3	3 × 12 = 36
13	0	0 × 13 = 0
14	1	1 × 14 = 14
Totals	49	445

So mean shoe size is
$445 \div 49 = 9.1$

EXERCISE 6

1 The heights of a group of oak trees were measured.

Height (metres)	7	8	9
Frequency	12	17	1

Calculate the mean height of the oak trees.

2 The heights of a group of beech trees were measured.

Height (metres)	4	5	6	7
Frequency	2	8	5	35

Calculate the mean height of the beech trees.

3 A survey was made of 100 families, to investigate the number of children in each family.

Here is a frequency table showing the results of the survey.

Find the mean number of children in a family.

Number of Children	Frequency
0	10
1	25
2	23
3	26
4	14
5	0
6	1
7	0
8	1

4 The letters in each of the first 200 words of a book were counted.

This frequency table shows the results.

(a) Find the median length of a word from this sample.

(b) Calculate the mean length of a word from this sample.

Number of letters	Frequency
1	16
2	23
3	15
4	51
5	62
6	24
7	7
8	0
9	1
10	1

5 The number of people travelling in cars (including the driver) was counted. Here are the results.

Number of people	Frequency
1	208
2	101
3	46
4	40
5	4
6	1

(a) Write down the median.

(b) What is the modal number of people in a car?

(c) Calculate the mean, correct to 1 decimal place.

(d) Which measure of average is the most useful?

6 (a) Draw up a frequency table for the shoe sizes for the female students on Resource Sheet F: *Y10 data*.

(b) Calculate the mean shoe size for the female students.

Means of grouped frequency distributions

▶ Resource Sheet F: *Y10 data*

This table shows the arm spans for the 49 male students on Resource Sheet F: *Y10 data*.

$165 \leq a < 170$ means an arm span of between 165 and 170, including 165 but not 170.

Arm span (a cm)	Frequency
$160 \leq a < 165$	7
$165 \leq a < 170$	10
$170 \leq a < 175$	10
$175 \leq a < 180$	9
$180 \leq a < 185$	9
$185 \leq a < 190$	3
$190 \leq a < 195$	1

From this table, you cannot know the exact arm span of all 49 students.

So you have to assume that, for example, everyone in the class interval 165 cm to 170 cm has an arm span of 167.5 cm which is the middle value of the interval.

You then calculate the mean in the same way as before.

EXERCISE 7

1 Copy and complete this table to find the mean arm span for the male students on Resource Sheet F: *Y10 data*.

Arm span (*a* cm)	Frequency	Middle value	Frequency × middle value
$160 \leq a < 165$	7	162.5	7 × 162.5 =
$165 \leq a < 170$	10	167.5	10 × 167.5 =
$170 \leq a < 175$	10		
$175 \leq a < 180$	9		
$180 \leq a < 185$	9		
$185 \leq a < 190$	3		
$190 \leq a < 195$	1		
Totals	49		

2 (a) Draw up a grouped frequency table for the arm spans of the female students on Resource Sheet F: *Y10 data*.

(b) Calculate the mean arm span for the female students.

3 (a) Use your tables from Questions 1 and 2 to draw up a grouped frequency table for the arm spans of *all* the students on Resource Sheet F: *Y10 data*.

(b) Calculate the mean arm span for all the students.

(c) What can you conclude from the three different means you have calculated in this question and in Questions 1 and 2?

4 (a) What is the modal class for male arm spans, female arm spans and for the arm spans of all students on Resource Sheet F: *Y10 data*?

(b) Do these modal classes support what you said in Question 3 part (c)?

5 Work out the mean wage for the staff at a hotel, whose earnings are shown in this table.

Wage (£*w*)	Frequency
$0 \leq w < 50$	18
$50 \leq w < 100$	22
$100 \leq w < 150$	28
$150 \leq w < 200$	6
$200 \leq w < 250$	1
$250 \leq w < 300$	1
$300 \leq w < 350$	1
$350 \leq w < 400$	0
$400 \leq w < 450$	1

6 A cat welfare group conducted a survey to find the average weight of healthy cats. From this they hope to judge whether cats are being maltreated.

Weight (w kg)	Middle value	Frequency
$2.5 \leq w < 3.5$		32
$3.5 \leq w < 4$		13
$4 \leq w < 4.5$		9
$4.5 \leq w < 5.5$	5.0	2

(a) Write down the median weight and the modal class of the sample.

(b) Calculate the mean weight of a healthy cat.

7 Work out the mean exam mark for this set of marks.

Mark (out of 100)	Frequency
0 – 9	1
10 – 19	1
20 – 29	9
30 – 39	23
40 – 49	65
50 – 59	62
60 – 69	26
70 – 79	8
80 – 89	5
90 – 99	0

8 The manager of a busy supermarket recorded the amount of money spent by each customer during one day.

Work out the mean amount of money spent by each customer. Use £150 as the 'middle' value for the 'more than £100' interval.

Amount spent (£A)	Frequency
£10 or less	152
$10 < A \leq 20$	203
$20 < A \leq 30$	116
$30 < A \leq 40$	40
$40 < A \leq 50$	33
$50 < A \leq 60$	21
$60 < A \leq 70$	29
$70 < A \leq 80$	17
$80 < A \leq 90$	8
$90 < A \leq 100$	7
More than £100	23

9 A sample of students from one year group run 100 metres.
The times are grouped as shown here.

Time taken (t secs)	Frequency
$12.0 \leq t < 14.0$	3
$14.0 \leq t < 15.0$	14
$15.0 \leq t < 15.5$	8
$15.5 \leq t < 16.0$	12
$16.0 \leq t < 17.0$	5
$17.0 \leq t < 20.0$	10

Calculate the mean time taken in seconds.

10 For this question, you need Resource Sheet F: *Y10 data*.

(a) Choose suitable class intervals for the students' hand span measurements.

(b) Draw up a grouped frequency distribution for the hand spans of the male students.

(c) Work out the mean hand span for the male students.

(d) Repeat parts (b) and (c) for the female students.

(e) What is the modal class for the male and female hand spans?

(f) Write one or two statements about what your calculations show.

COURSEWORK OPPORTUNITY

A statistical investigation

Choose a hypothesis or question to investigate.
Here are some examples.

Y10 students in our school are absent more often than Y7 students.

How long does it take students to come to school in the morning?

Do the Y10 students in our school have similar arm spans and hand spans to the Y10 students in the Cornwall school (on Resource Sheet F: *Y10 data*)?

Here are some points to consider when planning your coursework.

Understanding the question

- Is the question or hypothesis clear to other people?

Collecting and organising the data

- Will a computer database be helpful?
- Will working in a group with other students be helpful? If so, who will do what?
- What data needs to be collected?
- How will the data be collected?
- How many people will be asked? How will they be chosen?

Representing the data

- What type of diagrams will be helpful?

Analysing the data

- What calculations are needed to answer the question?
- Are there any other calculations that might be interesting?

Interpreting the data

- What have you found out?

CHAPTER SUMMARY

A **statistical investigation** has four stages:

- questioning
- collection
- analysis
- interpretation

Hypothesis ... an idea that underlies the questions asked in a statistical investigation.

Different types of data

Qualitative, e.g. hair colour
Discrete (counting), e.g. number of children in a family
Continuous (measuring), e.g. height in centimetres

Representing data

Bar chart
(qualitative data or discrete data)

Histogram
(continuous data)

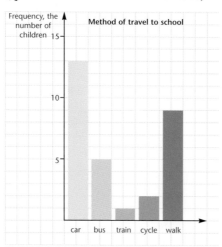

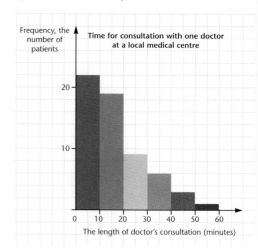

Frequency polygon (continuous data) obtained by joining up the mid-points of tops of bars on histogram

Pie chart: This is how the information shown in the bar chart above can be put into a pie chart.

There are 30 students altogether. So each student is represented by $360° \div 30 = 12°$.

Type of transport	Number of children	Size of angle in pie chart
Car	13	$13 \times 12° = 156°$
Bus	5	$5 \times 12° = 60°$
Train	1	$1 \times 12° = 12°$
Cycle	2	$2 \times 12° = 24°$
Walk	9	$9 \times 12° = 108°$
Total	30	$360°$

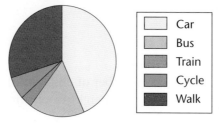

Calculating averages

Mean

- Add all the items of data together.
- Divide by the number of items.

Median

- List all the items in order of size.
- Pick out the item in the middle of the list.

Mode or modal class

The item of data or group of data occurring most frequently

Range

This is the difference between the largest and smallest items of data. It tells you how spread out the data is.

Mean of a frequency distribution

Example: Find the mean number of children in the families of this Y10 class.

Number of children	1	2	3	4	5
Frequency	6	12	4	2	1

This means that there are four families with 3 children.

Number of children	Frequency	Total number of children
1	6	$6 \times 1 = 6$
2	12	$12 \times 2 = 24$
3	4	$4 \times 3 = 12$
4	2	$2 \times 4 = 8$
5	1	$1 \times 5 = 5$
Total	25	55

The mean number of children is $55 \div 25 = 2.2$

Mean of grouped frequency distribution

Example: Find the mean hand span of students in this Y10 class.

Hand span ($h$cm)	Frequency	Middle value	Frequency × middle value
$16 \leq h < 17$	3	16.5	$3 \times 16.5 = 49.5$
$17 \leq h < 18$	2	17.5	$2 \times 17.5 = 35$
$18 \leq h < 19$	1	18.5	$1 \times 18.5 = 18.5$
$19 \leq h < 20$	4	19.5	$4 \times 19.5 = 78$
$20 \leq h < 21$	4	20.5	$4 \times 20.5 = 82$
$21 \leq h < 22$	2	21.5	$2 \times 21.5 = 43$
$22 \leq h < 23$	4	22.5	$4 \times 22.5 = 90$
$23 \leq h < 24$	2	23.5	$2 \times 23.5 = 47$
Total	22		443

The mean hand span is $443 \div 22 = 20.1$cm (to 1 decimal place).

AREA AND PYTHAGORAS' THEOREM

This chapter is about:

- finding areas of triangles, parallelograms and composite shapes
- using and interpreting coordinates in all four quadrants
- understanding squares and square roots
- understanding and using Pythagoras' theorem.

▶ Resource Sheet B:
Square dot

Finding areas of triangles

DISCUSSION POINT
Copy these triangles on centimetre-squared dot paper.

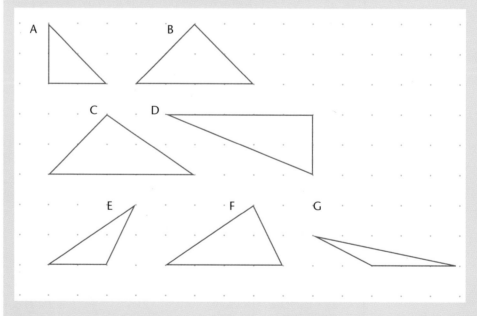

Find the area of each triangle.

Draw some more triangles and find their areas.

Can you find a quick way of finding the area of a triangle?

Can you write a formula for finding the area of a triangle?

1 Find the areas of these triangles.

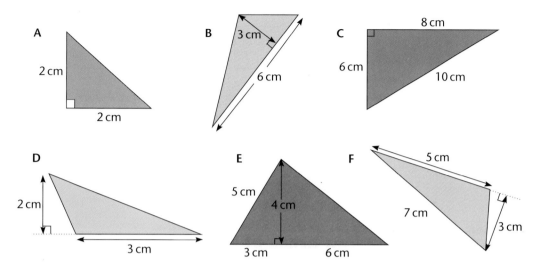

2 Find the areas of these shapes.

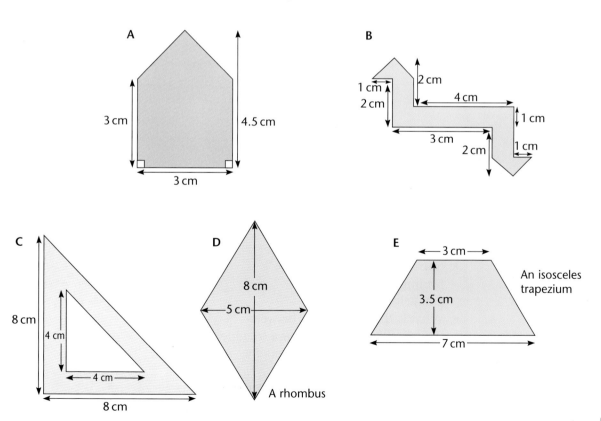

3 Copy and complete this table, which is about four different triangles.

Base of triangle (cm)	Height of triangle (cm)	Area of triangle (cm²)
6		12
	7	35
8		28
	20	100

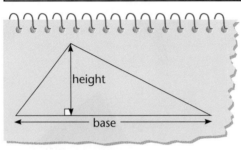

Finding areas of parallelograms

DISCUSSION POINT

Copy these parallelograms on centimetre-squared dot paper.

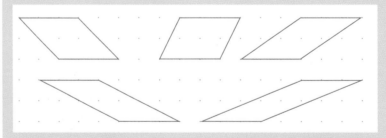

- What is the same about all these parallelograms?
  Find the area of each
  parallelogram.
- Show how each of your
  parallelograms can be turned
  into a 3 cm-by-2 cm rectangle.
- Can you write a formula for
  finding the area of a
  parallelogram?
- What is the connection between
  the formula for the area of a triangle
  and the formula for the area of a
  parallelogram.
  Can you explain this connection?

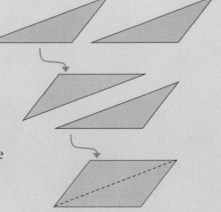

EXERCISE 2

1 Copy these shapes on centimetre-squared dot paper and find their areas.

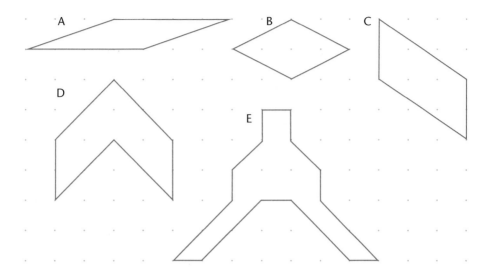

2 Find the areas of these parallelograms.

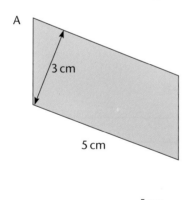

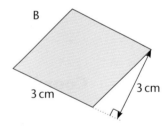

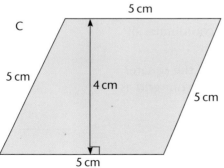

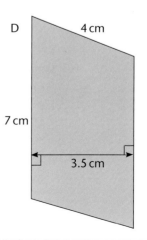

3 Find the areas of these shapes.

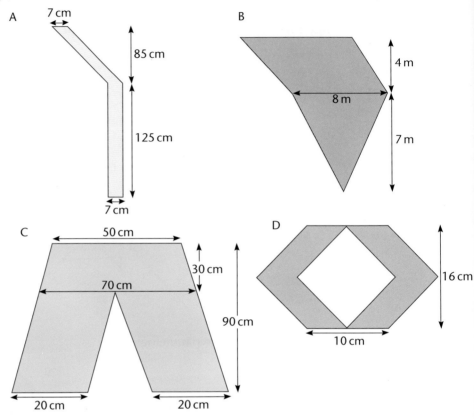

A

7 cm

85 cm

125 cm

7 cm

B

4 m

8 m

7 m

C

50 cm

30 cm

70 cm

90 cm

20 cm

20 cm

D

16 cm

10 cm

Coordinates and area

EXERCISE 3

1 Three corners of a square are at the points (3, 2), (3, –3) and (–2, 2).

(a) Plot these points and draw the square.

(b) Write down the coordinates of the fourth corner.

(c) What is the area of the square? (Use one square on your grid as the unit of area.)

For each question in this exercise, you will need a set of axes like this.

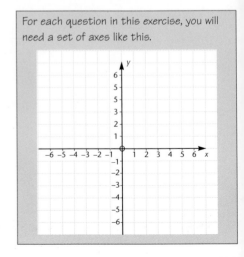

2 One side of a square joins the points (–2, 1) and (–2, 3).

   (a) Plot these two points.

   (b) What must the area of the square be?

   (c) There are two different ways to complete the square.
   Complete it in these two ways and write down the coordinates of the
   other two corners for each way.

3 One side of a rectangle joins the points (–2, 1) and (0, 1).
   The area of the rectangle is 8 squares.

   (a) Draw in the two possible positions of the rectangle.

   (b) For each possibility write down the coordinates of the other two corners.

4 Three corners of a square are at the points (1, 3), (1, –3) and (4, 0).

   (a) Plot these points and draw in the square.

   (b) Write down the coordinates of the fourth corner.

   (c) What is the area of the square?

5 Three corners of a square are at the points (3, 4), (–1, 4) and (1, 2).

   (a) Plot these points and draw in the square.

   (b) Write down the coordinates of the fourth corner.

   (c) What is the area of the square?

To find the area of
the square in
Question 6, you
could cut it up into
a square and four
right-angled
triangles.

6 Three corners of a square are at the points (–2, 1), (–3, –1) and (0, 0).

   (a) Plot these points and draw in the square.

   (b) Write down the coordinates of the fourth corner.

   (c) What is the area of the square?

7 Three corners of a square are at the points (–1, 3), (–3, –2) and (2, –4).

   (a) Plot these points and draw in the square.

   (b) Write down the coordinates of the fourth corner.

   (c) Find the area of the square.

8 Three corners of a rhombus are at the points (–5, 3), (3, 3) and (–1, 1).

   (a) Plot these points and draw in the rhombus.

   (b) Write down the coordinates of the fourth corner.

   (c) Find the area of the rhombus.

9 Three corners of a rectangle are at the points (–3, 0), (7, 0) and (6, –3).

   (a) Plot these points and draw in the rectangle.

   (b) Write down the coordinates of the fourth corner.

   (c) Find the area of the rectangle.

10 Two corners of a square are at the points (–1, –1) and (–1, 3).

    (a) How many different possible ways are there of completing the square?

    (b) Draw each possible square and find its area.

11 Two corners of a square are at the points (–1, 5) and (1, 1).

    (a) How many different possible ways are there of completing the square?

    (b) Draw each possible square and find its area.

12 Three corners of a kite are at the points (–4, 3), (–1, 5) and (2, 3).
The area of the kite is 18 squares.
Find the coordinates of the fourth corner of the kite.

13 Three corners of a parallelogram are at the points (1, 3), (–2, 3) and (3, 0).

    (a) Plot the points and draw in a parallelogram.

    (b) What is the area of your parallelogram?

    (c) There are two other ways to complete the parallelogram. Plot the points again and draw in these parallelograms. What are their areas?

    (d) What do you notice about the areas of the three parallelograms? Can you explain this?

14 Three corners of an isosceles trapezium are at the points (–3, 4), (2, 4) and (–1, –2).

    (a) There are three possible positions for the fourth corner of the trapezium. Draw all three possible trapezia.

    (b) Find the area of each of your trapezia.

▷ Centimetre-squared paper

DISCUSSION POINT

Copy this diagram on centimetre-squared paper.
- What is the area of the yellow square?
- What is the length of one side of the yellow square?
- ☑√ How does this button on your calculator help you to find this length?

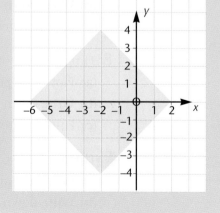

EXERCISE 4

1 What is the length of one of the sides of each of these squares?

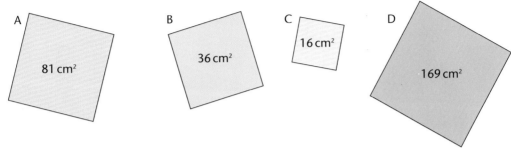

A 81 cm²   B 36 cm²   C 16 cm²   D 169 cm²

Give your answers
correct to 3 s.f.

2 What is the length of one of the sides of each of these squares?

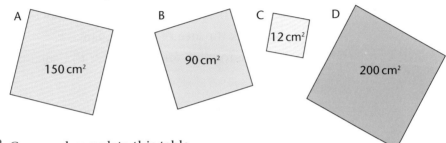

A 150 cm²   B 90 cm²   C 12 cm²   D 200 cm²

3 Copy and complete this table.

Area of square (cm²)	Length of one side of square (cm)
1	
2	
3	
4	
5	
6	
7	
8	
9	
10	

4 One side of a square is x cm and $x^2 = 50$. What is the value of x?

Use centimetre-
squared dot paper
for Questions 5
and 6.

5 Join up four dots to form a square with area:
   (a) 2 cm²   (b) 8 cm²

6 (a) Can you form a square with an area of 10 cm² by joining up four dots?
   (b) What other areas, less than 20 cm², can you make by forming squares
      on centimetre-squared dot paper?

Finding the areas of tilted squares

▶ Resource Sheet B:
Square dot

DISCUSSION POINT

Copy these squares on centimetre-squared dot paper.

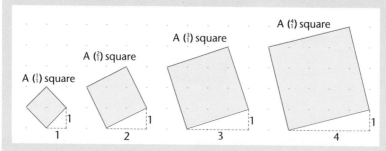

Find the area of each square. Discuss the best way of doing this.

What do you think the area of a $\binom{10}{1}$ square is?

Can you suggest a formula for the areas of $\binom{m}{1}$ squares?

Making and testing
generalisations

▶ Resource Sheet B:
Square dot

EXERCISE 5

1 (a) Copy these squares on your copy of Resource Sheet B: *Square dot*.

Making and testing
generalisations

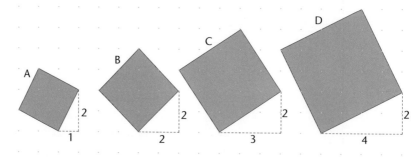

(b) Find the area of each square.

(c) Work out a rule for finding the area of any square of this type.

(d) Write down a formula for the areas of $\binom{m}{2}$ squares.

2 Repeat Question 1 for the areas of $\binom{m}{3}$ squares.

3 Look at your formulae for $\binom{m}{1}$, $\binom{m}{2}$ and $\binom{m}{3}$ squares. Suggest a formula for $\binom{m}{4}$ squares. Test it by trying some examples.

4 Suggest and test a formula for $\binom{m}{n}$ squares.

Proving the area formula for tilted squares

Justifying a generalisation

DISCUSSION POINT

Use these diagrams to prove that the area of any $\binom{m}{n}$ square is $m^2 + n^2$.

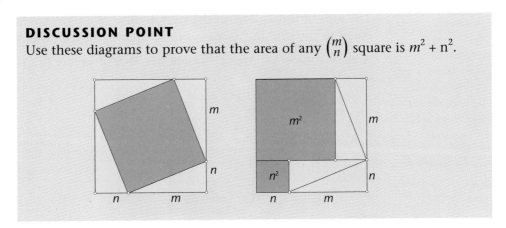

Pythagoras' theorem

DISCUSSION POINT

Here is a $\binom{3}{2}$ tilted square.

The area of this square is $3^2 + 2^2 = 13$.

Now look at this drawing.

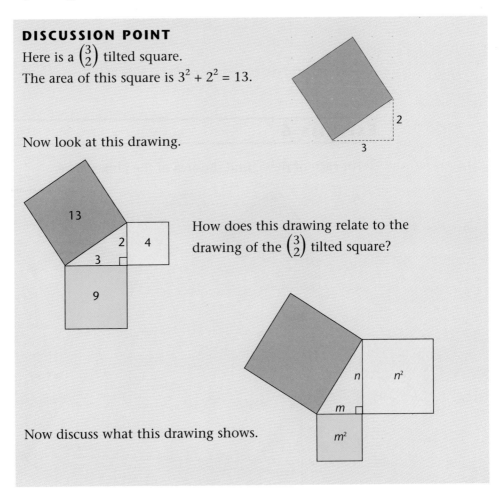

How does this drawing relate to the drawing of the $\binom{3}{2}$ tilted square?

Now discuss what this drawing shows.

The Babylonians knew about Pythagoras' theorem 1000 years before Pythagoras, and the theorem was also known about in India and in China.

Pythagoras lived about 2500 years ago. His famous theorem states that:

The area of the square on the **hypotenuse** of a right-angled triangle is equal to the sum of the areas of the squares on the other two sides.

Area of square A + Area of square B = Area of square C

or

$a^2 + b^2 = c^2$

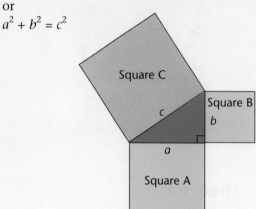

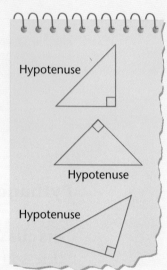

EXERCISE 6

1 For each of these, find the area of the pink square.

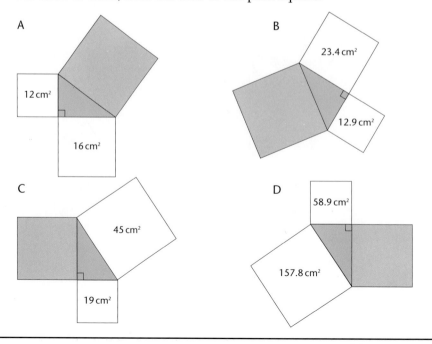

2 Look at this diagram.

  (a) What is the area of square A?

  (b) What is the area of square B?

  (c) What is the area of square C?

  (d) What is the length of the hypotenuse of the blue triangle?

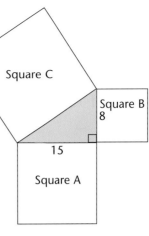

3 Look at this diagram.

  (a) What is the area of square C?

  (b) What is the area of square B?

  (c) What is the area of square A?

  (d) What is the length of the shortest side of the blue triangle?

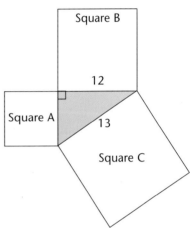

You do not have to keep drawing the squares to use Pythagoras' theorem. You can just remember this:

$$a^2 + b^2 = c^2$$

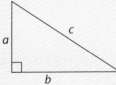

Example 1

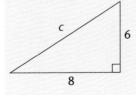

$c^2 = 6^2 + 8^2$

$ = 36 + 64$

$ = 100$

$c = \sqrt{100}$

$ = 10$

Example 2

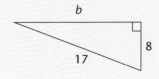

$8^2 + b^2 = 17^2$

$64 + b^2 = 289$

$ b^2 = 289 - 64$

$ = 225$

$ b = \sqrt{225}$

$ = 15$

EXERCISE 7

1 Find the length of the third side in each of these triangles.

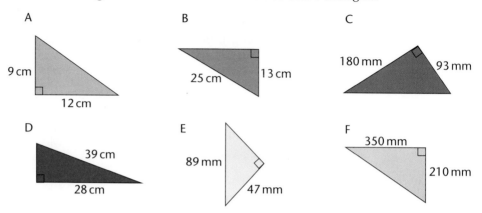

A

9 cm

12 cm

B

25 cm

13 cm

C

180 mm

93 mm

D

39 cm

28 cm

E

89 mm

47 mm

F

350 mm

210 mm

2 Find the lengths of the diagonals in each of these shapes.

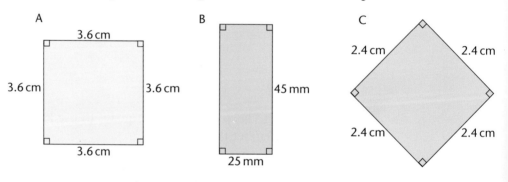

A

3.6 cm

3.6 cm   3.6 cm

3.6 cm

B

45 mm

25 mm

C

2.4 cm   2.4 cm

2.4 cm   2.4 cm

3 Find the length marked *x* in each of these diagrams.

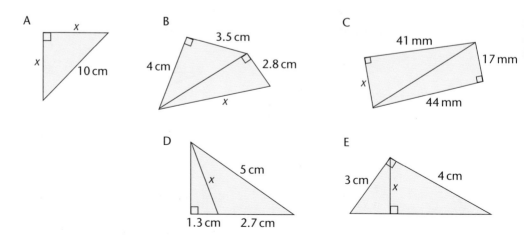

A

x

x

10 cm

B

3.5 cm

4 cm

2.8 cm

x

C

41 mm

17 mm

x

44 mm

D

5 cm

x

1.3 cm   2.7 cm

E

3 cm

x

4 cm

4 (a) Find the distance of the point A (6, 5) from the origin.

(b) Find the distance of the point B (−3, 2) from the origin.

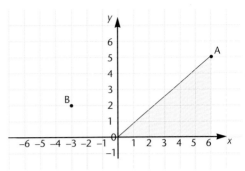

5 (a) Find the distance between the points A (−2, 2) and B (3, 4).

(b) Find the distance between the points C (−3, 1) and D (1, −3).

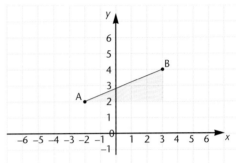

6 The vertices of a triangle are at the points (1, 5), (4, 1) and (6, 5).

(a) Find the lengths of the sides of this triangle.

(b) What is this type of triangle called?

7 The vertices of a quadrilateral are at the points (1, 2), (4, 3), (3, 0) and (−1, −2).

(a) Find the lengths of the sides of this quadrilateral.

(b) What is this type of quadrilateral called?

8 (a) Find the height of this isosceles triangle.

(b) Hence, find the area of the triangle.

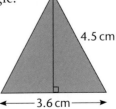

4.5 cm

3.6 cm

9 Find the area of an equilateral triangle with sides of length 8 cm.

10 The diagonals of a square are each 20 cm long. Find the perimeter of the square.

DISCUSSION POINT

Sensible degrees of accuracy

Use Pythagoras' theorem to answer this question.

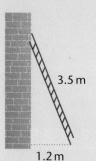

A ladder, 3.5 m long, is leaning up against a wall.
The foot of the ladder is 1.2 m away from the wall.

How far up the wall does the ladder reach?

3.5 m

1.2 m

How accurately should you give your answer to this question? What would be a sensible degree of accuracy?

In this exercise, give your answers, correct to a sensible degree of accuracy.

EXERCISE 8

1 A ladder is propped against the wall of a house.

The bottom of the ladder is 2.8 m from the wall and the top of the ladder reaches 4.8 m up the wall.

How long is the ladder?

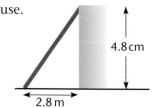

4.8 cm

2.8 m

2 A ladder 3.8 m long is leaning up against a wall.
It reaches 3.6 m up the wall.
How far away from the wall is the foot of the ladder?

3 If you travel 6 miles North and, then, 5 miles East, how far are you away from your starting point?

4 A square field has each side of length 110 m.
You want to walk from one corner to the opposite corner.
How much further is it to walk round the edge than to walk diagonally across the field?

5 A box for a geometry set has a base 20.3 cm by 10.9 cm.
What is the length of the longest pencil which would fit inside the box and lie flat on the base?

6 This map shows the road system connecting the three towns Ayton, Beaton and Seaton.

(a) What is the distance between Ayton and Seaton, as the crow flies?

(b) What is the distance between Ayton and Seaton, by road?

(c) A new road is to be built straight from Beaton to Seaton.
When it is built, will it shorten the journey from Ayton to Seaton and, if so, by how much?

7 A shelf is 25 cm wide.
A supporting bracket for the shelf is fixed to the wall 15 cm below the shelf and to the shelf 7 cm from its outer edge.

Find the length of the bracket.

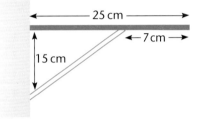

8 This picture shows the side view of a tilted flower vase, ABCD. NC is the water line and XBY is the horizontal ground.

(a) Find the area of triangle NCD.

(b) Find the area of quadrilateral ANCB.

(c) Find the length of NC.

(d) Find the area of triangle ANB.

(e) Use your answers to parts (b), (c) and (d) to find the height of the water level NC above the ground.

(f) Find the height of corner D above the ground.

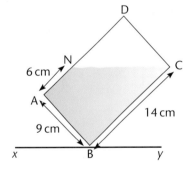

The isosceles right-angled triangle

EXERCISE 9

1 (a) Cut out a 16 cm-by-16 cm square. Cut it into four isosceles right-angled triangles. Label each triangle with the number 1.

(b) What is the area of each of your four triangles?

(c) Calculate the lengths of the sides of one of the triangles.

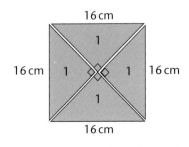

2 Now cut one of your triangles in half again. Label each half with the number 2.

(a) Explain why the new smaller triangles are still isosceles right-angled triangles.

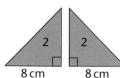

16 cm   8 cm   8 cm

(b) What is the area of one of these smaller triangles?

(c) What are the lengths of the sides of one of these triangles?

3 (a) Record your answers to Questions 1 and 2 in a table, like this.

Triangle no.	Area (cm²)	Length of hypotenuse (cm)	Length of side (cm)
1	64	16	11.314
2	32	11.314	
3			
4			
5			
6			
7			
8			

(b) Continue cutting up and numbering your isosceles right-angled triangles, and complete the table.

4 Imagine that you could keep cutting up your triangles. Describe how the patterns of numbers in the table would continue, by explaining how each row can be calculated from the numbers in the previous row.

Try drawing the design on centimetre-squared paper starting with a 16 cm-by-16 cm square.

5 Look at these two diagrams.

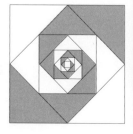

(a) The first diagram shows shading in green.
  (i) What fraction of the total area is shaded green?
  (ii) Imagine that you could keep the same pattern going for ever. What fraction would be shaded green then?

(b) The second diagram shows another way of shading the same drawing, this time in orange.
  (i) What fraction of the total area is shaded orange?
  (ii) Imagine that you could keep the same pattern going for ever. What fraction would be shaded orange then?

Isosceles right-angled triangles

Explore in more detail some of the ideas suggested in Exercise 10.
Different designs using right-angled triangles can be created and explored.

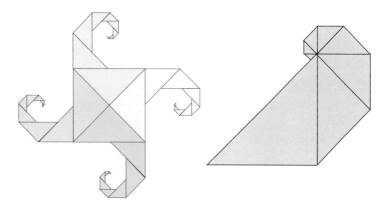

CHAPTER SUMMARY

Area of a triangle

All these triangles have the same area, because they have the same base and
height.

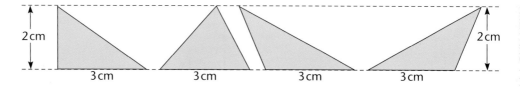

The area is $\frac{1}{2} \times 3\,\text{cm} \times 2\,\text{cm} = 3\,\text{cm}^2$.

The area of any triangle is $\frac{1}{2} \times$ **base** $\times$ **height**.

The height must always be measured at right angles to the base. The base may
be in any orientation.

In this triangle, the base is 5 cm
and the height is 4 cm.

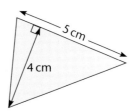

The area is $\frac{1}{2} \times 5\,\text{cm} \times 4\,\text{cm} = 10\,\text{cm}^2$.

Area of a parallelogram

All these parallelograms have the same area, because they have the same base and height.

Area = 3 cm × 2 cm = 6 cm²

The area of any parallelogram is **base** × **height**.

Pythagoras' theorem

Area of square A + Area of square B = Area of square C

or

$a^2 + b^2 = c^2$

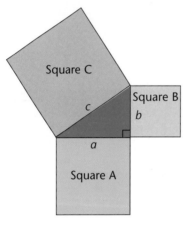

Square C

Square B

c

b

a

Square A

Example 1

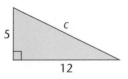

5

c

12

$c^2 = 5^2 + 12^2$

$= 25 + 144$

$= 169$

$c = \sqrt{169}$

$= 13$

Example 2

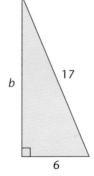

b

17

6

$6^2 + b^2 = 17^2$

$36 + b^2 = 289$

$b^2 = 289 - 36$

$= 253$

$b = \sqrt{253}$

$= 15.9$ (to 3 s.f.)

6 PERCENTAGES

This chapter is about:

- the equivalence between fractions, decimals and percentages
- finding percentages of quantities
- working out percentage changes and VAT
- finding one number as a percentage of another
- using percentages to compare amounts
- repeated percentage change
- reverse percentage problems
- using mental, written and calculator methods to solve problems.

Percentages, fractions and decimals

DISCUSSION POINT
What is the connection between 25%, $\frac{1}{4}$ and 0.25?

EXERCISE 1

1 Copy and complete this table.

Percentage	Fraction	Decimal
		0.5
10%		
30%		
	$\frac{2}{5}$	
		0.6
	$\frac{3}{4}$	
5%		
		0.01
90%		
	$\frac{7}{10}$	

2 Estimate the percentage of each of these containers that has been filled.

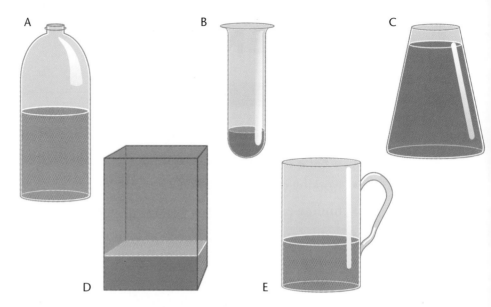

DISCUSSION POINT
Some percentages are not so easy to change into decimals or fractions.
How would you change 12.5% into a decimal?
How would you change it into a fraction?
What is the simplest fraction equal to 12.5%?

EXERCISE 2

1 Change each of these percentages into a decimal.

$\frac{1}{3} = 33\frac{1}{3}\%$

(**a**) 4%   (**b**) 24%   (**c**) 14%   (**d**) 87%

(**e**) 48%   (**f**) 37.5%   (**g**) 6.25%   (**h**) 68.75%

(**i**) $17\frac{1}{2}$ %   (**j**) $66\frac{2}{3}$ %

2 Change each of the percentages in Question 1 into a fraction, in its simplest form.

Calculating percentages of quantities

DISCUSSION POINT
Some percentages can be worked out *without* a calculator.
How would you find 40% of £25?

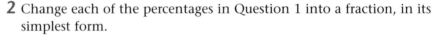

1 Copy these diagrams and show the percentage given by shading the correct amount of squares.

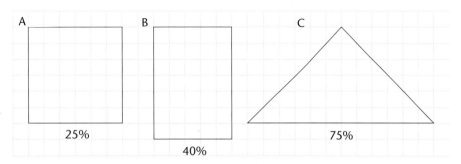

A

25%

B

40%

C

75%

2 Find these percentages.

(a) 10% of £2   (b) 20% of £6   (c) 30% of £40   (d) 15% of £5

(e) 40% of £105   (f) 15% of £240   (g) 70% of £60   (h) 37% of £10

Percentage change

DISCUSSION POINT

A shop has to increase its prices by 10%. What is the new price for each of these items?

90p

£1.20

£13

Another shop decreases its prices by 15% in a sale. What are the sale prices for these items?

£65

£33

£29

Nelson GCSE Maths   PERCENTAGES (INTERMEDIATE)

EXERCISE 4

1 An armchair usually costs £250. In the sale, there is 20% off.
What is the sale price?

2 A shop decides to increase the price of a table by 15%. The old price is £60.
What is the new price?

3 Work out the sale prices of these items.

A £20

30% off
all items in
SALE

B £65

C £130

4 A classic car is expected to increase its value by 7% over the next year. Its
current value is £2000. What is its value expected to be in a year's time?

5 Increase each of these amounts by the percentage shown.

    (**a**) 40 by 25%   (**b**) 250 by 60%   (**c**) 12.5 by 40%

    (**d**) 1000 by 42%   (**e**) 27 by 50%   (**f**) 460 by 75%

6 Decrease each of these amounts by the percentage shown.

    (**a**) 40 by 25%   (**b**) 250 by 60%   (**c**) 225 by 30%

    (**d**) 500 by 8%   (**e**) 27 by 50%   (**f**) 460 by 75%

DISCUSSION POINT
What is VAT?
How would you work out the VAT at 17.5% on a bill of £64, *without*
using a calculator?

EXERCISE 5

1 Work out the VAT at 17.5% for each of these items.

   A Tyre £48 + VAT   B Double glazing £2000 + VAT   C Garden shed £380 + VAT

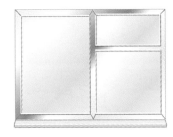

   D Gateau £5.60 + VAT   E Restaurant meal £7.50 + VAT   F Necklace £45 + VAT

2 Work out the total price for each of the items in Question 1.

EXERCISE 6

1 A drink can label says that it contains an extra 20%. The previous size was 275 ml. How much drink does the new size contain?

2 A tin of sweet corn advertises that it contains an extra $33\frac{1}{3}$% free. It normally contains 150 g of sweet corn.
   (a) How much extra sweet corn is there in this tin?
   (b) How much sweet corn is there altogether?

3 A tin of tuna chunks normally contains 185 g. In a special offer, it claims to contain an extra 10% free.
The new tin contains 205 g of tuna. Is it a fair claim?

4 Text books cost £8.50 each, but if you buy 15 or more you receive a 15% discount on your total bill. How much do you save on 20 books?

5 The same type of camera is sold at two different shops.
The normal price of the camera is £72.

Shop A    Shop B

Special offer
£15 off

Discount 20%

Both shops make special offers on the camera. Shop A reduces the price by
£15 and Shop B reduces it by 20%. Which shop offers the best price for the
camera? Explain how you decided.

6 This table of nutrition information has been taken from the side of a
Breakfast Wheat box.

(**a**) Write down the
percentage of
carbohydrate
present in
Breakfast Wheat.

(**b**) A normal serving
is two Breakfast
Wheats.
What is the weight
of two Breakfast
Wheat biscuits?

(**c**) Has the amount
of carbohydrate
in a serving of
two biscuits been
calculated correctly
on the box?

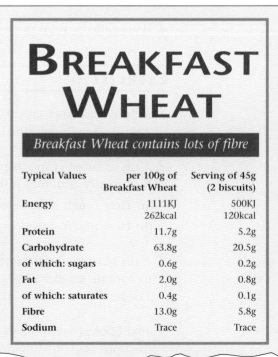

BREAKFAST WHEAT

Breakfast Wheat contains lots of fibre

Typical Values	per 100g of Breakfast Wheat	Serving of 45g (2 biscuits)
Energy	1111KJ	500KJ
	262kcal	120kcal
Protein	11.7g	5.2g
Carbohydrate	63.8g	20.5g
of which: sugars	0.6g	0.2g
Fat	2.0g	0.8g
of which: saturates	0.4g	0.1g
Fibre	13.0g	5.8g
Sodium	Trace	Trace

Finding one number as a percentage of another

Sometimes you need to calculate one thing as a percentage of another.

There are 30 students in a class and 21 of them are girls.

To find the percentage of girls, work out

$\frac{21}{30} \times 100 = 70$

So 70% of the students are girls.

A tin of beans costs 21p. In a special offer, it is reduced to 17p.
What is the percentage reduction?
The actual reduction is 4p.

So, the percentage reduction is

$\frac{4}{21} \times 100 = 19.04761$

So, the reduction is 19%, to the nearest whole number.

EXERCISE 7

1 In a school which has 680 students, 238 of the students travel to school by bus. What percentage of students in this school travel by bus?

2 The capacity of a football ground is 35 000.
At a certain match, the attendance was 16 483.
What percentage of the ground was full?

3 The inventor of a new can-opener earns 6p for each can-opener sold.
A shop is selling these can-openers for 87p each.
What percentage of the price does the inventor earn?

4 Someone bought a bike for £20, spent £2.50 on smartening it up and sold it for £27.50.
What was the percentage profit on his total cost?

5 A car was bought for £5785 and sold three years later for £3500.
What was the percentage loss?

6 A dealer buys a car in very poor condition for £2300 and spends £1200 repairing it.
It is sold for £5350.
What is the profit expressed as a percentage of the *selling* price?

7 These were the milometer readings for a car journey.

Start of journey	38651
Lunch stop	38787
End of the journey	38855

What percentage of the journey was done before lunch?

8 A builder estimates that a building job will take 15 days.
It actually takes 19 days.

(a) What is the percentage increase in the time taken?

(b) The builder estimated the job would cost £3000.
   If the cost of the job is increased by the same percentage as the time,
   what does the job cost?

9 A supermarket normally sells packets of a breakfast cereal for 78p each.
With a special offer, you can buy 8 packets for £5.50.
What is the percentage reduction with the special offer?

10 A chemist has some special offers.

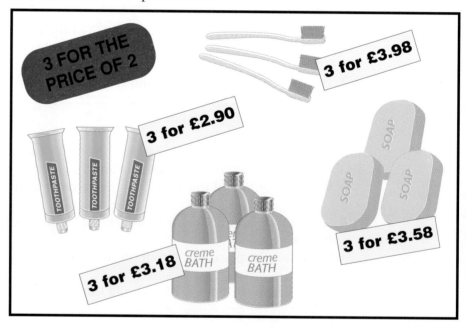

(a) (i) What would three tubes of toothpaste cost, at the normal price?
   (ii) What is the percentage saving on the special offer for toothpaste?

(b) Find the percentage saving on the special offer for

   (i) tooth brushes　　(ii) soap　　(iii) cream bath

Using percentages to compare amounts

A hockey team wins 12 out of its 17 matches.
A second team wins 16 out of a total of 22 matches.
Which of the two teams is the most successful?

The answer to this question may not be obvious because the teams have played a different number of matches.
You can use percentages to compare the teams. First, write both sets of results as a fraction, then change them to a percentage.

Team A won $\frac{12}{17}$ of their matches.	Team B won $\frac{16}{22}$ of their matches.
This is $12 \div 17 \times 100\%$ of their matches.	This is $16 \div 22 \times 100\%$ of their matches.
Team A won **71%** (nearest 1%)	Team B won **73%** (nearest 1%)

So, team B was slightly more successful!

EXERCISE 8

1 The makers of one type of cat food claim that nine out of ten cats prefer their cat food.
Another maker claims that 95% of cats prefer their product.
Which of the two claim the greater amount of popularity among cats?

2 (a) Change $\frac{13}{15}$ to a percentage.
(b) Change $\frac{8}{}$ to a percentage.
(c) Which of these two fractions is the larger?

3 (a) Turn each of these fractions into a percentage.
$$\frac{3}{5} \quad \frac{2}{3} \quad \frac{4}{7} \quad \frac{3}{8} \quad \frac{7}{11}$$
(b) List the five fractions in order of size, starting with the smallest.

4 In a survey, 220 boys and 185 girls were asked whether they smoked.
Of those who admitted they smoked, 55 were boys and 48 were girls.
From these results, would you say the highest percentage of smokers were boys? Or, were they girls?

5 A skilled worker who earned £255 per week was given a wage rise of £15 per week. Her unskilled assistant, who earned £160 per week was given a rise of £12 per week. Who received the highest percentage wage rise?

6 A television survey asks this question.

Do you think that a man should be paid more than a woman if they are both doing exactly the same job?

Out of a total of 24096 telephone calls, 16344 were from women and the rest were from men.

Of the women, 331 of them thought a man should be paid more; and 308 men thought they should be paid more than a woman.

Did a higher percentage of the women than the men think that men should be paid more?

7 Look at this.

'Hard core' drink drive offenders

THE Christmas drink-drive figures for Cornwall have revealed that a hard-core of offenders are still willing to risk their lives – and those of others – by getting behind the wheel after enjoying a festive drink.

Between December 18 and January 2, 266 underwent road-side breath-tests and 42 people were arrested after failing. Nearly a dozen had been involved in accidents.

Across Devon and Cornwall there were 908 breath-tests and 144 people are set to face the shame of a court appearance. Last Christmas there were 130 arrests from 841 breath-tests.

A conviction will bring a driving ban – the minimum is 12 months – and a probable fine, the severity of the punishment rising with the alcohol reading. Persistent offenders, and those who drive while banned, face the very real threat of prison.

For many the decision to drink and drive will have massive consequences, several years off the road often leading to job losses and great hardship for families.

Police say the figures are very similar to the levels of recent years and are "disappointed" that some motorists still do not heed the very clear warnings.

The worst offenders are in the 17–25 age group, while the 50–60 age group is also a problem.

Assistant Chief Constable Alan Street told the Cornish Guardian this week: "The figures are about the same as last year – more arrests being recorded because we have breath-tested more people.

"It's very disappointing that there is still a hard-core of people who will drink and drive and this force will not give up its efforts to catch them and take them off the road."

Police stress that they are on the look-out for drink-drivers at all times of the year, not just Christmas, and say that one of the worst times for the offence is in the summer.

(a) Were more arrests made for drink-driving offences at Christmas 1995 or at Christmas 1996?

(b) In which year were more drivers breath-tested?

(c) Out of the drivers breath-tested, which year had the higher percentage of arrests?

Repeated percentage changes

If you put a sum of money into a savings account at the bank, building society or Post Office, you will be given extra money, called **interest**.

Normally, you would be paid this after every year.

If you put £200 into the bank and they pay you 6% interest p.a. (per year), how much money will you have after three years?

As long as you do not take any money out, or put more money in, at the end of the first year, you will have your original £200 plus 6% of £200. This is

£200 + £12 = £212

But now you have £212 of your money in the bank for the next year. So, at the end of the second year, you will have

£212 + 6% of £212
= £212 + £12.72
= £224.72

At the end of the third year, you will have

£224.72 + 6% of £224.72
= £224.72 + £13.48
= £238.20

DISCUSSION POINT

To increase something by 6%, it is quicker just to multiply by 1.06. Discuss why this works.

Use this quicker method to check the answer of £238.20 given above.

EXERCISE 9

1 (a) Decrease 80 by 50%. Now decrease the answer by 50%.
Does this answer surprise you? Why?

(b) Decrease your answer to part (a) by 50% again. Do this again, and again. Will you ever reach zero, if you keep decreasing by 50%?

2 A bank pays 8% interest. You invest £400 in an account at the bank.

(a) How much would you have altogether, if you leave the money in the bank for one year?

(b) How much money would you have altogether, if you leave the money in the bank for three years?

(c) How much interest would you have earned altogether, after three years?

3 On average, the value of a car depreciates by 18% per year. If a new car costs £8500, what will it be worth when it is three years old?

4 An antique clock is valued at £250 and the owner is told that it should increase in value by 4% each year.
What might it be worth in five years' time?

5 A house is worth £65 000. It is predicted that house prices will increase in value over the next ten years by 2% each year.
How much might it be worth after ten years?

If you borrow money from a bank, you are charged interest. The interest is added on at the **start** of each year.

6 (a) If you borrow £500 for one year and the bank charges 22% interest per annum, how much money in total do you have to pay back to the bank at the end of one year?

(b) Another bank charges 1.8% per month.
Which bank would be the best to borrow the money from, if you pay all the money back after one year?

7 If you start with £1000 in savings, how long would it take to double your money, if you invested it at 20% interest per annum?

8 (a) In a salesman's first year at work, his total sales were £32 000.
In his second year, his sales increased by 8%.
What were his sales in the second year?

(b) The following year, the salesman's total sales increased again, this time by 6.5%.

'Well done!' said the manager. 'Your overall percentage rise over two years is 14.5%. What a pity you didn't reach a 15% increase. If you had, you would have received a bonus payment of £500.'

Was the manager being fair to the salesman? Explain your reasons.

9 The bus fares on a route were increased by 10%, then decreased by 15% and finally increased again by 12%.
What was the overall percentage change in the bus fares?

10 A shopkeeper announced that all prices had been increased by 10%.
Unfortunately for the shopkeeper, all the customers complained.

'OK,' the shopkeeper said, giving in. 'I'll take 10% off the new prices, so you should be happy with that.'

(a) The customers went away *very* happy. Why?

(b) Would it have made any difference if the shopkeeper had decreased the prices first and then increased them by 10%?

Winning £1000000

You are lucky enough to win £1000 000.

♦ What will you do with the money?

You may want to spend some money straight away, but you will also probably want to invest some.

♦ Where will you invest your money?

You could use a bank or a building society or the Post Office.

You may even want to invest in the stock market.

Reverse percentages

DISCUSSION POINT

The local bus company offers a 15% discount to students.
A student pays £5.44 for a journey.
What is the full fare for that journey?

EXERCISE 10

1 When a number is increased by 50%, the answer is 18.
What was the original number?

2 When a number is decreased by 25%, the answer is 45.
What was the original number?

3 The sale price of a pair of shoes is £54.
If the shoes had been reduced by 10%, what was the original price of the shoes?

4 On a particular day, a school has 60 students absent.
This represents 15% of all the students in the school.
How many students are there in the school altogether?

5 The cost of a table at a furniture warehouse is £350, including VAT at 17.5%.

(a) What is the original price of the table?

(b) How much was the VAT?

6 Students receive a discount of 25% on all train journeys with a student railcard.

If a student pays a fare of £19.50, what would be the full cost of the same journey?

7 A shop advertises that all items have been reduced by 25% in a sale.

(a) If the sale price of a pair of trainers is £36, what was the full price of the trainers?

(b) These pictures show some of the other items in the shop and their sale prices.

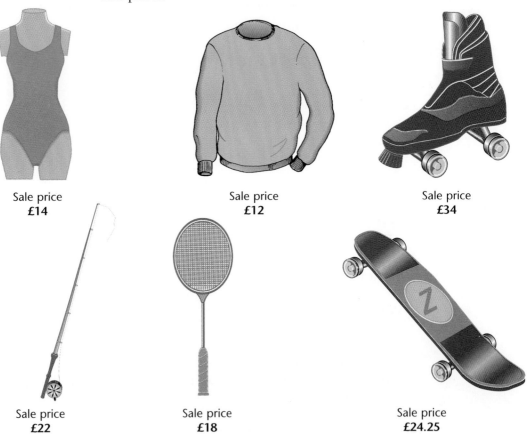

Sale price
£14

Sale price
£12

Sale price
£34

Sale price
£22

Sale price
£18

Sale price
£24.25

Work out the original price for each of the items shown.

8 'Wholewheat Biscuits' advertise an extra 33% free biscuits in a special offer box. There are 36 biscuits in this special offer box.

(a) How many biscuits do you think there are in a normal box?

(b) How accurate is the percentage in the advertisement for the special offer?

9 A newspaper report claims that, over the Christmas holiday period of 1996, the Devon and Cornwall Police charged 144 motorists with drink-driving offences.
This represented a rise of 10.8% on the total for 1995.
How many motorists were charged in 1995?

10 (a) You increase a number by 25%.
What percentage must you decrease the answer by, to return to the original number?

(b) You increase a number by 20%.
What do you decrease the answer by, to return to your original number?

CHAPTER SUMMARY

Recognising simple percentages

You should know these simple percentages.

$1\% = \frac{1}{100}$ $33\frac{1}{3}\% = \frac{1}{3}$

$10\% = \frac{1}{10}$ $50\% = \frac{1}{2}$

$20\% = \frac{1}{5}$ $75\% = \frac{3}{4}$

$25\% = \frac{1}{4}$ $100\% = 1$

Changing percentages to fractions and decimals

Percentage means 'out of 100'. So

$40\% = \frac{40}{100} = \frac{2}{5}$ or $40\% = 40 \div 100 = 0.4$

Changing fractions and decimals to percentages

Multiplying by 100% is the same as multiplying by 1. So

$\frac{4}{5} = \frac{4}{5} \times 100\% = \frac{400\%}{5} = 80\%$ and $0.8 = 0.8 \times 100\% = 80\%$

Finding percentages

If you can, work it out in your head! Otherwise, replace the % symbol with ÷ 100, and 'of' with ×.

VAT (value added tax) is an extra tax you have to pay on most things that you buy.

Finding one number as a percentage of another

Example: The sale price of a coat is £70. The original price was £120. What is the percentage saving?

You save £50 out of £120. Percentage saving is
$50 \div 120 \times 100\% = 42\%$ (to the nearest 1%)

Comparing amounts

Example: A student scores 17 out of 25 on a Science test, and 15 out of 20 on a Maths test. At which subject did she do best?

Change both scores to a percentage.
Science: $17 \div 25 \times 100\% = 68\%$
Maths: $15 \div 20 \times 100\% = 75\%$

The student was more successful at Maths.

Increasing by a percentage

Example: Increase £68 by 14%

Either:
First find 14% of £68.
$14 \div 100 \times £68 = £9.52$
Then add this to £68, giving
£68 + £9.52 = £77.52
Or:
14% = 0.14 so you can multiply by 1+ 0.14 = 1.14
£68 × 1.14 = £77.52

Decreasing by a percentage

Example: Decrease £68 by 14%

Either:
First find 14% of £68
$14 \div 100 \times £68 = £9.52$
Then subtract this from £68, giving
£68 – £9.52 = £58.48

Or:
You can multiply by 1 – 0.14 = 0.86
£68 × 0.86 = £58.48

Interest is the amount of money a bank will charge you if you borrow money from it, or the amount of money the bank will pay you if you give them your money to look after. Interest is normally added on each year or each month.

Repeated percentage increase: Keep multiplying by the same amount as many times as you need.

Example: If you put £800 into a bank for four years at 7.5% interest, you will end up with a total of

£800 × 1.075 × 1.075 × 1.075 × 1.075 = £1068.38

Reverse percentages

When a number is increased by 20% it becomes 48. What is the number?

Either:

The original number must be 100%

120% = 48

10% = 4 (divide both sides by 12)

100% = 40 (multiply both sides by 10)

Or:

To increase by 20% you multiply by 1.20.

So you divide by 1.20 to reverse the process.

48 ÷ 1.20 = 40

CUBES AND SEQUENCES

This chapter is about:

- making difference tables
- finding rules for number sequences
- using algebra to write formulae for number sequences
- explaining why rules and formulae work
- evaluating formulae
- drawing graphs
- finding surface areas of shapes made from cubes.

Cube models

▶ Interlocking cubes

EXERCISE 1

Try making some of the models from interlocking cubes.

1 Models are made by starting with a yellow cube.

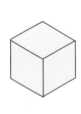 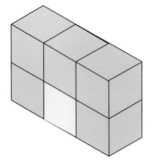 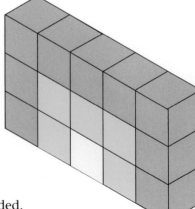

Cubes are then added in stages.

- At the first stage, five blue cubes are added.
- At the second stage, nine red cubes are added.

Check that at the next (third) stage, 13 cubes will be added.

(**a**) How many cubes will be added at the fourth stage?
How many will be added at the fifth stage?

(**b**) How many will be added at the tenth stage?

(**c**) Explain how you worked out your last answer.

(**d**) Copy and complete this table of results.

Stage number	1	2	3	4	5	6	7	8	9	10
Cubes added	5	9	13							

(**e**) This graph has some of the results from the table plotted on it.

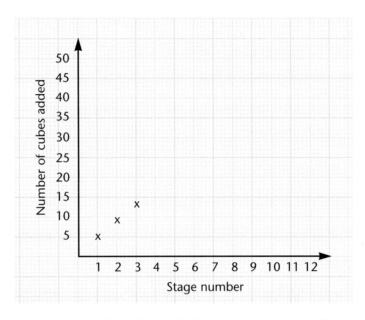

Copy this graph and plot all the results in your table from part (d).
The points will be in a straight line.

(**f**) Explain how you can use your graph to find the number of cubes
added at the twelfth stage.

Do not join up the
points on any of
your graphs in this
exercise.

2 Look at this sequence of models.

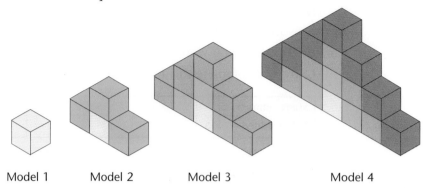

Model 1   Model 2   Model 3   Model 4

(a) Copy and complete this table of results.

Model number	1	2	3	4	5	6	7	8
Number of cubes in bottom row	1	3	5	7				

(b) How did you work out the number of cubes for models 5, 6, 7 and 8?

(c) Draw a graph for these results.

(d) Use your graph to find the number of cubes on the bottom row of the tenth model.

3 Look at this sequence of models.

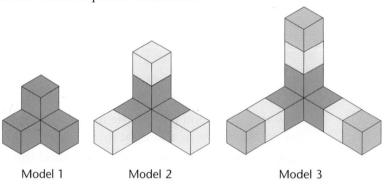

Model 1   Model 2   Model 3

This table contains results for this sequence of models.

Model number	1	2	3	4	5	6	7	8
Number of cubes	4	7	10	13				

(a) Copy and complete the table.
Explain how you worked out the number of cubes for models 5, 6, 7 and 8.

(b) Draw a graph for these results.

(c) How many cubes are needed for the twelfth model?

4 Look at this sequence of models.

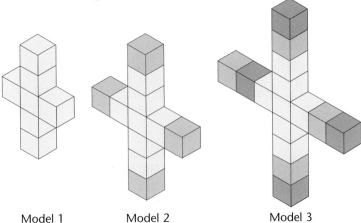

Model 1   Model 2   Model 3

(a) Make a table of results showing the model number and the number of cubes in the model.

(b) Draw a graph of your results.

(c) How many cubes are there in the eighth model?

5 Look again at this sequence of models.

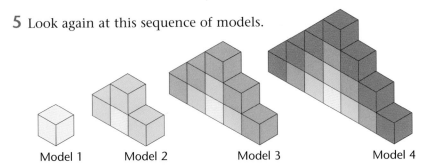

Model 1   Model 2   Model 3   Model 4

(a) Copy and complete this table, recording the model number and the *total* number of cubes in the model.

Model number	1	2	3	4	5	6
Total number of cubes	1	4				

(b) Draw a graph of these results.

(c) In what way is this graph different from the graphs drawn for Questions 1, 2, 3 and 4? In what way is the number pattern different?

DISCUSSION POINT
Why do you think you were told not to join the points on the graphs in the last exercise?

Formulae for linear sequences

To help you to find the formula for the nth term of a sequence, you can produce a **table of differences**.

This is how the formula for the sequence 5, 9, 13, ... can be worked out.

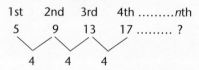

This tells us that $4n$ is part of the formula.

Look again at the table of differences.

Add another step to the beginning of the difference pattern.

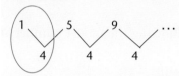

This tells us we need to add 1 to the $4n$.

So the formula for the sequence is $4n + 1$.

To be safe, you should check this formula.

For example, the formula says the third term in the sequence is

$4 \times 3 + 1 = 13$

which is correct.

EXERCISE 2

1 Work out the formulae for these number sequences.

(a) 7, 10, 13, 16, 19, ...

(b) 10, 19, 28, 37, 46, ...

(c) 1, 6, 11, 16, 21, ...

(d) 8, 12, 16, 20, 24, ...

(e) 5, 20, 35, 50, 65, ...

(f) 19, 39, 59, 79, 99, ...

(g) 20, 37, 54, 71, 88, ...

(h) 7, 40, 73, 106, 139, ...

2 To find the formulae for these sequences, you will need to use fractions, decimals or negative numbers, but you work them out in exactly the same way.

(a) −4, 1, 6, 11, 16, 21, ...

(b) −15, −11, −7, −3, 1, ...

(c) 1.6, 5.4, 9.2, 13, 16.8, ...

(d) $3\frac{1}{2}, 7\frac{1}{2}, 11\frac{1}{2}, 15\frac{1}{2}, 19\frac{1}{2}, ...$

(e) $5, 8\frac{1}{2}, 12, 15\frac{1}{2}, 19, 22\frac{1}{2}, ...$

(f) 24, 19, 14, 9, 4, ...

EXERCISE 3

1 Models are made by starting with two yellow cubes.

Cubes of different colours are then used.

At the first stage, six blue cubes are added.

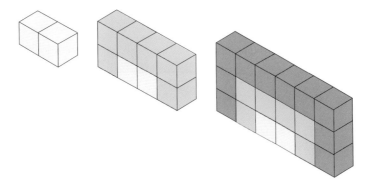

(a) How many red cubes are added at the second stage?

(b) How many cubes are added at the third stage?

(c) Write down the number of cubes added at each of the first five stages.

(d) Work out the formula for the sequence in part (c).

(e) Use your formula to work out the number of cubes added at each of these stages.

    (i) 10th   (ii) 20th   (iii) 33rd

2 Another sequence of models, similar to the one in Question 1, starts with *three* yellow cubes.

(a) Write down the number of cubes added at each of the first five stages.

(b) Work out the formula for the sequence in part (a).

(c) Use your formula to work out the number of cubes added at each of these stages.

    (i) 10th   (ii) 20th   (iii) 33rd

3 Answer Question 2 for a sequence of models starting with *four* yellow cubes.

DISCUSSION POINT

Look back at the formulae you worked out for the questions in Exercise 3. What would be the formula if you started a similar sequence of models with *y* yellow cubes?

Making general statements

Extended difference tables

Not all sequences give the same answer in the first row of differences. Sometimes, you need to work out more than one row of differences.

Example
A sequence of 'staircases' can be made like this.

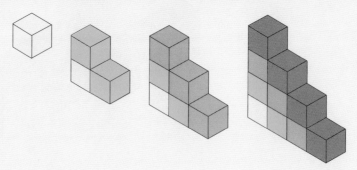

The sequence formed from the number of cubes in each model is 1, 3, 6, 10, ...

Here is the difference table for this sequence.

This time a constant difference appears in the second row of differences.

EXERCISE 4

1 (a) Use the difference table above to help you to predict the next five numbers in this sequence.

(b) What special name is given to this sequence?

2 This diagram shows a difference table.

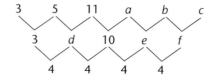

What number does each letter stand for?

3 The sequence of square numbers is described by the formula n^2.
  (a) Write down the first ten square numbers.
  (b) Create a table of differences for the numbers you have written.
  (c) What number is repeated in the second row of differences?

4 The nth term of a sequence is described by the formula $2n^2$.
  (a) Write down the first eight terms of this sequence.
  (b) Create a table of differences.
  (c) Use your difference table to predict the next three numbers in the $2n^2$ sequence.
  (d) What number is repeated in the second row of differences?

5 (a) Draw up a difference table for this sequence of numbers.
     3, 6, 12, 21, 33, 48, 66, 87, ...

  (b) Use the difference table to predict the next three numbers in the sequence.

6 Create a table of differences for each of these sequences.
  (a) $2n^2 + 3$ **(b)** $2n^2 + n$ **(c)** $2n^2 + 3n - 5$
  (d) $3n^2$ **(e)** $4n^2 + 2n$ **(f)** $5n^2 - 3$

7 Look at your tables of differences in Question 6.
   What is the connection between the table of differences and the n^2 part of the formula?

8 All the numbers in the second row of a difference table are 6.
   What can you write down about the formula for the sequence?

Finding formulae for quadratic sequences

If the differences become constant in the second row of differences, it means that there will be a term with n^2 somewhere in the formula.
The number of n-squareds can be found by dividing the number in the second row of differences by 2.

Example

To find the formula for the sequence 5, 18, 37, 62, 93, ...

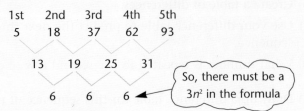

So, there must be a $3n^2$ in the formula

Draw a difference table.
Write the sequence down again, and then subtract the $3n^2$ sequence to see what else is there.

$$5, 18, 37, 62, 93, ...$$
$$3, 12, 27, 48, 75, ...$$
$$\overline{2, \ 6, \ 10, \ 14, \ 18, \ ...}$$

You already know how to deal with sequences like 2, 6, 10, 14, 18, ...

The formula for this sequence is
$4n - 2$

So the complete formula is
$3n^2 + 4n - 2$

Check your answer: the third term should be
$(3 \times 3^2) + (4 \times 3) - 2 = 37$

which is correct.

EXERCISE 5

1 Find the formula for each of these sequences.

(a) 3, 12, 27, 48, 75, 108, ...

(b) 4, 16, 36, 64, 100, 144, ...

(c) $\frac{1}{2}$, 2, $4\frac{1}{2}$, 8, $12\frac{1}{2}$, 18, ...

(d) 3, 6, 11, 18, 27, 38, ...

2 Find the formula for each of these sequences. You may find these take you a little longer to work out.

(a) 2, 6, 12, 20, 30, 42, ...

(b) 4, 10, 18, 28, 40, 54, ...

(c) 3, 10, 21, 36, 55, 78, ...

(d) 6, 13, 24, 39, 58, 81, ...

(e) 6, 12, 20, 30, 42, 56, ...

(f) 2, 9, 18, 29, 42, 57, ...

3 This is the sequence of triangle numbers.
1, 3, 6, 10, 15, 21, 28, 36, ...

(**a**) What is the formula for this sequence?

(**b**) What is the 15th triangle number?

▶ Interlocking cubes

EXERCISE 6

Making general
statements

1 (**a**) This is the first model in a sequence of double-staircases. Make this
model out of cubes. Check that its surface area is 18 squares.

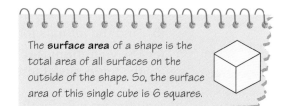

The **surface area** of a shape is the
total area of all surfaces on the
outside of the shape. So, the surface
area of this single cube is 6 squares.

(**b**) The next model in the sequence looks like this.

What is the surface area of this model?
You may need to make it first.

(**c**) Make the next two models in the sequence.
What are their surface areas?

(**d**) Draw a table of differences for the sequence
of surface areas.

(**e**) Use the difference table to predict the surface area of the tenth model
in the sequence.

2 (**a**) Build this sequence of cubes.

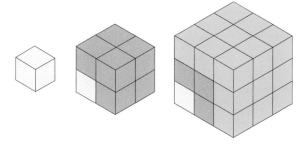

(**b**) Work out the surface area of each model.

(**c**) What is the formula for this sequence of surface areas?

(**d**) What will be the surface area for the 20th model in this sequence?

Nelson GCSE maths   CUBES AND SEQUENCES (INTERMEDIATE)

3 Look at this sequence of models.

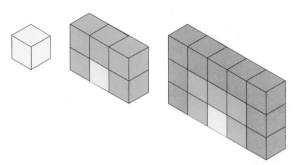

(a) Write down the sequence formed by the *number of cubes* in each model.

(b) Find the formula for this sequence.

(c) Use your formula to work out how many cubes would be needed for the tenth model in this sequence.

4 Find the formula for the sequence of surface areas of the models in Question 3.

Explaining your results

Quite often you have to explain why a sequence of models has a particular formula. To do this, it may be useful to look at how models have been made, or to rearrange the models.

DISCUSSION POINT

You have met this sequence of models earlier in this chapter.

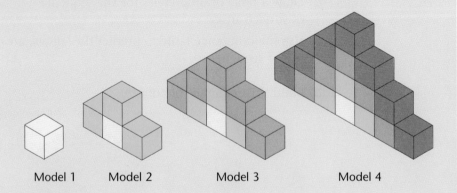

Model 1   Model 2   Model 3   Model 4

Writing down the number of cubes for each model gives this sequence.
   1, 4, 9, 16, ...
You should recognise this as the sequence of square numbers, and so the formula is n^2.
Why does this sequence of 'double staircases' give the square numbers?

Making and justifying generalisations

EXERCISE 7

1 In this octagon, the number of diagonals that can be drawn from any one vertex is 5.

(a) Copy and complete this table to show the number of diagonals that can be drawn from one vertex of different polygons.

Number of sides in polygon	3	4	5	6	7	8	9	10
Number of diagonals from one vertex						5		

(b) What is the formula connecting the number of sides in the polygon to the number of diagonals that can be drawn from one vertex?

(c) Explain why your formula works.

(d) This diagram shows the total number of diagonals that can be drawn in the octagon. There are 20 diagonals altogether!

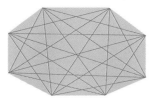

Copy and complete this table to show the *total* number of diagonals that can be drawn in any polygon.

Number of sides in polygon	3	4	5	6	7	8	9	10
Total number of diagonals						20		

(e) The formula connecting the number of sides in the polygon to the total number of diagonals can be written as

$d = \frac{1}{2}n(n - 3)$

Check this formula works for your results.

(f) Explain why this formula works.

2 These are called skeleton cubes.

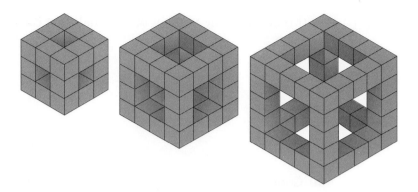

(a) Write down the number of cubes in each model.

(b) Make the next two models in the sequence.

How many cubes are needed for each?

(c) Find the formula for the number of cubes needed for each of the models.

(d) Explain why you cannot have a skeleton cube with less than three small cubes along each edge.

(e) Explain why the numbers in the sequence go up by 12 each time.

(f) Explain the other term in your formula.

3 Look at this sequence of 'square holes'.

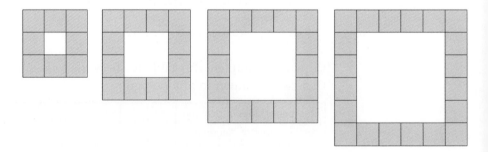

(a) Write down the sequence of the number of squares needed to make each pattern.

(b) Find the formula for this sequence.

(c) Explain your formula by looking at the patterns.

4 Look at this sequence of cube models.

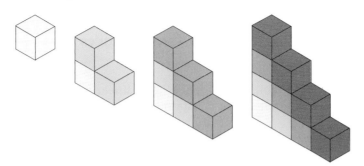

(a) Write down the sequence of the number of cubes needed to make each model.

(b) Find the formula for this sequence.

(c) Explain this formula by taking two identical models and fitting them together.

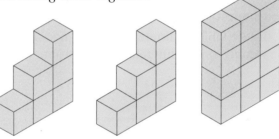

Sequences of cube models

In this piece of work, try to explain the sequences of numbers which you obtain.

♦ You could investigate the surface areas of skeleton cubes.

♦ You could investigate the number of cubes needed to make hollow cubes.

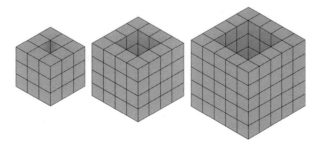

♦ You could make up your own sequences of cube models, and investigate them.

Finding formulae for sequences

Linear sequences

In the table of differences for a linear sequence, the numbers in the first row of differences are constant.

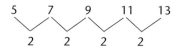

The formula for this sequence begins $2n$ because the first row of differences is always 2.

The full formula is $2n + 3$ because $5 - 2 = 3$.

Quadratic sequences

In the table of differences for a quadratic sequence, the numbers in the second row of differences are constant.

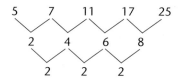

Remember to divide the number by 2 to find the number of n-squareds in the formula.

This formula will begin with $1n^2$ (although you write just n^2). Now take the n^2 sequence away from the original sequence to work out the formula for the sequence left over.

Evaluating formulae

Example: If the formula for the nth term of a sequence is

$2n^2 - n + 5$

then the sixth term (when $n = 6$) is

$2 \times 6^2 - 6 + 5$

$= 72 - 6 + 5$

$= 71$

The surface area is the total area of all the surfaces on the outside of a shape.

8

RATE AND RATIO

This chapter is about:

- using ratio to solve problems
- proportional division
- map scales and reading maps
- scale drawings and plans
- solving problems involving speed.

Ratio

Ratios are used to compare different amounts. Look at this recipe for toad-in-the-hole which is used in school kitchens.

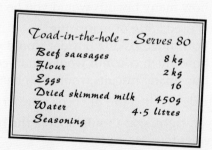

Toad-in-the-hole – Serves 80

Beef sausages	8 kg
Flour	2 kg
Eggs	16
Dried skimmed milk	450g
Water	4.5 litres
Seasoning	

You can compare the amount of sausages to the amount of flour using the ratio 8:2. This means eight 'lots' of sausages to every 2 'lots' of flour.
The 'lots' can be anything: it does not matter how much you have as long as there is four times the amount of sausage as flour.
This ratio can be simplified to 4:1, by dividing both numbers by two.
It must not be written 1:4. This would mean four times as much flour as sausage, and the toad-in-the-hole would not taste the same!

DISCUSSION POINT

Why do you need to change the units before you use ratio to compare the amount of flour to skimmed milk?
Can you use ratio to compare the amount of skimmed milk to water?

1 Look at this recipe used in school kitchens for gypsy cream biscuits.

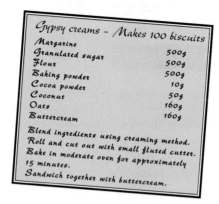

Gypsy creams – Makes 100 biscuits

Margarine	500g
Granulated sugar	500g
Flour	500g
Baking powder	10g
Cocoa powder	50g
Coconut	160g
Oats	160g
Buttercream	

Blend ingredients using creaming method.
Roll and cut out with small fluted cutter.
Bake in moderate oven for approximately
15 minutes.
Sandwich together with buttercream.

(a) Rewrite this recipe to make 200 biscuits.

(b) Rewrite the recipe to make 10 biscuits.

(c) If you used 2 kg of flour
    (i)   how much sugar would you need?
    (ii) how much coconut would you need?
    (iii) how many biscuits would you be making?

(d) If you used 750 g of margarine
    (i)   how much baking powder would you need to use?
    (ii) how much coconut would you need?
    (iii) how many biscuits would you be making?

(e) Write down the ratio of cocoa powder to oats, in its simplest form.

(f) Do you think you should double the baking time if you double the ingredients?
Explain your answer.

2 Here is a list of ingredients for jam and cream puffs.

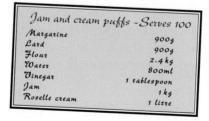

Jam and cream puffs – Serves 100

Margarine	900g
Lard	900g
Flour	2.4 kg
Water	800ml
Vinegar	1 tablespoon
Jam	1 kg
Roselle cream	1 litre

(a) Write the ratio of margarine to flour as simply as you can.

(b) What is the ratio of cream to water in this recipe?

(c) Rewrite the recipe to make 75 jam and cream puffs.

3 (a) In a bag, there are 12 green cubes and 8 pink cubes.

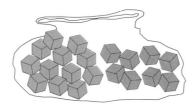

Write down the ratio of green:pink cubes in its simplest form.

(b) Four brown cubes are added to the bag.
What is the ratio of colours now?

(c) In a second bag, there are 18 green cubes. The green, pink and brown cubes in this bag are in the same ratio as in the first bag.
How many pink and brown cubes are there in the second bag?

4 (a) In a school, there are 1200 students and 60 teachers.
What is the student to teacher ratio?

(b) How many teachers would you expect a school of 800 students to have?

5 In a school of 1170 students, there are 540 girls.
What is the ratio of boys to girls in the school?

6 Write these sets of numbers or amounts as ratios, in their simplest form.

   (a) 12, 18   **(b)** 3.5, 2.5   **(c)** 27, 18, 45   **(d)** 40p, £2.50

   (e) 3 kg, 250 g   **(f)** 90 cm, 1.8 m   **(g)** 1 cm, 1 km   **(h)** 25p, 75p, £2

7 The Fibonacci sequence begins:
1, 1, 2, 3, 5, 8, 13, 21, 34, 55, ...
Pick pairs of numbers from the Fibonacci sequence to satisfy these statements.

A: The ratio of the numbers is 4:1.

B: The ratio of the numbers is 17:4.

C: The ratio of the numbers is 29:1.

D: The ratio of the numbers is 122:11.

EXERCISE 2

1 A 250-g jar of coffee costs £3.60, and a 200-g jar costs £2.98.
Which is the best buy?

2 A 500-g box of breakfast cereal costs £1.35.
A 150-g box of the same cereal costs 90p.

(**a**) Explain why the larger size gives better value for money.

(**b**) Why might some people still prefer to buy the smaller size?

3 Two rival double glazing firms both announce special offers.
One company offers seven windows for £1995, while the other offers five windows for £1425.
Which company is providing the best value for money?

4 A box of 60 pencils is sold for £4.75.
A box of 144 similar pencils costs £9.99.
Which box gives the best value for money?

5 Computer discs can be bought in packs of 40 for £18.75 or packs of 10 for £4.75.

Which is the best buy?

6 A pack of four Mammoth Bars costs 99p.
Five Monster Bars cost £1.20.
Which is the best buy?

DISCUSSION POINT

People all over the world are becoming more aware of endangered species in nature.

For instance, in the early 1990s, it was estimated that there were

- 30000 Asian elephants
- 5000 cheetahs
- 800 tigers
- 350 northern right whales
- 8 sacred ibises.

Who counts these animals?

How do they go about it?

Why do they do it?

EXERCISE 3

1 In the jungle, 200 tigers are captured and tagged.
Some time later, a second sample of tigers is captured.
Estimate the number of surviving tigers in the wild, if these are the results of the second sample.

(a) 30 tagged tigers and 120 untagged tigers

(b) 15 tagged and 45 untagged tigers

(c) 16 tagged and 56 untagged tigers

2 In the jungle, 80 mountain gorillas are captured, tagged and then returned to the wild.
A year later, some more gorillas are captured. 14 gorillas are tagged and 56 are untagged.
Estimate the number of gorillas surviving in the wild.

3 One summer, 2000 cranes are captured, tagged and then released.
Some time later another 840 cranes are captured, of which 60 are found to be tagged and the rest untagged.
Estimate the number of cranes left in the wild.

4 One day, 100 fish are pulled from a small lake.
They are tagged and then returned to the lake.
Two days later, 150 fish are pulled from the lake and 17 of them are tagged.

(a) Estimate the number of fish in the lake.

(b) How accurate do you think your estimate is?

Capture and recapture

You can use tagging to estimate the number of cubes in a bag.

You are then 'modelling' the method used to estimate an animal population.

♦ Ask somebody to put a large number of cubes (or counters, or buttons, or …) in a bag.

♦ Take out a number of cubes, write down how many, mark them and put them back in the bag.

Marking each cube before putting it back into the bag is like tagging an animal before releasing it.

♦ Give the bag a good shake and then take out some more cubes.

Write down the number of tagged and untagged cubes.

♦ Estimate the number of cubes in the bag.

♦ How could you make your estimate more accurate?

♦ How is this experiment like estimating animal populations?

How is it different?

What other problems might an animal researcher have?

♦ If you want to, you can count the cubes in the bag to see how accurate your estimate was.

Proportional division

Example

Share £45 between three people in the ratio 2:3:4.

One person receives two shares, the second receives three shares and the third receives four shares.

$2 + 3 + 4 = 9$

So, altogether you need to divide the money into 9 shares.

$£45 \div 9 = £5$

So, each share is worth £5, and the three amounts of money will be

$2 \times £5 = £10$

$3 \times £5 = £15$

$4 \times £5 = £20$

You can check your answer.

$£10 + £15 + £20 = £45$

which is correct.

1 Divide £20 in the ratio 7:1.

2 Divide £36 in the ratio 3:1:5.

3 In a class of 28 students, the ratio of boys to girls is 3:4.
 (a) How many boys are there?
 (b) What fraction of the total class are boys?
 (c) What fraction are girls?

4 To make a fruit-juice cocktail, you mix pineapple juice, grapefruit juice and lemonade in the ratio 2:1:3.
 (a) How much pineapple juice do you need to make 3 litres of the cocktail?
 (b) If you have 7.5 litres of lemonade
  (i) how much cocktail can you make?
  (ii) how much pineapple juice will you need?
 (c) What fraction of the cocktail is lemonade?
 (d) What fraction of the cocktail is pineapple juice?

5 On a building project, a bricklayer works for five days, a carpenter for four days and a plasterer for two days.
 They are paid a total of £4290 and agree to share it in the ratio of the number of days worked.
 (a) How much did they each receive?
 (b) What fraction of the money did the plasterer receive?

6 A brother and sister share £600 so that the brother receives twice as much as his sister.
 (a) Write down the amounts of money received by the brother and sister, as a ratio.
 (b) How much does the sister receive?
 (c) What fraction of the money does the brother receive?

7 (a) The lengths of the sides of a triangle are in the ratio 5:6:9.
  If the perimeter of the triangle is 70 cm, what is the length of the longest side?
 (b) The triangle is enlarged so that the shortest side is now 27.5 cm.
  What is the perimeter of the enlarged triangle?

Map scales

DISCUSSION POINT

You may have seen ratios used on maps and plans.

Two ratios commonly used on maps for walking are 1:50 000 and 1:25 000.
What do these ratios mean?

Explain why a ratio of 1:50 000 is the same as 2 cm to 1 km.

EXERCISE 5

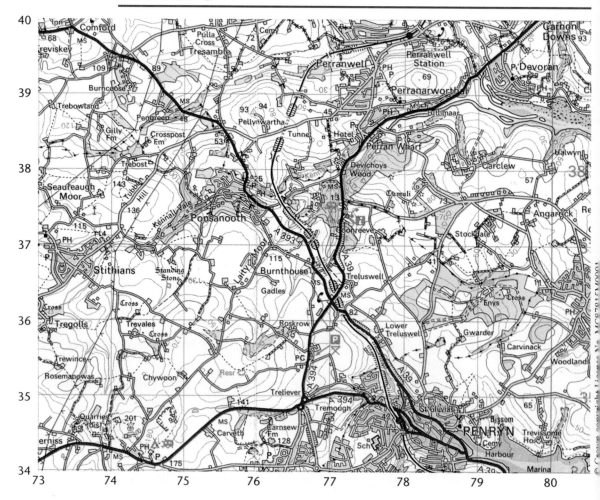

1 The railway station at Penryn has the grid reference 780 348.
What is the name of the small village at grid reference 789 380?

2 What building can be found at these grid references?

(a) 772 384   (b) 776 344

3 Give the grid references of the churches in these villages.

   (a) Stithians   (b) Devoran

4 Has there been a fire at grid reference 768 367? Name the village.

5 The scale of the map is 1:50 000.
   What does 1 cm on the map represent in real life

   (a) in centimetres?   (b) in metres?   (c) in kilometres?

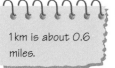

1 km is about 0.6 miles.

6 You are travelling between the railway stations at Penryn and Perranwell Station.

   (a) Estimate how far it is in kilometres, if you travel

      (i) by rail   (ii) by road

   (b) What are the distances you found in part (a), in miles?

7 Halwyn is the name of a tiny village at grid reference 804 382.
   A person living at Halwyn drives to church at Devoran.
   Estimate the length of the journey

   (a) as the crow flies, in kilometres   (b) as the crow flies, in miles

   (c) by road, in kilometres   (d) by road, in miles

EXERCISE 6

1 Look at this map of a walk in Staffordshire.

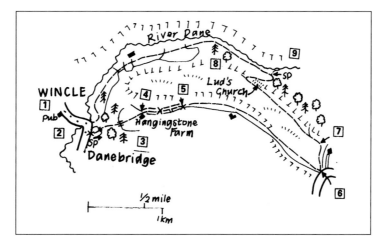

   (a) Use the scale given to *estimate* the length of the walk in miles.

   (b) Measure the scale line to the 1 km mark and work out the scale of the map in the form 1:*n*.

2 Look at this map of a walk in Northumberland.

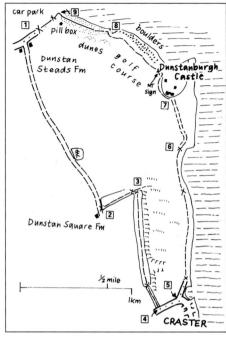

(a) Estimate the length of the walk in miles.

(b) Work out the scale of the map in the form 1:*n*.

3 A distance of 5 cm on a map represents a distance of 100 km in real life.
What is the map scale in the form 1:*n*?

4 A road map is drawn to a scale of 4 cm to 1 km.

(a) Write the map scale as a ratio in its simplest form.

(b) The real distance between two points is 12 km.
What distance is this on the map?

(c) Two points on the map are 16 cm apart.
What is the real distance between these points?

5 (a) This is the scale used in an atlas for a map of The Netherlands.

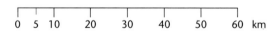

Measure it, and work out the map scale in the form 1:*n*.

(b) The same atlas uses this scale to show Amsterdam in more detail.

Measure this scale, and work out the map scale in the form 1:*n*.

6 A map of South-East Australia has a scale of 1:6 000 000 (or 1:6M).
The distance from Melbourne to Brisbane, as the crow flies, is 1380 km.
How far is this on the map?

7 A map of the African continent has a scale of 1:24M. The distance on the map between Casablanca in Morocco, and Johannesburg in South Africa, is 30.5 cm. What is the real distance between these two towns?

Scale drawing

EXERCISE 7

1 A student wanted to work out the height of a building. She made this rough sketch and marked on it the measurements she took.

(a) Use the information given to produce an accurate scale drawing, using a scale of 1:100.

(b) Use your drawing to estimate the height of the building.

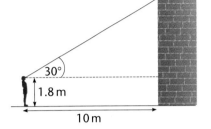

2 A student was estimating the width of a road. He made some measurements and put them on a rough sketch.

Use the information given to draw an accurate diagram to a scale of 1:50.

From your diagram, estimate the width of the road.

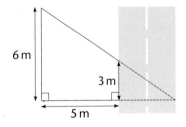

3 This diagram shows the dimensions of a football pitch.

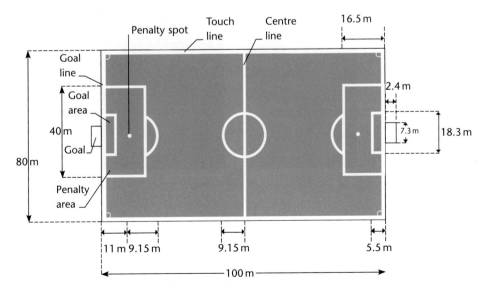

Choose a suitable scale and make a scale drawing of the football pitch.

Nelson GCSE Maths   RATE AND RATIO (INTERMEDIATE)

4 The height of this scale model is 4 cm. The real car is 1.6 m high.

(a) What is the scale of the model?

(b) What is the length of the real car, if the model is 11 cm long?

(c) The wheels on the real car have a diameter of 66 cm.
What is the diameter of the wheels on the model?

(d) There are four wheels on the model car.
How many wheels will there be on the real thing?

5 One of these photographs is an enlargement of the other.

6 cm   9 cm

(a) What is the scale factor of the enlargement?

(b) If the height of the larger photograph is 12 cm, what height is the smaller one?

(c) What is the ratio of the areas of the photographs?

Scale drawing

Think of a situation in your life where it may be helpful to make a scale drawing.

♦ You might want to redesign your bedroom. You could make a scale drawing of the room and the furniture you might want to include. You could then experiment with different arrangements of the furniture.

♦ You might want to redesign another room in the house.

♦ You might want to make a scale drawing of a garden and try out different designs for it, including, for example, a patio, some flower beds and a lawn.

♦ You might want to create a visitors' map to help people to find your school, or to find interesting landmarks in the town or village where you live.

♦ You might want to design a layout for your school sports field.

♦ You might want to design a piece of furniture, such as a computer desk, or bird feeding table, or somewhere to keep your CDs.

Speed

A man runs a 1500-metre race in 4 minutes 5 seconds.
His speed varies at different points in the race, but his **average speed** can be calculated like this.

Distance run = 1500 metres
Time = 245 seconds
Average speed = 1500 metres ÷ 245 seconds
　　　　　　 = 6.1 metres per second

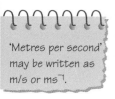

'Metres per second' may be written as m/s or ms^{-1}.

A woman travels from Leicester to Peterborough.
Her journey is 33 miles.
The journey takes 47 minutes.

Distance travelled = 33 miles
Time taken = 47 minutes
　　　　　 = 47 ÷ 60 hours
　　　　　 = 0.783 hours

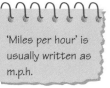

'Miles per hour' is usually written as m.p.h.

Average speed = 33 miles ÷ 0.783 hours
　　　　　　 = 42 miles per hour

This is the formula for average speed.
average speed = distance ÷ time

Nelson GCSE Maths　RATE AND RATIO (INTERMEDIATE)

In this exercise, give all your answers to a sensible degree of accuracy.

EXERCISE 8

1 A cyclist allows three hours for a journey.

She estimates her average cycling speed as 15 m.p.h.

How many miles is the journey?

2 A bus travels on average at 10 m.p.h.

How long will it take to complete a journey of 15 miles?

3 A high-speed train travels from London to Paris in three hours.

The distance travelled is approximately 220 miles.

Estimate the average speed.

4 A cyclist takes 2 hours to travel 36 miles.

How long will it take him to travel 50 miles at the same average speed?

Give your answer to the nearest ten minutes.

5 A car travels at an average speed of 45 m.p.h.

If it maintains the same average speed, how far will it travel in these lengths of time?

(a) 2 hours (b) 5 hours (c) 30 minutes

(d) 20 minutes (e) 1 hour 40 minutes (f) 3 hours 10 minutes

6 An aeroplane's average speed is 420 m.p.h.

How far will it go in these lengths of time?

(a) 15 minutes (b) 5 minutes (c) 3 hours 25 minutes

7 The average speed of a snail is 7 centimetres per minute.

(a) How far can a snail travel in 1 hour?

(b) Write this speed in kilometres per hour.

(c) How long would it take a snail to travel 1 metre?

8 For a spacecraft to escape the Earth's gravitational pull, it must reach a speed of 11.2 kilometres per second.
Write this speed in kilometres per hour.

9 The speed of the Earth, as it travels around the Sun, is approximately 30 kilometres per second.
How far do you travel every day, even if you stand still?
Give your answer to 1 significant figure.

10 A cheetah's top speed is about 110 kilometres per hour, but it can only maintain this speed for about 400 m.

(a) Work out the cheetah's speed in metres per second.

(b) How long would it take the cheetah to cover 400 m?

(c) Linford Christie, the athlete, had a personal best time of 9.87 s for the 100 m. If it were possible for Linford to race a cheetah over 100 m, who would win? By how much?

11 The Moon is drifting away from the Earth at a rate of 4 cm per year.

(a) How long will it take to drift 1 m away?

(b) How long would it take for the Moon to drift 1 km?

(c) Write the speed of the Moon's drift in kilometres per hour.
Give your answer to 1 significant figure.

12 A car covers 32 miles in 40 minutes.

(a) What is its average speed?

(b) How long will it take for the same journey if the average speed is doubled?

(c) How long would it take if the average speed was increased by 50%?

(d) How long would it take if the average speed was decreased by $\frac{1}{3}$?

(e) How long would it take if the average speed was decreased by 25%?

(f) If the time taken for the same journey was increased to 1 hour, what would the average speed be?

(g) If the journey time is increased by 25% what happens to the average speed?

(h) If the journey time is decreased by 25% what happens to the average speed?

Ratio

Ratios are used to compare different amounts.

Sausages and flour are in the ratio 4:1
(*not* 1:4).
Ratio of flour to skimmed milk is
   2 kg:450 g
   = 2000 g:450 g
   = 40:9

Toad-in-the-hole – Serves 80

Beef sausages	
Flour	8 kg
Eggs	2 kg
Dried skimmed milk	16
Water	450 g
Seasoning	4.5 litres

Proportional division

Example: Share £90 in the ratio 2:3:5.

You need to divide the money into 10 shares (because 2 + 3 + 5 = 10).
   £90 ÷ 10 = £9
Each share is worth £9.

The three amounts of money will be:
   2 × £9 = £18
   3 × £9 = £27
   5 × £9 = £45

You can check your answer: £18 + £27 + £45 = £90, which is correct.

Maps

Many maps use six-figure grid references which are like coordinates, e.g. the grid reference 345 678 can be thought of as the point (34.5, 67.8) on the map.

Map scales: A scale of 1:50 000 means every 1 cm on the map is worth 50 000 cm in real life.

50 000 cm is the same as $\frac{1}{2}$ km, so 1 cm on the map is worth $\frac{1}{2}$ km in real life.

Speed

Speed = distance ÷ time
This triangle may help you
to remember the three formulae
connected with speed.

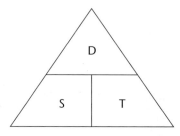

9 TRIGONOMETRY

This chapter is about:

- accurate drawing and measuring using a ruler and protractor
- sketching, plotting and reading graphs
- finding rules connecting sets of numbers
- the link between multiplication and division
- multiplication and division by a decimal less than 1
- selecting the appropriate degree of accuracy
- using sine, cosine and tangent to solve problems about right-angled triangles.

Naming sides of triangles

The hypotenuse is the longest side and is opposite the right angle.

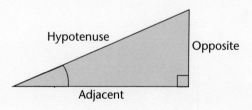

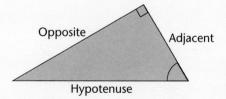

Of the other two sides: the opposite side is opposite the marked angle, and the adjacent side is next to the marked angle.

Exercise 1

1 Make a rough copy of each of these right-angled triangles.

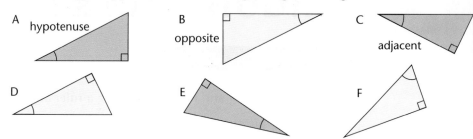

2 Label each side of the triangles from Question 1 as 'opposite', 'adjacent', or 'hypotenuse'.

Sketching and drawing right-angled triangles

DISCUSSION POINT
Check you know how to use a protractor.

EXERCISE 2

▶ Protractor

1 Estimate the size of these angles. Then measure them accurately, using a protractor.

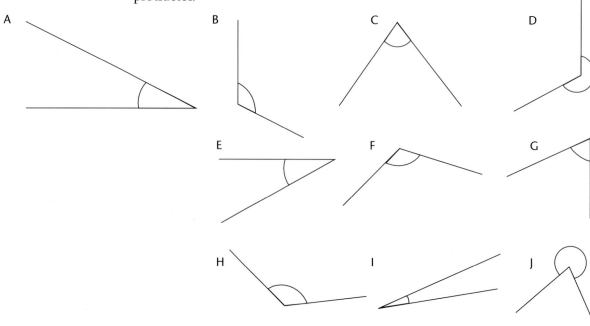

2 Sketch each of these angles. Then give them to your partner to measure accurately, using a protractor.

(a) 45°   (b) 60°   (c) 30°   (d) 135°

(e) 260°   (f) 310°   (g) 15°   (h) 80°

EXERCISE 3

1 This is a right-angled triangle with a hypotenuse of 10 cm.

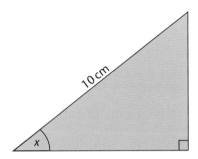

Use a protractor and a ruler to draw more right-angled triangles, each with a hypotenuse of 10 cm, but using different angles for *x*, as listed in this table.

Angle *x*	Length of opposite side (cm)	Length of adjacent side (cm)
5°		
10°		
20°		
30°		
40°		
45°		
50°		
60°		
70°		
80°		
85°		

For each triangle, measure the length of the opposite side and the length of the adjacent side. Copy and complete the table.

2 What angle has the opposite and adjacent sides of the same length?

3 What angles have the opposite side longer than the adjacent side?

4 What angles have the opposite side shorter than the adjacent side?

5 Copy these axes and, using your results from Question 1, plot the graph accurately to show what happens to the length of the *adjacent* side as the angle changes.

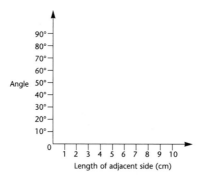

Join the points up with a smooth curve.

6 Draw axes like those for Question 5.

Using your results from Question 1, plot the graph accurately to show what happens to the length of the *opposite* side as the angle changes.

DISCUSSION POINT

Look at this right-angled triangle.

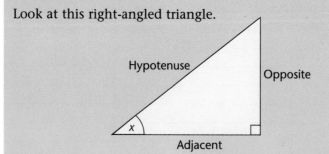

Imagine rotating the hypotenuse so that the angle *x* changes.
Think what happens to the lengths of the other two sides as the angle *x* changes.
- What angle *x* would give the longest possible adjacent side?
- What angle *x* would give the shortest possible adjacent side?
- What angle *x* would give the longest possible opposite side?
- What angle *x* would give the shortest possible opposite side?
- How long is the adjacent side when the opposite side is as long as possible?
- How long is the adjacent side when the opposite side is as short as possible?

A **sketch** is a rough drawing which gives you an idea of what is involved in a problem.

A sketch may also be labelled to help you to do any calculations.

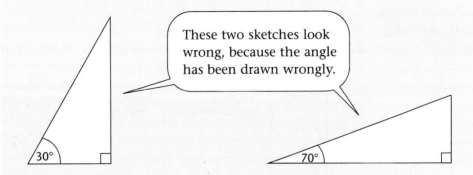

These two sketches look wrong, because the angle has been drawn wrongly.

30°

70°

- If the angle is less then 45°, the adjacent side is longer than the opposite.
- If the angle is more than 45°, the adjacent is shorter than the opposite.

EXERCISE 4

1 Each of these statements describes a right-angled triangle. Sketch and label these ten triangles.

A: Angle: 30°; opposite side: 5 cm

B: Angle: 60°; adjacent side: 12 cm

C: Angle: 45°; hypotenuse side: 37 km

D: Angle: 70°; opposite side: 12 miles

E: Angle: 10°; adjacent side: 3 mm

F: Angle: 55°; hypotenuse: 15 inches

G: Angle: 80°; hypotenuse: 43 m

H: Angle: 22°; hypotenuse: 62 mm

I: Angle: 76°; hypotenuse: 1500 km

J: Angle: 65°; hypotenuse: 1.75 m

2 For each of your triangles in Question 1, decide if the opposite side or the adjacent side is the longer side.

Put a tick to show which of the two is the longer.

Sine, cosine and tangent as multipliers

EXERCISE 5

Resource Sheet G: *60° right-angled triangles*

1 On your copy of Resource Sheet G: *60° right-angled triangles*, label each side of each triangle as adjacent, opposite or hypotenuse.

2 (**a**) Measure the lengths of the sides of each triangle on the resource sheet.

(**b**) Put your results in a table like this.

Triangle	Length of hypotenuse (cm)	Length of opposite side (cm)	Length of adjacent side (cm)
A	1		
B	2		
C	4		
D	8		
E	3		
F	6		
G	9		
H	5		
I	10		
J	12		

Making general statements

DISCUSSION POINT

What are the rules connecting the three columns in the table you completed in Question 2 of Exercise 5?

Some of your rules may not work exactly with all the numbers in the table. Why is this?

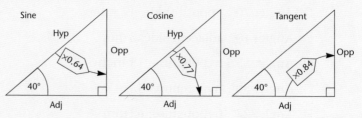

The number you have to multiply the hypotenuse by, to obtain the length of the opposite side is called the **sine multiplier**.

The number you have to multiply the hypotenuse by, to obtain the length of the adjacent side is called the **cosine multiplier**.

The number you have to multiply the length of the adjacent side by, to obtain the length of the opposite side is called the **tangent multiplier**.

The sizes of the sine, cosine and tangent multipliers depend on the angle.

EXERCISE 6

1 (**a**) On your copy of Resource Sheet H: *20° right-angled triangles*, label each side of each triangle as adjacent, opposite or hypotenuse.

(**b**) Measure the lengths of the sides of each of the triangles.

(**c**) Put your results in a table like the table in Question 2 of Exercise 5.

(**d**) Find the three multipliers (sine, cosine and tangent) for the 20° angle.

> It may be useful to share the questions in this exercise with others in the class. Collect everyone's results together at the end.

2 Answer Question 1 for the triangles on your copy of Resource Sheet I: *40° right-angled triangles*.

3 Answer Question 1 for the triangles on your copy of Resource Sheet J: *80° right-angled triangles*.

> Instead of drawing and measuring triangles to find the sine, cosine and tangent multipliers, you can use your calculator.
>
> Make sure your calculator is in DEG mode before you start, otherwise you will be given the wrong answers.
>
> Use the sin, cos and tan buttons.

EXERCISE 7

1 Use your calculator to check your answers to Question 2 in Exercise 5 and all three questions in Exercise 6.

2 Copy and complete this table, using your calculator.

Multiplier	10°	20°	30°	40°	50°	60°	70°	80°
Sine								
Cosine								
Tangent								

DISCUSSION POINT
How do the multipliers change as the angle becomes bigger?

Finding the length of a side

The measurements given for the triangles in this exercise are correct to the nearest millimetre. Give your answers to a sensible degree of accuracy.

EXERCISE 8

1 In each of these three right-angled triangles, you are given the size of one angle and the length of one side. Another side has been marked with a question mark.

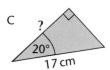

Use either your calculator or your table to help you to calculate the length of the side marked ? in each triangle.

2 Calculate the length of the side marked ? in each of these three triangles.

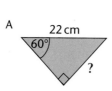

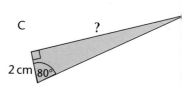

3 Calculate the length of the side marked ? in each of these four triangles.

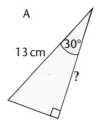
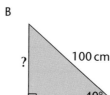
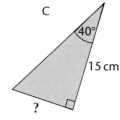
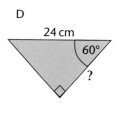

Finding the length of the hypotenuse

DISCUSSION POINT

So far you have been given the length of the hypotenuse and asked to use the **sine multiplier** to find the length of the opposite side.

• How would you use the **sine multiplier** to find the length of the hypotenuse, if you were given the length of the opposite side?

• How would you use the **cosine multiplier** to find the length of the hypotenuse, if you were given the length of the adjacent side?

• How would you use the **tangent multiplier** to find the length of the adjacent side, if you were given the length of the opposite side?

EXERCISE 9

1 Copy and complete these diagrams.

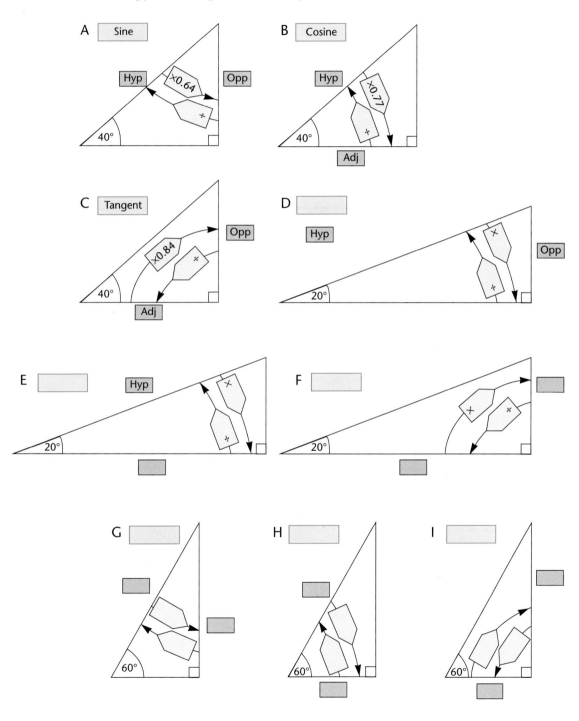

A Sine

Hyp   ×0.64   Opp

÷

40°

B Cosine

Hyp   ×0.77

÷

40°   Adj

C Tangent

×0.84   Opp

÷

40°   Adj

D

Hyp   ×

Opp

÷

20°

E

Hyp   ×

÷

20°

F

÷   ÷

20°

G

60°

H

60°

I

60°

Nelson GCSE Maths   TRIGONOMETRY (INTERMEDIATE)

2 Copy and complete these diagrams.

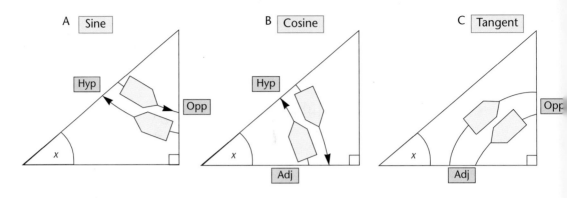

The measurements given in this exercise are correct to the nearest millimetre. Give your answers to a sensible degree of accuracy.

EXERCISE 10

1 Use your calculator to help you to calculate the length of the side marked ? in each of these triangles.

A
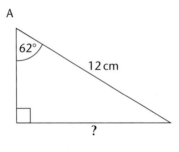

B
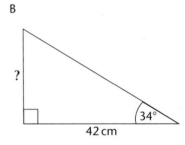

C
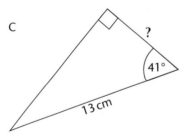

D
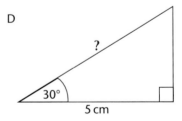

E
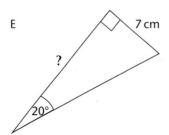

2 Use your calculator to help you to calculate the length of the sided marked ? in each of these triangles.

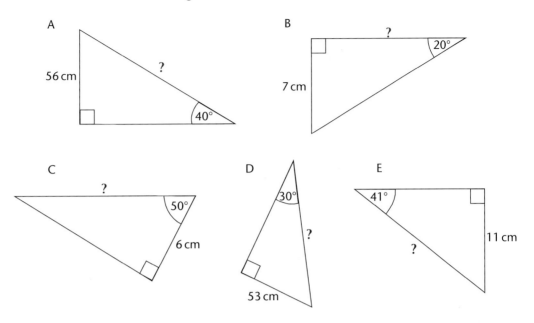

A 56 cm ? 40°

B 7 cm ? 20°

C ? 50° 6 cm

D 30° ? 53 cm

E 41° ? 11 cm

3 Use your calculator to help you to calculate the length of the side marked ? in each of these triangles.

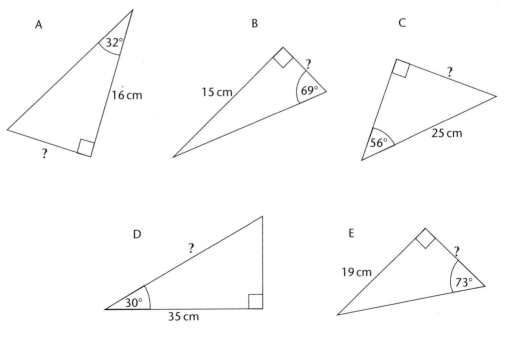

A 32° 16 cm ?

B 15 cm ? 69°

C ? 25 cm 56°

D ? 30° 35 cm

E 19 cm ? 73°

The trigonometric graphs

EXERCISE 11

1 Copy these axes. Label your axes 'Angle' and 'Sine'.

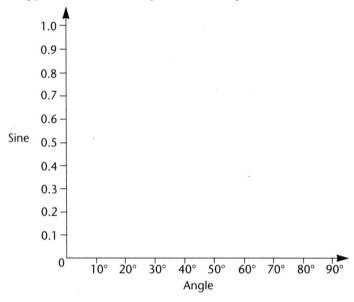

Plot the graph of the sine of an angle against the angle.

2 Make another set of axes like the ones in Question 1 but, this time, label your axes 'Angle' and 'Cosine'.
Plot the graph of the cosine of an angle against the angle.

3 Copy these axes. Label your axes 'Angle' and 'Tangent'.

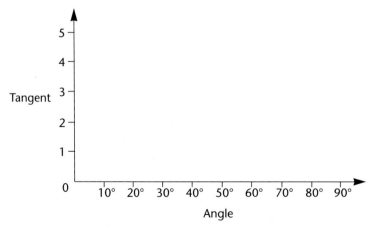

Plot the graph of the tangent of an angle against the angle.

Sine, cosine and tangent are usually shortened to sin, cos and tan.

4 Using your three graphs from Questions 1, 2 and 3, estimate these values.

(a) $\cos 56°$ (b) $\tan 37°$

(c) $\sin 73°$ (d) $\sin 18°$

(e) $\tan 84°$ (f) $\cos 35°$

(g) The angle whose sine is 0.5   (h) The angle whose tangent is 1.7

(i) The angle whose cosine is 0.74   (j) The angle whose cosine is 0.95

(k) The angle whose sine is 0.95   (l) The angle whose tangent is 0.5

Finding angles

DISCUSSION POINT

You have used your graphs to find out the angle when you know the sine of that angle.

- How can you do this on your calculator?
- How do you find the angle when you know the cosine of that angle?
- How do you find the angle when you know the tangent of that angle?

EXERCISE 12

1 Find the size of the angle marked ? in each of these triangles.

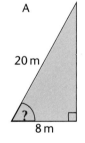

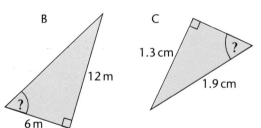

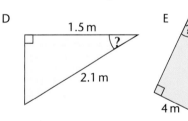

2 Find the size of the angle marked ? in each of these triangles.

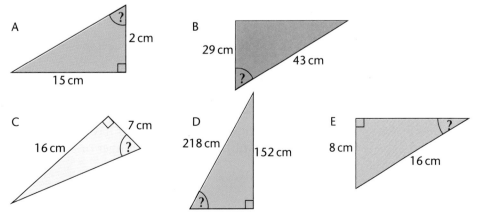

For a right-angled triangle, there are three different ways of writing each of the sine, cosine and tangent formulae.

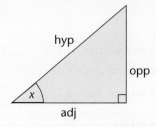

$$\begin{array}{lll}
\text{opp} = \text{hyp} \times \sin x & \text{hyp} = \text{opp} \div \sin x & \sin x = \text{opp} \div \text{hyp} \\
\text{adj} = \text{hyp} \times \cos x & \text{hyp} = \text{adj} \div \cos x & \cos x = \text{adj} \div \text{hyp} \\
\text{opp} = \text{adj} \times \tan x & \text{adj} = \text{opp} \div \tan x & \tan x = \text{opp} \div \text{adj}
\end{array}$$

These diagrams may help you to remember the formulae.

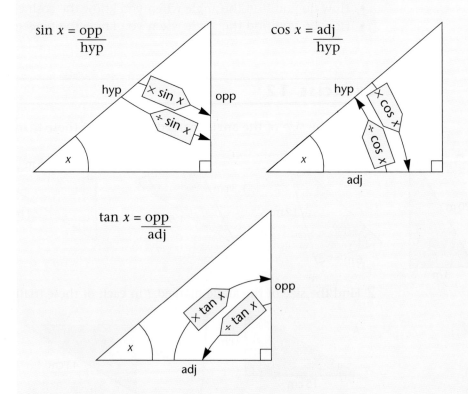

$$\sin x = \frac{\text{opp}}{\text{hyp}}$$

$$\cos x = \frac{\text{adj}}{\text{hyp}}$$

$$\tan x = \frac{\text{opp}}{\text{adj}}$$

You need to make a note of these formulae.

If you cannot remember whether you have to multiply or divide, try to decide if you want the length of a longer or a shorter side.

Using trigonometry to solve problems

Here is a typical exam question.

A 2m long ladder is leaning at an angle of 60° against a wall. How far away from the wall is the bottom of the ladder?

The examiner expects you to sketch the problem and to calculate the answer using sine, cosine or tangent. **To use sine, cosine or tangent, you must draw a right-angled triangle.**

Look at these two sketches.

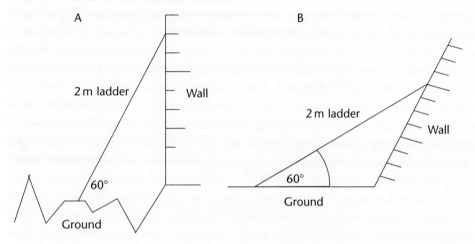

In sketch A, you cannot solve the problem because the ground is not level.

In sketch B, you cannot solve the problem because the wall is not at right angles to the ground.

You also do not know how accurately the ladder was measured. If it was to the nearest metre, it could be anything between 1.5 m and 2.5 m. So you do not know how accurately to give your answer.

The examiner has assumed that

- the ground is level
- the wall is at right angles to the ground
- you can guess how accurately the ladder was measured.

EXERCISE 13

In this exercise, answer the question and then list the assumptions you have made.

1 A ladder 2.5m long is resting against a wall. How high up the wall does the ladder reach, if it is leaning at an angle of 68°?

2 A spotlight is situated on the ground and angled to illuminate the top of a tower which is 26 m high. The light is 12 m from the foot of the tower. At what angle must the spotlight be fixed?

3 A flag pole is held up by two wire guys.
Find the angle each guy makes with the ground, if each guy is 4 m long
and is attached to the pole at a height of 2.1m.

4 A mountain railway is 8 km long and climbs a height of 900m.
At what angle does the train climb?

5 A swimmer is 250 m away from the base of a cliff. She looks up at an angle
of 18.7° to see the top of the cliff. How high is the cliff?

6 Make up some problems of your own. Give them to your partner to solve.
Check your partner's answers.

An **angle of elevation** is measured from the horizontal in an *upwards*
direction.

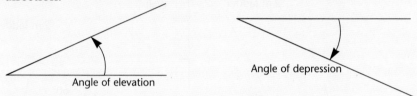

Angle of elevation   Angle of depression

An **angle of depression** is measured from the horizontal in a *downwards*
direction.

EXERCISE 14

For this exercise,
draw a sketch for
each question, and
calculate your
answer to a
sensible degree of
accuracy.

1 A ladder 15 m long leans against a wall so that the top of the ladder is 12 m
above the ground. What angle does the ladder make with

    (a) the ground?   **(b)** the wall?

2 A kite is flying at the end of a piece of string which is 43m long.
The string rises at an angle of 47°.
How far above the ground is the kite?

3 A railway line rises 120 m vertically. The track is inclined at 9° to the
horizontal. What is the length of the track?

4 A pipe of length 0.7 km is laid on sloping ground to carry water across a
horizontal distance of 0.57 km.
Find the angle the pipe makes with the horizontal.

5 A ladder is 10.4 m long and leans against a wall at an angle of 75°.
How far is the foot of the ladder from the bottom of the wall?

6 A ski lift travels a distance of 7 km to climb a mountain 2km high.
Find the angle it makes with the horizontal.

7 A children's slide is 10.5 m long. It is at an angle of 25° to the ground.
One end is on the ground. How high is the other end?

8 The height of a radio mast is 35 m.
Four wires, which are attached to the top of the mast and the ground,
support the mast. Wire A is 40m long, wire B is 45 m long, wire C is 55 m
long and wire D is 70m long.
Find the angle each wire makes with the ground.

9 From the top of a cliff which is 40 m high, a lifeguard sees a struggling
swimmer. She measures the angle of depression as 28°.
How far from the base of the cliff is the swimmer?

10 At a distance of 70 m, the angle of elevation of a church spire is 14°.
How tall is the spire?

11 A house is 7.4 m high. From the roof of the house, the angle of elevation
of a block of flats, 63 m away, is 19°.
How high is the block of flats?

12 Find the angle of depression from the top of a tower 35 m high to a point
60 m from the base of the tower.

13 Find the angle of elevation to the top of a tree, 18 m high, from a point
30 m from the foot of the tree.

14 A plane flies 12 km after take-off and climbs to 5000 m.
Calculate the angle at which it flies.

15 A flagpole is supported by a wire which is 8.5 m long.
The wire slopes at an angle of 55° to the ground.
How far from the foot of the pole is the wire fixed to the ground?

16 An aircraft takes off and flies for 3 km at an angle of 25°.
What horizontal distance has it travelled?

17 A kite flies at a height of 30 m.
The string makes an angle of 35° with the ground.
How long is the string?

18 A ladder is 10 m long. It leans against a wall, with its foot 4 m from the
wall. What is the angle between the ladder and the ground?

The sides of a right-angled triangle

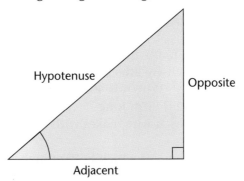

The trigonometric formulae

$\sin x = \dfrac{\text{opp}}{\text{hyp}}$

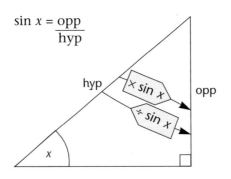

$\cos x = \dfrac{\text{adj}}{\text{hyp}}$

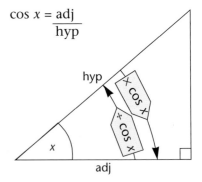

$\tan x = \dfrac{\text{opp}}{\text{adj}}$

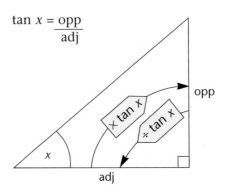

The three trigonometric graphs for angles from 0° to 90° look like this.

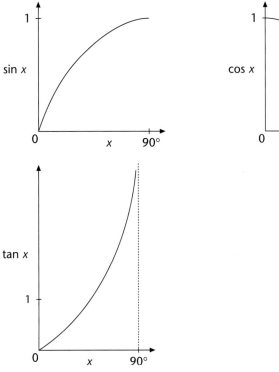

An **angle of elevation** is measured from the horizontal in an *upwards* direction.

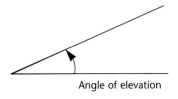

Angle of elevation

An **angle of depression** is measured from the horizontal in a *downwards* direction.

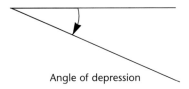

Angle of depression

PROBABILITY

- the probability line
- knowing that the total probability of mutually exclusive events is 1
- giving estimates of probability
- relative frequency, including graphical representation
- using equally likely outcomes or experimental evidence
- comparing estimated and theoretical probability
- adding, subtracting and multiplying fractions
- identifying all the outcomes of a combination of two experiments
- using tabulation and tree diagrams
- calculating the probability using AND and OR.

Using equally likely outcomes

A bag of cubes contains five cubes which are identical, except for their colour. Two are red, two are blue and one is yellow.
A cube is drawn from the bag *at random*.
- The probability that the cube is red is $\frac{2}{5}$.
- The probability that the cube is yellow is $\frac{1}{5}$.

EXERCISE 1

1 A bag contains four cubes which are identical, except for colour. Three of the cubes are red, and one is blue.
A cube is drawn *at random* from the bag. What is the probability that:

    (a) the cube is red?   **(b)** the cube is blue?

2 A bag contains eight cubes which are identical, except for colour. Four are red, three are blue, and one is yellow. A cube is drawn at random from the bag. What is the probability of drawing

    (a) a yellow cube?   **(b)** a red cube?

3 A bag contains 20 cubes which are identical, except for colour.
Six are red, nine are blue, three are yellow, and two are green.
What is the probability of drawing

(**a**) a yellow cube?   (**b**) a red cube?

(**c**) a cube which is *not* blue?   (**d**) a cube which is *not* blue and *not* red?

4 A bag contains nine cubes which are identical, except for colour.
Six are red, and three are blue.
How many yellow cubes should be added to the bag, so that

(**a**) if a cube is drawn at random, there is an even chance of drawing a red cube?

(**b**) there is an even chance of drawing a yellow cube?

(**c**) there are equal chances of drawing a yellow cube and a blue cube?

(**d**) there is a probability of $\frac{1}{10}$ of drawing a blue cube?

5 In the game of Scrabble, 100 tiles are used. The tiles are identical, apart from the letters written on them. Two of the tiles are blank.

The number of tiles with each letter is shown in this table.

A	9	G	3	M	2	S	4	Y	2
B	2	H	2	N	6	T	6	Z	1
C	2	I	9	O	8	U	4	blank	2
D	4	J	1	P	2	V	2		
E	12	K	1	Q	1	W	2		
F	2	L	4	R	6	X	1		

All 100 Scrabble tiles are placed in the bag, and a tile is drawn at random.

(**a**) What is the probability that the tile is a T?

(**b**) Which letter has the greatest probability of being drawn?

(**c**) What is the probability that the letter drawn is

(**i**)   a vowel?

(**ii**) one of the letters in the word SCRABBLE?

(**iii**) *not* one of the letters in the word PROBABILITY?

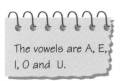
The vowels are A, E, I, O and U.

6 A bag contains eight cubes which are identical, except for their colour.
Four cubes are red, and four are blue.

Someone draws a cube at random from the bag. It is red.
She replaces the cube and draws a cube at random again. It is red again.
She replaces the cube in the bag.
Someone else then says, 'I bet you won't get a red cube again.'

What is the probability that she *will* draw a red cube at random from the bag, a third time?

Nelson GCSE Maths   PROBABILITY (INTERMEDIATE)

Drawing conclusions from experiments

▶ Cubes

DISCUSSION POINT

Ask a partner to put eight cubes in a bag.

There should be cubes of just three colours (say red, blue and yellow).

There can be as many cubes as your partner likes of each colour, and your partner must not tell you how many cubes there are.

You must not look in the bag.

As an experiment, draw a cube at random from the bag. Write down its colour. Replace it in the bag.

• Repeat this experiment four times.

From the four colours you have written down, forecast how many of each colour there are in the bag.

Still do not look at the cubes in the bag.

• Now do the experiment four more times.

You should now have eight colours written down altogether.

From these eight colours, forecast again how many of each colour there are in the bag.

Still do not look at the cubes in the bag.

• Do the experiment eight more times.

From the 16 colours you have written down, forecast again how many of each colour there are in the bag.

• Now look at the cubes in the bag.

Which of your three forecasts was most accurate?

Now repeat the whole experiment, but this time your partner can use a different mix of coloured cubes in the bag.

Also, your partner should tell you how many cubes there are, in total.

Your partner could tell you how many different colours they are using or this could be left secret, for you to discover.

EXERCISE 2

1 A bag contains four cubes.

Someone draws a cube from the bag and then puts it back.

She does this four times.

These are the colours she pulls from the bag. RED   BLUE   RED   RED

For each of these three statements, write down if it is *impossible, possible* or *certain.*

A: There are exactly three red cubes in the bag.

B: There is at least one blue cube in the bag.

C: There is at least one yellow cube in the bag.

2 A bag contains four cubes.

Someone draws a cube from the bag and then puts it back.

He does this ten times. These are the colours he pulls from the bag.

RED BLUE RED YELLOW BLUE RED YELLOW RED RED BLUE

For each of these seven statements, write down if it is *impossible, possible* or *certain*.

A: There are exactly two red cubes in the bag.

B: There are exactly two blue cubes in the bag.

C: There are exactly three red cubes in the bag.

D: There is at least one yellow cube in the bag.

E: There is a green cube in the bag.

F: There are more blue cubes than yellow cubes in the bag.

G: There are more yellow cubes than red cubes in the bag.

3 A bag contains 40 cubes.

Someone draws a cube from the bag and then puts it back.

She does this ten times. These are the colours she pulls from the bag.

RED BLUE RED YELLOW BLUE RED YELLOW RED RED BLUE

For each of these six statements, write down if it is *impossible, possible* or *certain*.

A: The are exactly 20 red cubes in the bag.

B: There are exactly eight blue cubes in the bag.

C: There are more than 20 red cubes in the bag.

D: There is at least one yellow cube in the bag.

E: There is at least one green cube in the bag.

F: There are more green cubes than red cubes in the bag.

4 A bag contains a number of cubes.

Someone draws a cube from the bag and puts it back.

He does this ten times. These are the colours he pulls from the bag.

RED BLUE YELLOW BLUE RED BLUE BLUE YELLOW BLUE YELLOW

(a) For each of these four statements, write down if it is *impossible, possible* or *certain*.

A: There are exactly two cubes in the bag.

B: There are exactly ten cubes in the bag.

C: There are more blue cubes than red cubes in the bag.

D: The number of yellow cubes in the bag is a multiple of three.

(b) You are now told that there are in fact 36 cubes in the bag.

(i) Estimate the number of red cubes, the number of blue cubes and the number of yellow cubes in the bag.

(ii) How certain are you about your estimates?

DISCUSSION POINT

Dice game

To play this game, two or more players take turns to throw a dice. When it is your turn, you throw a dice and write down the number shown.
- If you throw a 1, you *must* stop your turn, and your score for that turn is zero.
- If you do *not* throw a 1, you have to make a decision. You can decide to stop, *or* you can decide to throw the dice again. If you decide to stop before you throw a 1, you score the total of *all* the numbers you have thrown in that turn.

After each turn, you add your score for that turn (if any) to your previous score. The first person to reach 100 is the winner.

Play the game several times. Think about how you decide when to stop your turn. It may be useful to keep a note of how many times you throw the dice each time you have a turn.

The questions in this exercise are about the dice game just discussed.

EXERCISE 3

1 Write down whether you agree or disagree with each of these statements.
   A: There are only six numbers on the dice. So nobody could throw the dice more than five times before throwing a 1.
   B: For one turn, 10 is quite a good score.
   C: For one turn, 20 is quite a good score.
   D: For one turn, 30 is quite a good score.
   E: It would be impossible for someone to score 100 in one turn.
   F: It is always best to play safe and stop after your first throw.
   G: A good policy is never to throw the dice more than three times.
   H: If you have thrown three high numbers it is best to stop, because the next number is bound to be low, even if it is not a 1.
   I: If you have thrown several low numbers carry on because the next number is bound to be high.

2 A cautious player always throws the dice once and then stops.
   (a) What is the probability that he will score zero?
   (b) List all the possible scores he could have for one turn.
   (c) What is the mean amount he will score each turn?

3 Another player waits until the last minute before she decides whether she is going to stop. In one turn, she throws the dice three times and decides to carry on. Two throws later, she wonders whether to stop. Is she more likely to throw a 1 after five throws than she was after three throws?

Probabilities based on experimental evidence

If you are using an unbiased dice or coin or pack of playing cards, you can assume that all the possible outcomes are equally likely. So, for example

Probabilities can be stated as fractions, as decimals or as percentages.

- the probability of throwing tails is $\frac{1}{2}$ (or 0.5)
- the probability of throwing a 4 on a dice is $\frac{1}{6}$ (or 0.167)
- the probability of drawing a spade from a shuffled pack of playing cards is $\frac{1}{4}$ (or 0.25)

and so on.

Alternatively, you can estimate probabilities from experimental evidence. Here are the results of 100 throws of a dice.

You might estimate the probability of throwing a six as $\frac{43}{100}$ (or 0.43) and might conclude that the dice is biased.

Or, if you throw a coin 50 times and it lands on heads 40 times, you might estimate the probability of throwing heads as $\frac{40}{50}$ (or 0.8) and conclude that the coin is biased.

Outcome	Frequency
6	43
5	14
4	13
3	17
2	10
1	3

Sometimes, the only way of estimating a probability is experimentally. If you say that a candidate has a probability of $\frac{1}{4}$ (or 0.25) of passing the driving test, this can only be based on the number of people who have taken and passed the test in the past.

EXERCISE 4

1 A fair coin is thrown 60 times.

  (a) About how many heads would you expect to throw?

  (b) Suppose everyone in your class throws a coin 60 times. Suppose they all obtain exactly the same number of heads as your answer to part (a). Would you be surprised? Write down why.

2 A dice was thrown 100 times. This table shows how many times each number was obtained.

  (a) According to these results, which number has the highest probability of being thrown?

  (b) According to these results, which number has the lowest probability of being thrown?

  (c) What is the probability of obtaining each of these numbers, if you assume that the dice is unbiased?

  (d) Do you think that the dice is biased?

Number	Times thrown
1	15
2	21
3	20
4	18
5	14
6	12

3 A drawing pin is thrown 40 times. This table records how the drawing pin lands.

(a) Estimate the probability that the drawing pin falls point down.

(b) Estimate the probability that the drawing pin falls point up.

Point up		24 times
Point down		16 times

(c) A drawing pin is thrown 100 times.
Estimate the number of times it will fall point up.

(d) Does it make sense to ask whether the drawing pin is biased?

4 A drawing pin is dropped ten times and a note is taken of how it lands: point up or point down.

(a) In what percentage of these ten drops has the drawing pin landed point up?

Number of drops	Point up	Point down
10	5	5

(b) The experiment is repeated another ten times. These are the results.

In what percentage of these 20 drops has the drawing pin landed point up?

Number of drops	Point up	Point down
20	12	8

(c) The experiment is repeated many more times.
All of the results are shown in this table.

Number of drops	Point up	Point down
10	5	5
20	12	8
30	19	11
40	24	16
50	28	22
60	34	26

Copy and complete this table.

Number of drops	10	20	30	40	50	60
Percentage of times drawing pin lands point up						

(d) Copy these axes and plot the points from your table.

(e) Estimate the probability of the drawing pin landing point up.

(f) What happens to the points on the graph as the number of drops increases?

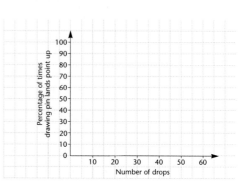

5 Someone questioned 300 people in a town and found that 267 described themselves as right-handed. The rest described themselves as left-handed.

For Question 5, give your answers to a sensible degree of accuracy.

    (a) Estimate the probability that the next person questioned would describe himself or herself as left-handed.

    (b) The population of the town is 250 000.
        Estimate the number of left-handed people in the town.

6 These are the results for throwing a dice which is suspected to be biased.

    (a) Estimate the probabilities of throwing each of the numbers with this dice.

    (b) Two people play a game. They each throw a dice 150 times. One uses this dice and the other uses an unbiased dice. Which person would you expect to throw more sixes? Estimate how many more sixes this person would throw.

Outcome	Frequency
1	12
2	14
3	17
4	15
5	19
6	23

Adding, subtracting and multiplying fractions

Adding and subtracting fractions

A bag contains 16 cubes. Eight of them are red. So, $\frac{8}{16}$ of the cubes in the bag are red.

In a second bag, there are 20 cubes. Ten of them are red. So $\frac{10}{20}$ of the cubes in the bag are red.

The same fraction of cubes in each bag is red.

$$\frac{8}{16} = \frac{10}{20} = \frac{1}{2}$$

Another bag contains 12 cubes.

- $\frac{1}{4}$ of the cubes in the bag are red. That is three cubes, so $\frac{3}{12}$ of the cubes are red.
- $\frac{1}{3}$ of the cubes in the bag are yellow. That is four cubes, so $\frac{4}{12}$ of the cubes are yellow.

If you count red *and* yellow cubes, there are seven, so $\frac{7}{12}$ of the cubes are red or yellow. So

$$\frac{1}{4} + \frac{1}{3} = \frac{3}{12} + \frac{4}{12} = \frac{7}{12}$$

A bag contains 16 cubes, and $\frac{3}{4}$ of the cubes are either blue or green. So, 12 cubes are either blue or green.

$\frac{12}{16}$ of the cubes are either blue or green.

$\frac{5}{16}$ of the cubes in the bag are green. So, five cubes are green.

This means that seven cubes are blue. $\frac{7}{16}$ of the cubes are blue. So

$$\frac{3}{4} - \frac{5}{16} = \frac{7}{16}$$

EXERCISE 5

1 (a) Two-thirds of the cubes in a bag are red.
How many cubes are red, if the bag contains
(i) 6 cubes? **(ii)** 15 cubes? **(ii)** 24 cubes?

(b) The fraction $\frac{2}{3}$ can also be written as $\frac{4}{6}$. Write $\frac{2}{3}$ in two more ways.

2 It may be useful in answering this question to think of bags containing different numbers of cubes. Write $\frac{3}{4}$ in four different ways.

3 Write $\frac{2}{5}$ in four different ways.

4 In a bag of 20 cubes, $\frac{1}{4}$ of the cubes are red and $\frac{2}{5}$ of the cubes are blue.
How many cubes are either red or blue?
What is $\frac{1}{4} + \frac{2}{5}$?

For Questions 5 and 7, you may want to think about bags of cubes. Decide how many cubes need to be in the bag, so both fractions are possible.

5 Work out these.

(a) $\frac{1}{4} + \frac{3}{8}$ **(b)** $\frac{1}{3} + \frac{1}{2}$ **(c)** $\frac{1}{6} + \frac{3}{4}$ **(d)** $\frac{3}{5} + \frac{1}{10}$ **(e)** $\frac{2}{3} + \frac{1}{6}$

(f) $\frac{2}{3} + \frac{1}{12}$ **(g)** $\frac{3}{4} + \frac{1}{16}$ **(h)** $\frac{2}{5} + \frac{4}{15}$ **(i)** $\frac{1}{6} + \frac{7}{12}$ **(j)** $\frac{5}{8} + \frac{1}{3}$

6 In a bag of 24 cubes, $\frac{3}{4}$ of the cubes are green or yellow and $\frac{1}{3}$ of the cubes are green.
How many cubes are yellow?
What is $\frac{3}{4} - \frac{1}{3}$?

7 Work out these.

(a) $\frac{3}{4} - \frac{1}{8}$ **(b)** $\frac{1}{2} - \frac{1}{3}$ **(c)** $\frac{2}{3} - \frac{1}{4}$ **(d)** $\frac{4}{5} - \frac{3}{10}$ **(e)** $\frac{5}{6} - \frac{1}{3}$

(f) $\frac{3}{4} - \frac{5}{12}$ **(g)** $\frac{5}{8} - \frac{3}{16}$ **(h)** $\frac{1}{2} - \frac{1}{12}$ **(i)** $\frac{1}{6} - \frac{1}{9}$ **(j)** $\frac{5}{6} - \frac{3}{4}$

Multiplying fractions

A bag contains 24 cubes, some large and some small.

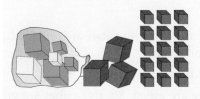

$\frac{3}{4}$ of the cubes are red. So 18 cubes are red.

$\frac{1}{6}$ of the red cubes are large. So, three of the red cubes are large, and $\frac{3}{24}$ (or $\frac{1}{8}$) of the cubes in the bag are large red cubes.

So $\frac{1}{6} \times \frac{3}{4} = \frac{3}{24} = \frac{1}{8}$

EXERCISE 6

1 In a bag of 30 large and small cubes, $\frac{2}{5}$ of the cubes are blue and $\frac{1}{3}$ of these blue cubes are large.

How many large blue cubes are there?

What is $\frac{1}{3} \times \frac{2}{5}$?

> For Question 2, you may want to think about bags of cubes.

2 Work out these.

(a) $\frac{1}{2} \times \frac{1}{4}$ (b) $\frac{1}{4} \times \frac{2}{3}$ (c) $\frac{1}{4} \times \frac{3}{5}$ (d) $\frac{2}{3} \times \frac{3}{10}$

(e) $\frac{3}{4} \times \frac{4}{5}$ (f) $\frac{3}{5} \times \frac{5}{8}$ (g) $\frac{3}{4} \times \frac{3}{4}$ (h) $\frac{1}{3} \times \frac{1}{6}$

(i) $\frac{1}{2} \times \frac{2}{3} \times \frac{3}{4}$ (j) $\frac{3}{4} \times \frac{4}{5} \times \frac{5}{6}$

Probabilities of more than one event

DISCUSSION POINT

This is a game for two teams to play.

The teams sit facing each other with a large sheet of paper between them, which represents the sea.

- Each team draws 12 ships on their side of the paper and numbers them 1 to 12.
- Each team is given ten counters or cubes, each representing a piece of cargo. .
- Each team places their cargo in their ships, however they wish.
  More than one piece of cargo can go in the same ship.
- The teams then take it in turns to roll two dice and add the scores on the dice.
  The answer decides from which numbered ship that team can remove one piece of cargo.
  If the ship is already empty, no cargo is moved.
- The winning team is the first team to clear all its cargo.

Here is a variation of the same game.

- When a ship's number is thrown, the team removes *all* the cargo from that ship in one go, no matter how much is on it.

Discuss the strategies you would use when playing these games.

A bag contains three cubes: two red, and one blue. Apart from colour, the cubes are identical. Someone draws a cube from the bag at random. The cube is replaced in the bag and a cube is drawn at random from the bag, a second time. What is the probability that a red cube is drawn both times?

One way to answer this question is look at all the **outcomes**, which means all *possible* things which can happen. There are three cubes and so, if you use R for red and B for blue, you can show the outcomes in a table like this.

Second draw

	R	R	B
R	RR	RR	RB
R	RR	RR	RB
B	BR	BR	BB

First draw

It can be seen from the table that there are 9 possible outcomes (3 × 3 = 9).
In 4 of these outcomes, a red cube is drawn twice.
So, the probability of drawing a red cube twice is $\frac{4}{9}$.

DISCUSSION POINT

Imagine that a yellow cube is added to the bag just described.
Make a copy of the table but add an extra row and an extra column for the yellow cube.
Two cubes are drawn from the bag of cubes as before.
What is the probability of drawing

- a red cube twice?
- a blue cube followed by a red cube?
- a blue cube just once?

- a blue cube twice?

- *no* yellow cube at all?

EXERCISE 7

1 A bag contains four cubes, identical except for colour.
Two cubes are blue, and two are yellow.

(a) Copy and complete this table, to show all the possible outcomes of drawing a cube at random from the bag, replacing it in the bag, and then drawing another.

(b) How many different possible outcomes are there?

(c) What is the probability that
(i) first cube drawn is blue and the second is yellow?
(ii) both cubes drawn are blue?
(iii) one cube drawn is blue and one is yellow?

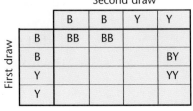

Second draw

	B	B	Y	Y
B	BB	BB		
B				BY
Y				YY
Y				

First draw

2 A bag contains four cubes, identical except for colour.
Two cubes are blue, one is yellow, and one is green.
A cube is drawn at random from the bag, replaced in the bag, and then another cube drawn.

(a) Copy and complete this table, show all the possible outcomes.

(b) How many different possible outcomes are there?

(c) What is the probability that
   (i)   the first cube drawn is blue and the second is yellow?
   (ii)   both cubes drawn are green?
   (iii)   both cubes drawn are *not* green?
   (iv)   both cubes drawn are blue?
   (v)   just one of the cubes drawn is blue?
   (vi)   at least one of the cubes drawn is green?
   (vii)   just one of the cubes drawn is yellow?
   (viii) neither of the cubes drawn is yellow?

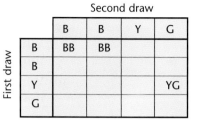

Second draw

First draw	B	B	Y	G
B	BB	BB		
B				
Y				YG
G				

3 Two coins are thrown.
One of the possible outcomes is HH, meaning the first coin and the second coin are both heads.

(a) How many other possible outcomes are there?
What are they?

(b) What is the probability that both coins will show heads?

(c) What is the probability that just one of the coins will show heads?

4 (a) Copy and complete this table to show all the possible outcomes of throwing two normal unbiased dice.

(b) How many different possible outcomes are there?

(c) What is the probability that
   (i)   the first dice shows 3 and the second dice shows 4?
   (ii)   the first dice shows 5 and the second dice shows an even number?
   (iii)   both dice show an even number?
   (iv)   the second dice shows a multiple of 3?
   (v)   the second dice shows a multiple of 3 and the first dice shows an odd number?
   (vi)   the first dice shows a multiple of 3 and the second dice does not?
   (vii)   neither dice shows a multiple of 3?

Second dice

First dice	1	2	3	4	5	6
1	1,1	1,2	1,3	1,4	1,5	1,6
2	2,1	2,2				
3	3,1					
4						
5						
6						

Nelson GCSE Maths PROBABILITY (INTERMEDIATE)

5 Two normal unbiased dice are thrown. The two numbers they show are added together to give the **sum**.

(a) Copy and complete this table.

(b) What is the probability that the sum of the numbers is 5?

(c) What is the most likely sum? What is the probability of throwing this sum?

(d) What is the probability of throwing a
  (i)   sum of 12?
  (iii) a sum greater than 9?
  (ii) a sum of 1?
  (iv) an even sum?

Second dice

First dice

SUM	1	2	3	4	5	6
1	2	3	4	5	6	7
2	3	4	5			
3						
4						
5						
6						

Multiplying probabilities

A bag contains five cubes. Three cubes are red, and two are blue.
This table shows there are 25 possible outcomes.

Second draw

First draw

	R	R	R	B	B
R	RR	RR	RR	RB	RB
R	RR	RR	RR	RB	RB
R	RR	RR	RR	RB	RB
B	BR	BR	BR	BB	BB
B	BR	BR	BR	BB	BB

Imagine that someone draws a cube from the bag at random, replaces the cube in the bag and then draws a cube from the bag a second time.

What is the probability that the first cube drawn is red and the second cube is blue?

This question can be answered by looking at the block of six outcomes (R, B). There are 25 outcomes altogether and so the probability required is $\frac{6}{25}$.

Another way of looking at this is to think about the shapes of the blocks. The (R, B) block is a 3-by-2 rectangle. The block of all outcomes is a 5-by-5 square. So the probability of drawing red first time and blue second time is

$$\frac{3 \times 2}{5 \times 5}$$

This is the same as

The probability of the first cube being red is $\frac{3}{5}$.

$\frac{3}{5} \times \frac{2}{5}$

The probability of the second cube being red is $\frac{2}{5}$.

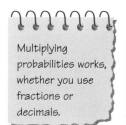

Multiplying probabilities works, whether you use fractions or decimals.

So, you can work out the probability of **both events** happening by **multiplying the probabilities** that each of them will happen.

You can only do this because the two events are **independent**. In other words, whatever colour is drawn the first time does not change the chance of drawing a particular colour the second time (as long as you shake the bag!). Cubes have no memory.

The rule for probabilities of independent events can be extended to three or more events.

You can work out the probability of several events *all* happening by multiplying the probabilities that *each* of them will happen.

EXERCISE 8

1 A bag contains five cubes, identical except for colour. Four of them are red and one is blue.

(a) A cube is drawn from the bag at random and then replaced.
What is the probability that it is red?

(b) A second cube is drawn from the bag.
What is the probability that it is blue?

(c) What is the probability that the first cube is red *and* the second cube is blue?

2 A bag contains eight cubes, identical except for colour. Four cubes are blue, three cubes are green and one cube is yellow. A cube is drawn from the bag at random and then replaced. A second cube is then drawn from the bag. What is the probability that

(a) the first cube is green?

(b) the second cube is blue?

(c) the first cube is green *and* the second cube is blue?

3 A bag contains 20 cubes, identical except for colour. Eight of the cubes are red, five are yellow, four are blue and three are green.
A cube is drawn from the bag and then replaced. A second cube is then drawn from the bag. What is the probability that

(a) (i) the first cube is red?   (ii) the second cube is blue?
(iii) the first cube is red *and* the second cube is blue?

(b) (i) the first cube is green?   (ii) the second cube is yellow?
(iii) the first cube is green *and* the second cube is yellow?

(c) (i) the first cube is blue?   (ii) the second cube is green?
(iii) the first cube is blue *and* the second cube is green?

4 A normal pack of playing cards is shuffled.

(**a**) A card is drawn from the pack and then replaced.
What is the probability that it is a red card?

(**b**) Another card is drawn from the pack.
What is the probability that it is a spade?

(**c**) What is the probability that the first card is a red card and the second card is a spade?

Adding probabilities

Here is the table for the bag containing five cubes, where three cubes are red and two are blue.

Second draw

		R	R	R	B	B
First draw	R	RR	RR	RR	RB	RB
	R	RR	RR	RR	RB	RB
	R	RR	RR	RR	RB	RB
	B	BR	BR	BR	BB	BB
	B	BR	BR	BR	BB	BB

You have already looked at the probability that the first cube drawn is red and the second cube is blue.

Suppose you want to look at the probability that *one* of the cubes drawn is red and *the other* cube is blue.

This can happen in two different ways.

- *Either:* The first cube drawn is red and the second cube is blue.
  Probability of (RB) = $\frac{3}{5} \times \frac{2}{5} = \frac{6}{25}$

- *Or:* The first cube drawn is blue and the second cube is red.
  Probability of (BR) = $\frac{2}{5} \times \frac{3}{5} = \frac{6}{25}$

The events (RB) and (BR) are **mutually exclusive**: this means they cannot both happen at the same time: the two shaded blocks do not overlap. So, to find the probability that either one happens or the other happens, you **add** the probabilities of each happening.

So, the probability that one cube is red and the other is blue is $\frac{6}{25} + \frac{6}{25} = \frac{12}{25}$

Suppose you now want to know the probability the *either* both cubes are red *or* both cubes are blue.

The probability that both cubes are red is $\frac{3}{5} \times \frac{3}{5} = \frac{9}{25}$

The probability that both cubes are blue is $\frac{2}{5} \times \frac{2}{5} = \frac{4}{25}$

So, the probability that either both cubes are red or both cubes are blue is

$\frac{9}{25} + \frac{4}{25} = \frac{13}{25}$

EXERCISE 9

1 A bag contains five cubes, identical except for colour. Four of them are blue and one is yellow. A cube is drawn from the bag at random and then replaced. Then a second cube is drawn. What is the probability that

(a) (i) the first cube is blue and the second cube is yellow?
   (ii) the first cube is yellow and the second cube is blue?
   (iii) one cube is blue and the other cube is yellow?

(b) (i) both cubes are blue?   (ii) both cubes are yellow?
   (iii) *either* both cubes are blue *or* both cubes are yellow?

2 A bag contains ten cubes, identical except for colour. Five of them are blue, three of them are red and two of them are green. A cube is drawn from the bag at random and then replaced. Then a second cube is drawn.

(a) What is the probability that
   (i) the first cube is red and the second cube is green?
   (ii) the first cube is green and the second cube is red?
   (iii) one cube is red and the other cube is green?

(b) What is the probability that both cubes are blue?

3 A normal pack of playing cards is shuffled. A card is drawn from the pack and then replaced. Another card is then drawn from the pack. What is the probability that

(a) the first card is a black card?

(b) the second card is a heart?

(c) the first card is a black card and the second card is a heart?

(d) one card is a black card and the other card is a heart?

(e) either both cards are black cards or both cards are hearts?

4 A particular drawing pin has a probability of 0.4 of landing point down when it is thrown and a probability of 0.6 of landing point up.
The drawing pin is thrown twice. What is the probability of its landing

(a) point up twice?   (b) point up once and point down once?

5 Two different drawing pins are thrown. One has a probability of 0.4 of landing point down when it is thrown; the other has a probability of 0.3 of landing point down when it is thrown.

Two players play a game. Player A wins if both drawing pins land the same way (either both point down or both point up). Player B wins if the drawings pins land in different ways (one point down and the other point up). What is the probability that

(a) player A wins?   (b) player B wins?

Who is more likely to win?

Tree diagrams

Tree diagrams can be used to help you to solve probability problems.

For example, Question 5 in Exercise 9, which is about drawing pins, can be solved like this.

First drawing pin	Second drawing pin	Outcome	Probability
	0.3 — Point down	Both point down A wins	$0.4 \times 0.3 = 0.12$
Point down			
0.4	0.7 — Point up	One down, one up B wins	$0.4 \times 0.7 = 0.28$
0.6	0.3 — Point down	One up, one down B wins	$0.6 \times 0.3 = 0.18$
Point up			
	0.7 — Point up	Both point up A wins	$0.6 \times 0.7 = 0.42$

EXERCISE 10

1 Two coins are thrown.

(a) Copy and complete this tree diagram to show all possible outcomes.

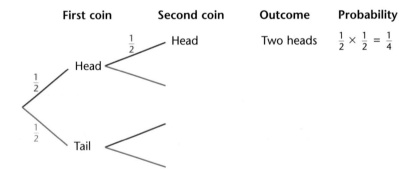

First coin	Second coin	Outcome	Probability
	$\frac{1}{2}$ — Head	Two heads	$\frac{1}{2} \times \frac{1}{2} = \frac{1}{4}$
$\frac{1}{2}$ Head			
$\frac{1}{2}$ Tail			

(b) What is the probability that both coins show tails?

(c) What is the probability that exactly one of the coins shows tails?

2 A red dice and a blue dice are both thrown.

(a) Copy and complete this tree diagram.

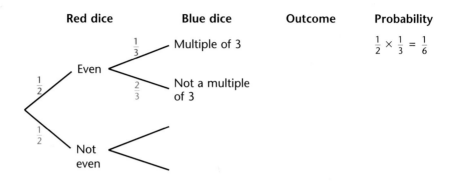

| Red dice | Blue dice | Outcome | Probability |

Even $\frac{1}{3}$ — Multiple of 3 $\frac{1}{2} \times \frac{1}{3} = \frac{1}{6}$

$\frac{1}{2}$ Even $\frac{2}{3}$ — Not a multiple of 3

$\frac{1}{2}$ Not even

(b) What is the probability that the red dice shows an even number and the blue dice shows a multiple of 3?

3 A blue dice and a yellow dice are both thrown.

(a) Copy and complete this tree diagram.

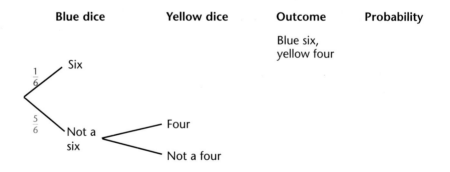

| Blue dice | Yellow dice | Outcome | Probability |

Blue six, yellow four

$\frac{1}{6}$ Six

$\frac{5}{6}$ Not a six — Four / Not a four

(b) What is the probability that the yellow dice shows a six and the blue dice shows a four?

(c) What is the probability that the yellow dice shows a six and the blue dice does not show a four?

4 Two drawing pins are thrown.

Each of the pins has a probability of 0.7 of landing point up.

Draw a tree diagram to find the probability that just one of the pins will land point up.

5 This spinner is spun twice.

(a) Copy and complete this tree diagram to find the probability that it lands on red once and on blue once.

First spin	Second spin	Outcome	Probability
	Red	Red, Red	
Red	Blue	Red, Blue	
	Yellow		
	Red		
Blue			
$\frac{1}{5}$			
Yellow			

(b) Use your tree diagram to find the probability that it does not land on yellow exactly once.

6 In a normal pack of playing cards, a picture card is a King, a Queen or a Jack. A card is drawn at random from the pack.

(a) What is the probability that a picture card is drawn?

(b) This card is replaced and another card is drawn. Draw a tree diagram to find the probability that both cards are picture cards.

(c) Use your tree diagram to find the probability that at least one of the cards drawn is a picture card.

7 Three dice (a red, a blue and a green dice) are thrown.

(a) Copy and complete this tree diagram.

Red dice	Blue dice	Green dice	Outcome	Probability
		Six	Three sixes	
	Six	Not a six	Two sixes	$\frac{1}{6} \times \frac{1}{6} \times \frac{5}{6} = \frac{5}{216}$
Six	Not a six			
Not a six				

(b) What is the probability that exactly two of the dice show sixes?

8 In a game with a dice, these are the rules.

- You lose if your first throw of the dice does not show a five or a six.
- If it shows a six, you throw again and win unless the dice shows one.
- If it shows a five, you throw again and win if the dice shows five or six.

Draw a tree diagram to find the probability of winning the game.

9 (a) When someone has her turn at the dice game on page 180, she always throws the dice twice (unless she throws a one first time) and then she stops.
Draw a tree diagram to find the probability that she will score zero in her turn.

(b) When someone else has his turn at the dice game, he always throws the dice three times (unless he throws a one first or second time) and then he stops.
Draw a diagram to find the probability that he will score zero in his turn.

COURSEWORK OPPORTUNITY

Digit probabilities

Consider these digits.

0   1   2   3   4   5   6   7   8   9

Pick one of these ten digits at random. Then pick another digit.
(You could choose the same digit twice.)

♦ In how many different ways can you pick the two digits?

Having picked your two digits make a 2-digit number with them.
With some selections of two digits, you can make two different 2-digit numbers.

♦ What is the probability that you will be able to make a square number?

♦ What is the probability that you will be able to make a multiple of 5?

♦ What is the probability that you will be able to make a prime number?

Choose some other kind of number.

♦ What is the probability of making this kind of number?

Now consider picking three digits at random ...

Probability line

Calculating probability for equally likely outcomes

Equally likely outcomes are when *all* the outcomes have the *same* chance of happening.

List all the equally likely outcomes and find how many times the event you want occurs in the list.

$$\text{Probability} = \frac{\text{number of times the event occurs}}{\text{total number of outcomes}}$$

Example: if a dice is thrown there are six outcomes: 1, 2, 3, 4, 5, 6.

If the event you want is to throw an even number this occurs three times in the list: 2, 4, 6.

So the probability of throwing an even number is

$$\frac{3}{6} = \frac{1}{2}$$

Estimating probability using experimental results

$$\text{Probability} = \frac{\text{number of times the event occurs}}{\text{number of times the experiment takes place}}$$

This is also called **relative frequency**.

Example: If 40 drawing pins are dropped on to a table and 26 of them land point up, the probability of the drawing pin landing point up is estimated to be $\frac{26}{40}$ or 0.65 or 65%.

Adding and subtracting fractions: Before adding or subtracting, the numbers at the bottom of each fraction must all be the same.

$$\frac{1}{4} + \frac{3}{8} = \frac{2}{8} + \frac{3}{8} = \frac{5}{8} \qquad\qquad \frac{3}{5} + \frac{1}{10} = \frac{6}{10} + \frac{1}{10} = \frac{7}{10}$$

$$\frac{5}{8} + \frac{1}{3} = \frac{15}{24} + \frac{8}{24} = \frac{23}{24} \qquad\qquad \frac{3}{4} - \frac{5}{16} = \frac{12}{16} - \frac{5}{16} = \frac{7}{16}$$

Multiplying fractions: You multiply the top numbers and then the bottom numbers.

$$\frac{1}{6} \times \frac{3}{4} = \frac{1 \times 3}{6 \times 4} = \frac{3}{24} = \frac{1}{8} \qquad\qquad \frac{2}{3} \times \frac{3}{10} = \frac{2 \times 3}{3 \times 10} = \frac{6}{30} = \frac{1}{5}$$

Probabilities of more than one event

Example: A bag contains two red cubes, one blue cube and one yellow cube. One cube is drawn and then replaced. Another cube is drawn.

Second draw

	R	R	B	Y
R	RR	RR	RB	RY
R	RR	RR	RB	RY
B	BR	BR	BB	BY
Y	YR	YR	YB	YY

First draw

So the probability of drawing a red followed by a blue is $\frac{2}{16} = \frac{1}{8}$.

The probability of drawing one red and one yellow is $\frac{4}{16} = \frac{1}{4}$.

Tree diagram

First draw	Second draw	Outcome	Probability

$\frac{2}{4}$

R
$\frac{2}{4}$ R   RR $\frac{2}{4} \times \frac{2}{4} = \frac{4}{16}$
$\frac{1}{4}$ B   RB $\frac{2}{4} \times \frac{1}{4} = \frac{2}{16}$
$\frac{1}{4}$ Y   RY $\frac{2}{4} \times \frac{1}{4} = \frac{2}{16}$

$\frac{1}{4}$ B
$\frac{2}{4}$ R   BR $\frac{1}{4} \times \frac{2}{4} = \frac{2}{16}$
$\frac{1}{4}$ B   BB $\frac{1}{4} \times \frac{1}{4} = \frac{1}{16}$
$\frac{1}{4}$ Y   BY $\frac{1}{4} \times \frac{1}{4} = \frac{1}{16}$

$\frac{1}{4}$ Y
$\frac{2}{4}$ R   YR $\frac{1}{4} \times \frac{2}{4} = \frac{2}{16}$
$\frac{1}{4}$ B   YB $\frac{1}{4} \times \frac{1}{4} = \frac{1}{16}$
$\frac{1}{4}$ Y   YY $\frac{1}{4} \times \frac{1}{4} = \frac{1}{16}$

So the probability of drawing a red followed by a blue is $\frac{2}{16} = \frac{1}{8}$.

The probability of drawing one red and one yellow is $\frac{2}{16} + \frac{2}{16} = \frac{4}{16} = \frac{1}{4}$.

CHAPTER

11 GRAPHS

This chapter is about:

- straight line graphs and their equations
- positive and negative gradients
- conversion graphs, lines of best fit and travel graphs
- non-linear graphs.

Making straight lines

DISCUSSION POINT

These four points lie in a straight line.

Give the coordinates of three more points in line with these four points.

What is the **equation** of this line?

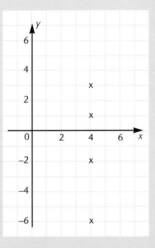

These five points lie in a straight line.

Give the coordinates of three more points in line with these five points.

What is the equation of this line?

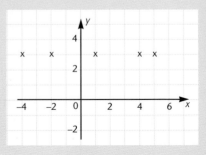

Find the coordinates of three more points in line with these five points.

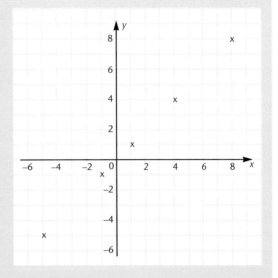

What is the equation of the line through these points?

Find some points on the line that do not have whole number coordinates.

Find some more points in line with these three points.

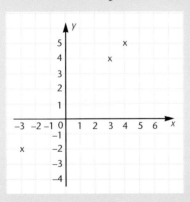

What is the equation of the line through these points?

Find some points on the line that do not have whole number coordinates.

Look at this set of points.

x	−8	−4	2	4
y	−4	−2	1	2

Can you find an equation that the points satisfy?

Find some points on the line that do not have whole number coordinates.

Now do the same for this set of points.

x	−8	−6	−1	3
y	2	0	−5	−9

Exercise 1

1 (a) For each of these diagrams, find an equation for the line the points lie on.

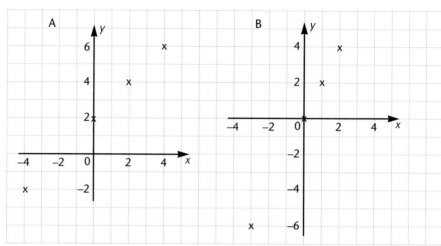

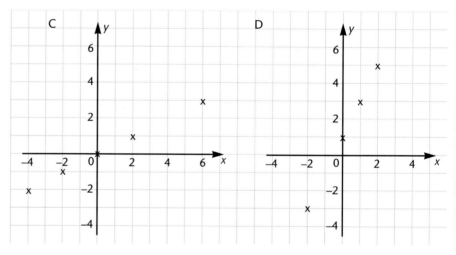

(b) In each case in part (a), the *x*-coordinate of another point on the line is 1.5. What is its *y*-coordinate?

2 Each of these sets of points lies on a straight line.

A: (−5, −1), (0, 0), (10, 2), (15, 3)

B: (−4, −2), (−1, 1), (3, 5)

C: (−3, −4), (−1, −2), (0, −1), (5, 4)

D: (4, −8), (1, −2), (−1, 2), (−2, 4)

For each set of points, find an equation for the line.

Nelson GCSE Maths · GRAPHS (INTERMEDIATE)

3 (a) For each of these diagrams, find an equation for the line the four points lie on.

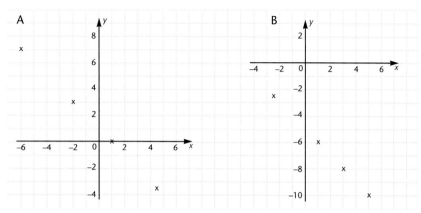

(b) In each case in part (a), the *x*-coordinate of another point on the line is 2.5. What is its *y*-coordinate?

4 (a) Each of these points lies on a straight line. Find an equation for this line.

x	−4	−2	0	2
y	9	7	5	3

(b) Repeat part (a) for this set of points.

x	−3	−1	1	3
y	0	−2	−4	−6

5 (a) For each of these diagrams, find an equation for the line the points lie on.

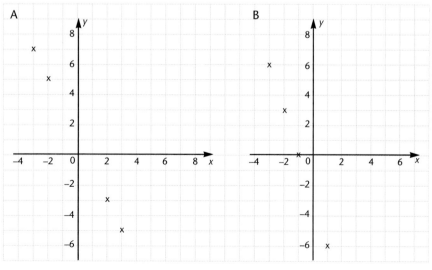

(b) In each case in part (a), write down the coordinates of two more points on that line for which the coordinates are not integers.

(c) What is the *y*-coordinate of the point on each line with *x*-coordinate 3.4?

6 Each of these sets of points lies on a straight line. For each set of points, find an equation for the line.

A: $(-2, -5)$, $(0, -1)$, $(\frac{3}{4}, \frac{1}{2})$, $(5, 9)$

B: $(-3, -6)$, $(-1, 0)$, $(\frac{2}{3}, 5)$, $(3, 12)$

C: $(-4, -18)$, $(-2.5, -12)$, $(0, -2)$, $(2, 6)$

D: $(-\frac{1}{2}, 5\frac{1}{2})$, $(1\frac{1}{2}, -\frac{1}{2})$, $(\frac{1}{3}, 3)$, $(-1\frac{1}{3}, 8)$

Exploring rules for straight lines

DISCUSSION POINT

This table is for points that fit the equation $y = x + 3$.

x	-2	-1	0	1	2
y	1				

Find the values of y not yet shown in the table.

Plot the points on a graph.

This table is for points that fit the equation $y = 2x + 3$.

x	-2	-1	0	1	2
y			3		

Find the values of y not yet shown in the table and plot the points.

Compare the graph of $y = 2x + 3$ with the graph of $y = x + 3$.

What is the same? What is different?

What happens to the line if the equation is changed to $y = 4x + 3$?

A graphical calculator may be useful for some of the questions in this exercise.

EXERCISE 2

1 (a) For each of these equations, find several points whose coordinates fit.

A: $y = x + 5$ B: $y = 2x + 5$ C: $y = 3x + 5$

D: $y = x - 1$ E: $y = 2x - 1$ F: $y = 3x - 1$

Draw the graph for each equation, using the same set of axes for all of them. Draw the axes for x between -6 and 6 and for y between -19 and 23. Label your graphs A to F.

(b) Which of these graphs are parallel?

(c) Which of these graphs have the same crossing point on the y axis?

(d) Without drawing the graph of $y = 2x + 7$, write down which graphs it would be parallel to. Where would it cross the y-axis?

(e) Answer part (d) for the graph of $y = 3x - 3$.

2 On a set of axes using x values between -6 and 6 and y values between -5 and 10, draw the graphs of $y = \frac{1}{2}x + 5$ and $y = \frac{1}{2}x - 1$.

3 (a) For each of these four equations, find at least three points whose coordinates fit the equation and then draw the graphs on the same set of axes. Label your graphs A to D.

A: $y = -2x + 3$ B: $y = -2x - 6$ C: $y = -3x + 4$ D: $y = -4x - 3$

  (b) Without drawing the graph of $y = -2x + 5$, write down which graphs it would be parallel to. Where would it cross the y-axis?

A graphical calculator may be useful for this discussion point.

DISCUSSION POINT
- Find the equations of three lines which are parallel.
  What is it about the equations that tells you the lines are parallel?
- Given the equations of two lines which are *not* parallel, what is it that tells you which line is steeper?
- What is it about the equation of a line which tells you whether it goes up or down (from left to right)?
- Find the equations of three lines which cross the y-axis at the point $(0, 3)$. What tells you that they cross the y-axis at the point $(0, 3)$?

Making and testing generalisations

Gradient of a line and where it crosses the y-axis

Gradient is a way of measuring the steepness of a line.

Look at this line. Its equation is $y = 2x + 4$.

To find the gradient, choose two points on the line, as shown.

$$\text{Gradient} = \frac{\text{distance up}}{\text{distance across}}$$

So, the gradient of this line is $\frac{6}{3} = 2$.

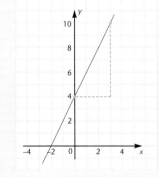

Now look at this line. Its equation is $y = -3x + 5$.

To find the gradient, choose two points on the line.

$$\text{Gradient} = \frac{\text{distance up}}{\text{distance across}}$$

Notice that this time the step is down, not up.
So, the distance up is -6.

So, the gradient of this line is $\frac{-6}{2} = -3$

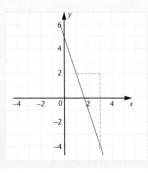

EXERCISE 3

1 Copy each of these diagrams on to squared paper. For each one, find the gradient of the line shown.

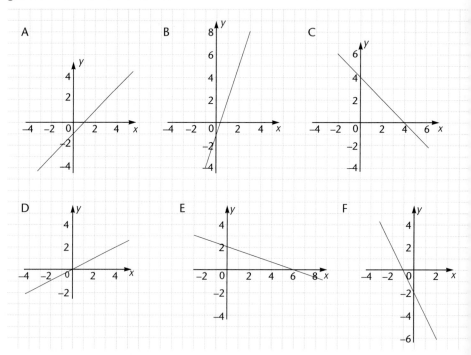

2 Here are the equations of eight lines. What are their gradients?

(a) $y = 2x + 5$ (b) $y = x - 3$ (c) $y = 4x$ (d) $y = -3x + 5$

(e) $y = -x$ (f) $y = 4 - x$ (g) $x + y = 6$ (h) $y - x = 2$

3 What is the gradient of the line joining the point (1, 3) to the point (4, 9)?

4 What is the gradient of the line joining each of these pairs of points?

(a) (3, 5) and (7, 9)   (b) (−1, −2) and (2, 7)   (c) (5, 2) and (2, 5)

(d) (−2, 6) and (1, −3)   (e) (0, 0) and (10, 30)   (f) (−2, 8) and (6, −8)

(g) (3, 5) and (7, 7)   (h) (6, 2) and (8, 7)

DISCUSSION POINT

Here are three tables of points (labelled P, Q and R), three equations (numbered 1, 2 and 3) and three diagrams showing straight line graphs (labelled A, B and C).

Table P

x	−1	1	3
y	7	3	−1

Table Q

x	−2	0	3
y	3	5	8

Table R

x	−3	1	3
y	−10	2	8

Equation 1: $y = 3x - 1$

Equation 2: $y = x + 5$

Equation 3: $2x + y = 5$

Graph A

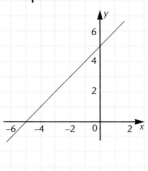

Graph B

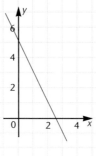

Graph C

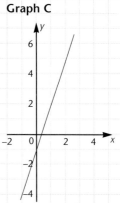

Match each table to an equation and to a graph, by deciding which points fit which equation and which equations match which graph.

How did you do the matching?

Now play the *Sorting game* on Resource Sheet K.

Sketch graphs are roughly done graphs that show the main features, such as where the graphs cross the axes.

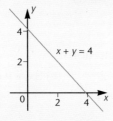

$x + y = 4$

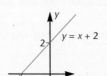

$y = x + 2$

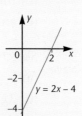

$y = 2x - 4$

1 Write down the gradients of the lines with these equations.

(a) $y = 2x + 5$ (b) $y = 3x - 6$ (c) $y = -x + 7$

(d) $y = -5x - 2$ (e) $y = \frac{1}{2}x + 5$

2 Write down the coordinates of the point where each line in Question 1 crosses the y-axis.

3 Copy and complete this table.

	Original equation	Rearranged as y = ...	Gradient	Crossing point on the y-axis
A	$3x + y = 12$	$y =$		
B	$x + y = 5$			
C	$2x + y = 10$			
D	$\frac{1}{2}x + y = 6$			
E	$y - 3x = 7$			
F	$3x + 2y = 8$			
G	$5x + 3y = 20$			
H	$x - y = 4$			
I	$2x - y = 5$			
J	$x - 3y = 6$			

4 Look at these sketch graphs.

A 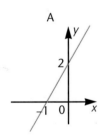   B 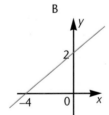   C 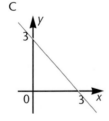   D 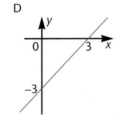   E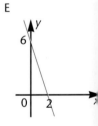

For each sketch graph, write down

(a) the gradient

(b) the crossing point on the y-axis

(c) an equation for the graph

5 Sketch the graphs of these equations.

(a) $y = 2x - 3$ (b) $y = -x + 2$ (c) $2x + y = 8$

(d) $3x - y = 9$ (e) $y = \frac{1}{2}x + 4$

Practical uses of straight line graphs

DISCUSSION POINT

This graph has been drawn through (0, 0) and (10, 22).

How does it relate to the
fact that 1 kg is about 2.2 lb?

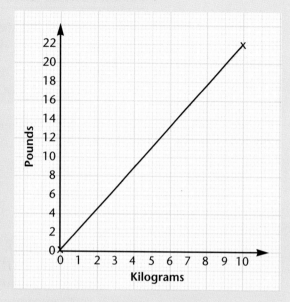

How can the graph be used to convert these amounts?
- 4.5 kg to pounds
- 16 lb to kilograms
- 80 kg to pounds

What is the gradient of the graph?

If p is the number of pounds and k the number of kilograms, what formula relates p and k?

EXERCISE 5

▷ Graph paper

1 In May 1997, £1 bought about $1.6 (US dollars) and so £100 bought $160.
   (a) Plot the two points (0,0) and (100, 160) and join them with a straight line.
   (b) Use your graph to estimate these conversions.
      (i) £40 to dollars   (ii) £85 to dollars   (iii) $64 to pounds
   (c) Find the gradient of your graph.
       How does it relate to the exchange rate?
   (d) Using p for the number of pounds and d for the number of dollars, write a formula connecting p and d.

2 (a) Copy and complete this table for travelling at a steady speed of 50 m.p.h.

Time (hours)	0	$\frac{1}{2}$	1	$1\frac{1}{2}$	2	$2\frac{1}{2}$	3
Distance travelled (miles)	0		50	75			

(b) Draw a graph of this data.

(c) Find from your graph the distance travelled after 1 hour 45min.

(d) How much time does it take to travel 80 miles?

(e) What is the gradient of the graph and what does it represent?

3 The freezing point of water is 0° Celsius and 32° on the Fahrenheit scale. Its boiling point is 100°C or 212°F.

The conversion formula is

$f = 1.8c + 32$

where c is the number of degrees Celsius and f is the number of degrees Fahrenheit.

(a) On a winter's morning, the temperature is –40°C. This is a very cold temperature. What is this temperature on the Fahrenheit scale?

(b) On a summer's day, the temperature is 35°C. This is a lot warmer! What is this temperature in degrees Fahrenheit?

(c) Using a scale of 2 cm for 10° on the c axis and 1 cm for 10° on the f axis, draw a graph of $f = 1.8c + 32$.

(d) Mark the two points (0, 32) and (100, 212) on your graph.

(e) Where does your graph cross the f-axis? What does this tell you?

(f) Find the gradient of your graph. How is your answer related to the conversion equation?

(g) Use your graph to find the Fahrenheit equivalent of these temperatures.
    (i) 5°C   **(ii)** 20°C   **(iii)** –5°C   **(iv)** –20°C

(h) Use your graph to find the Celsius equivalent of these temperatures.
    (i) 48°F   **(ii)** 59°F   **(iii)** 34°F   **(iv)** –5°F

4 A group of students design a print for a T-shirt and set up a printing block at a cost of £120. They then print T-shirts at a cost of £3 per shirt.

(a) Explain why the cost of setting up and printing 50 shirts is £270.

(b) Write a formula for the cost (£C) of setting up and printing n T-shirts. Why should the graph for this formula be straight?

(c) Draw a graph to show the formula for n from 0 to 300.

(d) Read from your graph the cost of 240 shirts.

(e) How many shirts are printed for £650?

5 This table shows the length of a spring when different masses were hung from it.

Mass in grams (M)	20	40	60	80	100	120
Length in mm (L)	72	89	104	119	136	162

(a) Plot the data on a graph. Draw a line of best fit for the data.

(b) What is the length of the spring with no mass hung on it?

(c) How much does the length change per gram? Use your line of best fit to answer this.

(d) Use the answers to (a) and (b) to find an equation for the graph.

6 When a weighing machine was checked for accuracy with some standard masses these results were obtained.

Standard mass in grams (s)	10	20	30	40	50
Mass showing in grams (m)	8	19.6	31.1	42.6	54.2

(a) Plot this data on a graph with 'standard mass' on the horizontal axis.

(b) Estimate where the machine was only inaccurate by up to 0.2 g.

(c) What standard mass would be on the machine when it registers 0?

(d) Find an equation relating s and m.

Nonlinear graphs

DISCUSSION POINT

Here is the graph of the equation $y = x^2$.

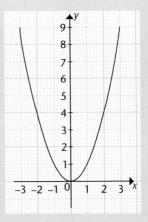

This is what you can do to understand why this graph fits the equation $y = x^2$.

- Copy and complete this table.

x	−3	−2	−1	−0.5	0	0.5	1	2	3
y	9		1			0.25		4	

- Plot the points from the table on to a graph.
- Join the points up with a smooth curve.

Nelson GCSE Maths   GRAPHS (INTERMEDIATE)

1 (a) Draw the graphs of the equations $y = x^2$ and $y = x^2 + 4$ on the same axes, using x values from −4 to 4 and y values from 0 to 20.

(b) How are the two graphs related?

2 (a) Draw the graphs of $y = x^2$ and $y = 2x^2$ on the same axes, using x values from −3 to 3 and y values from 0 to 20.

(b) How are the two graphs related?

3 (a) Draw the graph of $y = 4 - x^2$, using x values from −3 to 3 and y values from −6 to 6.

(b) How is this graph different from the graphs in Questions 1 and 2?

(c) Find the values of x at points on the graph when $y = 2$.

(d) Find the values of x at points on the graph when $y = -1$.

(e) For what x values on the graph is y greater than −1?

4 (a) Draw the graph of $y = 6x - x^2$, using x values from −1 to 7 and y values from −8 to 10.

(b) Write down the coordinates of the points where the graph crosses the x-axis.

5 (a) Draw the graph of $y = (x - 1)^2$ and $y = (x - 2)^2$ on the same axes, using values of x from −4 and 4.

(b) What is the relationship between these two graphs?

6 (a) Draw graphs of $y = 6 - x^2$ and $y = x^2 - 4x$ on the same axes, for values of x between −3 and 3.

(b) Write down the coordinates of the points where the graphs cross.

DISCUSSION POINT

- Compare the graphs of $y = x^2$, $y = x^2 + 1$, $y = x^2 - 2$ and so on. What does the graph of $y = x^2 + c$ look like for different values of c?

- Compare the graphs of $y = x^2$, $y = 2x^2$, $y = -x^2$, $y = -3x^2$ and so on. What does the graph of $y = ax^2$ look like for different values of a?

- Now look at the graphs of $y = 2x^2 + 4$, $y = x^2 + 4$, $y = -3x^2 + 4$ and so on. Or you could use a different number instead of 4. Describe how these graphs are related.

- Now look at the graphs of $y = x^2$, $y = (x - 1)^2$, $y = (x + 2)^2$ and so on. What does the number in the bracket with x do to the position of the graph?

Making and testing generalisations

1 Find the equation of each of these graphs.

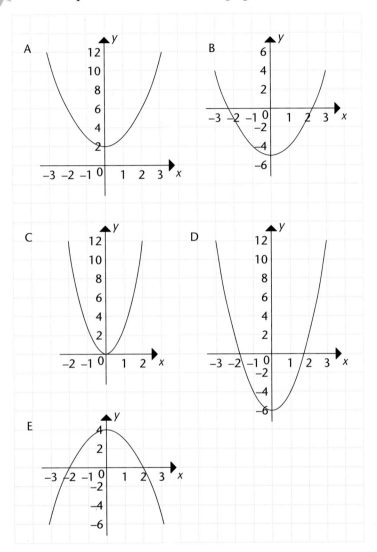

2 These three coloured graphs labelled A, B and C are

$y = x^2$

$y = 2x^2$

$y = \frac{1}{2}x^2$

Which is which?

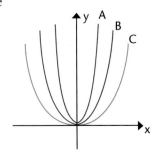

3 Look at these four graphs.

A

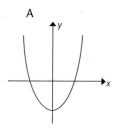

B

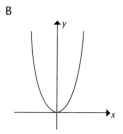

C

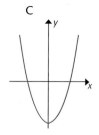

D

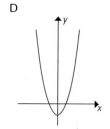

  (a) Which of these equations could fit graph A?

    $y = x^2$ $y = x^2 - 2$ $y = x^2 + 1$

  (b) Which of these equations could fit graph B?

    $y = 2x^2$ $y = -3x^2$ $y = x^2 + 1$

  (c) Which of these equations could fit graph C?

    $y = x^2 + 6$ $y = 6 - x^2$ $y = x^2 - 6$

  (d) Which of these equations could fit graph D?

    $y = 2x^2 - 1$ $y = 3x^2 + 1$ $y = -2x^2 - 1$

4 Look at these three graphs.

A

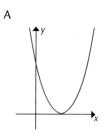

B

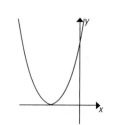

C

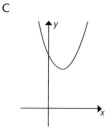

  (a) Which of these equations could fit graph A?

    $y = x^2$ $y = (x + 1)^2$ $y = (x - 2)^2$

  (b) Which of these equations could fit graph B?

    $y = (x - 2)^2$ $y = (x + 3)^2$ $y = (x - 4)^2$

  (c) Which of these equations could fit graph C?

    $y = (x - 1)^2$ $y = (x - 1)^2 + 2$ $y = (x - 1)^2 - 3$

5 Suggest equations for each of these sets of graphs.

A

B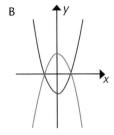

C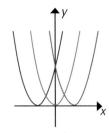

Patterns from equations

Find sets of equations that would make a tessellation of:

♦ squares

♦ rhombuses

♦ other shapes.

Find sets of equations that would make tartan patterns.

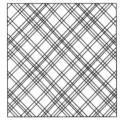

CHAPTER SUMMARY

Gradients

$y = 2x + 4$

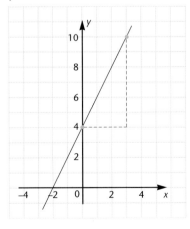

$y = -3x + 5$

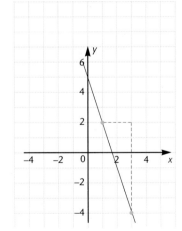

$$\text{Gradient} = \frac{\text{distance up}}{\text{distance across}}$$

$$= \frac{6}{3}$$

$$= 2$$

$$\text{Gradient} = \frac{\text{distance up}}{\text{distance across}}$$

$$= \frac{-6}{2}$$

$$= -3$$

Equations of graphs of straight lines

$y = mx + c$ is the equation for a straight line graph.

For example, $y = 2x + 5$, $y = -3x + 2$ and $y = \frac{1}{2}x - 1$ are all equations of straight line graphs.

The value of m is the gradient of the graph.

The value of c tells you where the graph crosses the y-axis.

For example, $y = 2x - 4$ has gradient 2 and crosses the y-axis at $(0, -4)$.

For example, $y = -3x + 2$ has gradient -3 and crosses the y-axis at $(0, 2)$.

Graphs involving x^2

Graphs of equations with x^2 in, such as $y = x^2$, $y = 2x^2 - 1$, $y = 3 - x^2$, and $y = (x - 2)^2$ are not straight lines.

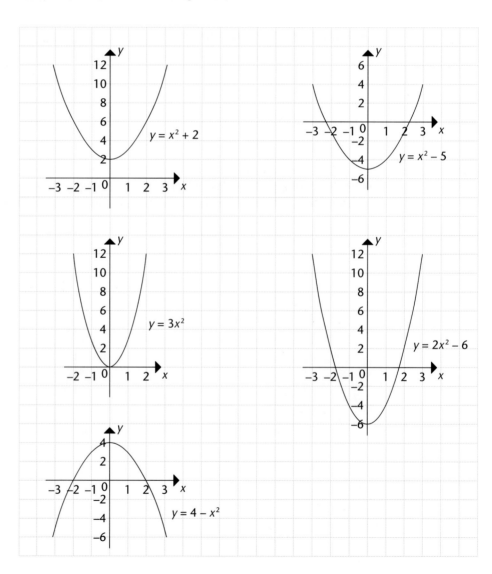

CHAPTER

12

MEASURES

This chapter is about:

- making sensible estimates using measures

- metric and Imperial units of measure

- the relationships between different units of measure

- circumference and area of a circle

- problems involving areas of two-dimensional shapes

- volumes and surface areas of prisms, including cuboids and cylinders.

Metric measures

DISCUSSION POINT

Estimate the height of a typical doorway in metres.
Estimate the height of a house in metres.
Estimate how tall a student of 16 years might be in centimetres.
Estimate how far it is to London in kilometres.
Estimate how many kilograms of potatoes you could carry home from the supermarket.
Estimate the weight of a 2-litre bottle of coke in kilograms.
Estimate the weight of this book in kilograms.

Length
1 km = 1000 m
1 m = 100 cm = 1000 mm
1 cm = 10 mm

Mass or weight
1 tonne = 1000 kg
1 kg = 1000 g
1 g = 1000 mg

Capacity or volume
1 litre = 1000 ml
1 m³ = 1000 litres
1 cm³ = 1 ml

Nelson GCSE Maths   MEASURES (INTERMEDIATE)

1 (a) Which of these could be the volume of a washing-up bowl?

   10 litres   100 litres   1000 litres   10000 litres

   (b) Which of these could be the weight of an apple?

   1.5 g   15 g   150 g   1500 g

   (c) Which of these could be the weight of a chair?

   50 g   500 g   5000 g   50000 g

   (d) Which of these could be the capacity of a wine glass?

   1.2 ml   12 ml   120 ml   1200 ml

   (e) Which of these could be the length of a car?

   0.004 m   0.04 m   0.4 m   4.0 m

2 (a) Change these lengths to millimetres.

   (i) 23.5 cm   (ii) 2.4 m   (iii) 0.23 cm

   (b) Change these lengths to centimetres.

   (i) 678 mm   (ii) 5.6 m   (iii) 0.0034 km

   (c) Change these lengths to metres.

   (i) 3478 mm   (ii) 5004 cm   (iii) 0.34 km

   (d) Change these lengths to kilometres.

   (i) 345 m   (ii) 5600 m   (iii) 13689 cm

3 (a) Change these weights to milligrams.

   (i) 3.6 g   (ii) 0.87 g   (iii) 0.04 kg

   (b) Change these weights to grams.

   (i) 5098 mg   (ii) 32.76 kg   (iii) 0.0654 kg

   (c) Change these weights to kilograms.

   (i) 2000 g   (ii) 8700 g   (iii) 4500000 mg

4 (a) Change these measures of capacity to millilitres.

   (i) 2.7 litres   (ii) 0.345 litres   (iii) 0.007 litres

   (b) Change these measures of capacity to litres

   (i) 2345 ml   (ii) 0.456 ml   (iii) 79804 ml

5 For each of these, find the amount which is different from the other two.

   (a) 500 ml, 0.5 litres, 5 litres

   (b) 8300 mm, 83 cm, 0.83 m

   (c) 600 m, 6 km, 0.6 km

   (d) 340 g, 34 g, 0.34 kg

Metric and Imperial measures

A 12-inch (30-cm)
ruler may be
helpful here.

DISCUSSION POINT

Estimate the height of a typical doorway in feet.

Estimate the height of a house in feet.

Estimate how tall a student of 16 years might be in feet and inches.

Estimate how far it is to London in miles.

Estimate how many pounds of potatoes you could carry home from the supermarket.

Estimate the weight of a 2-litre bottle of coke in pounds.

Estimate the weight of this book in pounds.

Length

1 mile = 1760 yards

1 yard = 3 feet = 36 inches

1 foot = 12 inches

Mass or weight

1 pound (lb) = 16 ounces (oz)

Capacity or volume

1 gallon = 8 pints

EXERCISE 2

This chart shows
how to change
measures of length
between metric and
Imperial measures.

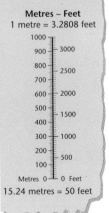

Metres – Feet
1 metre = 3.2808 feet

15.24 metres = 50 feet

1 (a) Which of these could be the volume of a washing-up bowl?

    1 pint   10 pints   50 pints   90 pints

(b) Which of these could be the weight of an apple?

    1 oz   6 oz   16 oz   60 oz

(c) Which of these could be the weight of a chair?

    0.5 pounds   3 pounds   7 pounds   25 pounds

(d) Which of these could be the capacity of a wine glass?

    0.01 pints   0.2 pints   0.5 pints   0.8 pints

(e) Which of these could be the length of a family car?

    1.5 feet   5 feet   10 feet   25 feet

2 (a) Change these measures of length to feet.

    (i) 423 m   (ii) 798 m

(b) Change these measures of length to metres.

    (i) 500 feet   (ii) 2170 feet

3 Look at this chart. It shows how to change measures of capacity between metric and Imperial measures.

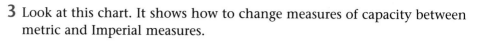
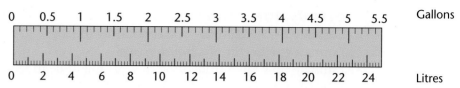

(a) Use the chart to change these measures of capacity to litres.

(i) 2 gallons (ii) 5 gallons

(b) Change these measures of capacity to gallons.

(i) 16 litres (ii) 5 litres

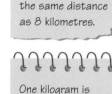

Five miles is about the same distance as 8 kilometres.

4 (a) Change these measures of distance to kilometres.

(i) 15 miles (ii) 250 miles

(b) Change these measures of distance to miles.

(i) 64 km (ii) 720 km

One kilogram is approximately 2.2 pounds (lb).

5 (a) Change these measures of weight to pounds.

(i) 5 kg (ii) 1000 kg

(b) Change these measures of weight to kilograms.

(i) 22 lb (ii) 154 lb

6 The heat setting of a gas oven is called its Gas Mark. A rough rule to change Gas Mark to a temperature in °C is 'multiply by 15, and add 100'.

(a) Use the rule to change Gas Mark 6 to a temperature in °C.

(b) Use the rule to change Gas Mark 4 to a temperature in °C.

(c) Estimate the Gas Mark which would give a temperature of about 130°C.

One litre of water weighs one kilogram. One litre of liquid has a volume of 1000 cm³.

7 (a) Change these measures of capacity to weights in kilograms.

(i) 350 cm³ of water (ii) 1500 ml of water

(iii) 750 ml of coke (iv) 1467 cm³ of water

(b) Change these weights of water to measures of capacity in litres.

(i) 500 g (ii) 756 g (iii) 28 kg (iv) 4 kg

8 A swimming pool is 18 metres long. In a sponsored swim, the recommended contribution is £5 per mile.

(a) Calculate a contribution per length of the swimming pool which is approximately the same as £5 per mile.

(b) A swimmer swam 800 lengths. Using your answer to (a), calculate the amount of money that might be collected from the sponsors.

Circumference and area of a circle

DISCUSSION POINT

A student measures the circumference, C, and the diameter, d, of various circles. In each case $C \div d$ is calculated.

Copy and complete this table, which shows the student's results.

Circumference (mm) C	Diameter (mm) d	$C \div d$
354	112	3.16
1041	331	
1324	421	
476	151	
626	201	

What do you notice about the numbers in the column $C \div d$?

If it were possible to make exact measurements, the numbers in the $C \div d$ column would all be exactly the same number.
This number is called π. The value of π is about 3.14.

Press the π button on your calculator. This will give you a more accurate value of π. This is much more accurate than you need in practice.

Circumference of a circle = $\pi \times$ diameter

EXERCISE 3

1 Work out the circumference of these circles.

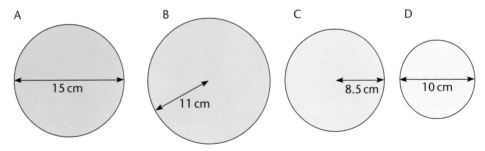

A   15 cm
B   11 cm
C   8.5 cm
D   10 cm

2 The circumference of a circle is 10.6 cm. What is its diameter?

3 The circumference of a circle is 15.8 cm. What is its radius?

4 Work out the perimeter of each of these shapes.

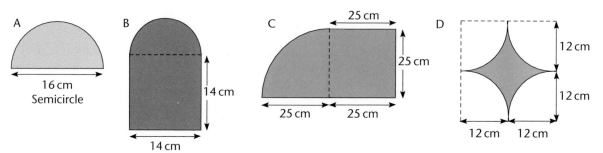

A

16 cm
Semicircle

B

14 cm

14 cm

C

25 cm

25 cm

25 cm   25 cm

D

12 cm

12 cm

12 cm   12 cm

Area of a circle = π × radius × radius
$$A = \pi r^2$$

▶ Resource Sheet L:
   Area of a circle

DISCUSSION POINT

This is one way of understanding why the formula for the area of a circle is true.

You need the Resource Sheet L: *Area of a circle*.

Cut the circle on the resource sheet into the twelve marked pieces, called **sectors**, and place eleven of them together as in this diagram.

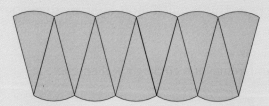

Cut the twelfth piece into two equal sectors and fit one on each end of your arrangement.

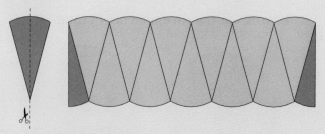

Your arrangement is approximately a rectangle.

Consider what would happen if the circle is cut into an increasing number of sectors.

Using the circumference and the radius of the circle, explain the formula for the area of any circle.

EXERCISE 4

1 Find the areas of these circles.

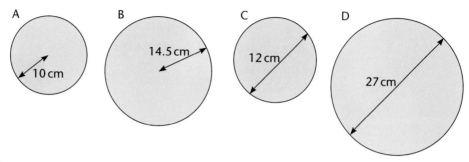

2 Find the area, in square centimetres, of a circle whose diameter is 1 metre.

3 Find, in square metres, the area of a circle whose diameter is 1 kilometre.

4 Find the areas of these shapes.

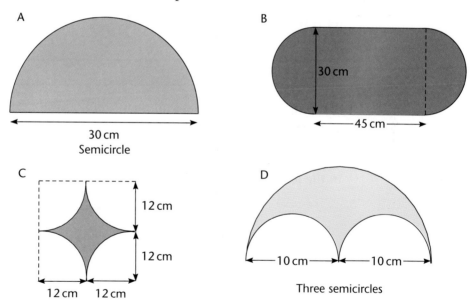

5 A regular hexagon has sides of length 4 cm.
The point S is the centre of the hexagon.

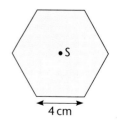

(**a**) Draw a circle of radius 4 cm. Draw the hexagon inside the circle.

(**b**) Calculate the perimeter of the hexagon.

(**c**) Use the diagram to explain why the circumference of the circle is larger than the perimeter of the hexagon.

(**d**) Calculate the circumference of the circle.

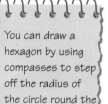
You can draw a hexagon by using compasses to step off the radius of the circle round the circumference.

6 The circumference of a circle is 30 cm.

(a) Find the diameter of the circle.   (b) Find the area of the circle.

7 This jug shape is made from four arcs of circles, the centres of which are at the corners of the dotted square.

This square has sides of length 26 cm.

Calculate the shaded area.

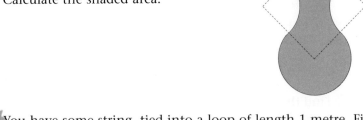

8 You have some string, tied into a loop of length 1 metre. Find in square centimetres the areas of these shapes made with the loop of string.

(a) A square   (b) A rectangle, in which one side is 15 cm

(c) A circle   (d) A rectangle, in which one side is $1\frac{1}{2}$ times the other

(e) A semicircle

EXERCISE 5

1 A young couple want to set up their own business.
They need to rent an office.
They reply to this advertisement in the local paper.

> **OFFICES TO LET**
> **Good size**
> *Most of our offices have a floor space greater than 20 square metres*

(a) The first office that they are shown has these floor measurements.

Without using a calculator, make a quick estimate of the floor area. Is the floor area greater than 20 square metres?

(b) The second office that they look at has these floor measurements.

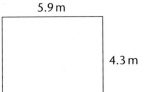

Use a calculator to find the floor area to the nearest square metre.

2 The grass in a garden needs reseeding. The shape of the grass is a rectangle which measures approximately 4.2 m by 9.1 m.
One box of grass seed contains enough seed to cover 10 m².
Estimate the number of boxes needed for one reseeding.

3 The manufacturer of granulated bone-meal garden fertiliser recommends using 140 g per square metre.
Estimate the weight of fertiliser required for these parts of the garden.

(a) A circular flower bed measuring 5.2 m in diameter

(b) A 2 m-wide rectangular border which is 9.1 m long

4 This diagram shows a window inside a plastic frame of width 4 centimetres.
The top is a semicircle and the measurements are shown in centimetres.

(a) Calculate the perimeter the glass in the window.

(b) Calculate the area of the glass in the window.

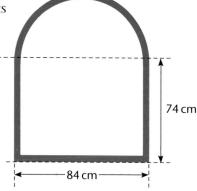

74 cm

84 cm

5(a) Calculate in acres the area of a field measuring 50 m by 100 m.

(b) A field is a rectangle with a width of 50 m. It has an area of 1.5 acres. Find the length of wire needed to electrify the fence surrounding this field.

6 A room is 2.6 m high and has floor measurements 5 m by 3.7 m.

(a) A roll of border paper is 8 m long.

   (i) Calculate the length of border needed to go around the room.

   (ii) How many rolls of border must be bought to complete the room?

(b) A roll of wallpaper is 52 cm wide and about 10 m long.

   (i) Calculate how many drops can be cut from one roll of paper.

   (ii) Estimate the number of rolls of wallpaper that must be bought to complete the room.

7 A wall measures 83 inches by 95 inches. Calculate the number of tiles needed to cover the whole wall with square tiles with an edge of

(a) 6 inches   (b) 108 mm

Nelson GCSE Maths   MEASURES (INTERMEDIATE)

223

8 Floor tiles measure 12 square inches. They are sold in packets of six tiles.

  (a) Estimate the number of floor tiles needed to cover a rectangular floor 5 m by 3.7 m.

  (b) Calculate many packets of tiles would be needed to cover the floor.

Volume

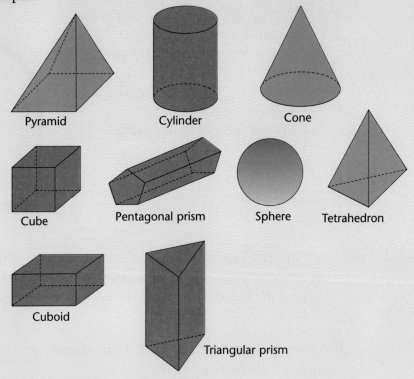

DISCUSSION POINT

What do the red shapes have in common which is different from the blue shapes?

Pyramid   Cylinder   Cone

Cube   Pentagonal prism   Sphere   Tetrahedron

Cuboid

Triangular prism

A shape with constant cross-section is called a **prism**.

The volume of a prism is the area of the base multiplied by the height.

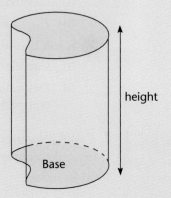

height

Base

Volume = base area × height

EXERCISE 6

1 Find the volume of each of these shapes.

A

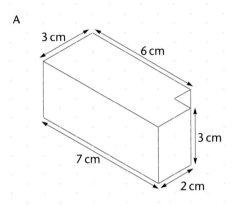

B

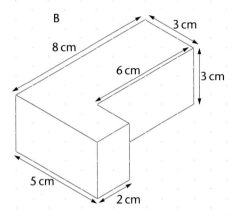

C

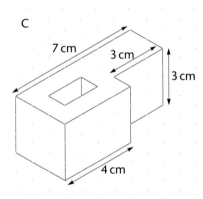

D

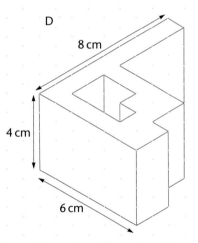

E

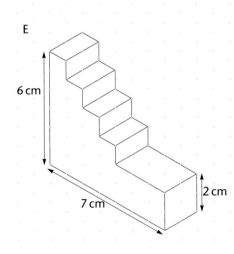

2 Find the volume of each of these shapes.

A

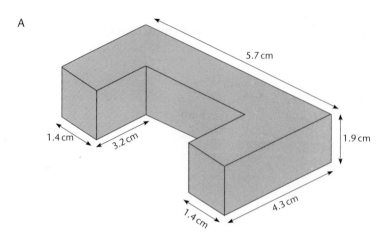

5.7 cm

1.4 cm   3.2 cm   1.9 cm

1.4 cm   4.3 cm

B

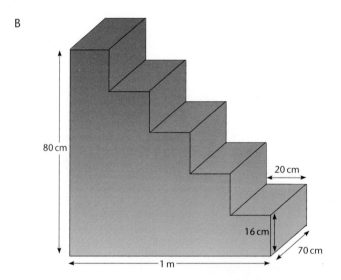

80 cm

20 cm

16 cm   70 cm

1 m

C

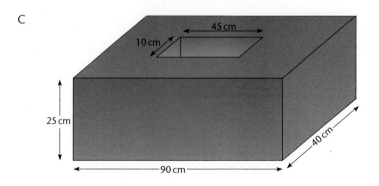

45 cm

10 cm

25 cm

90 cm   40 cm

3 Find the volume of each of these shapes.

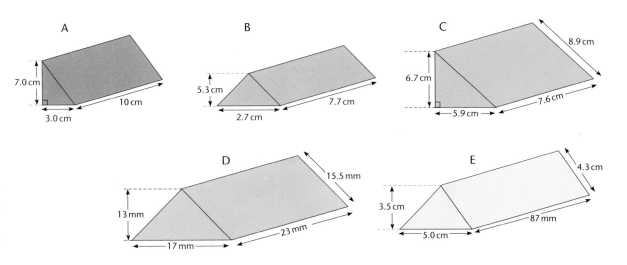

4 Find the volume of each of these cylinders.

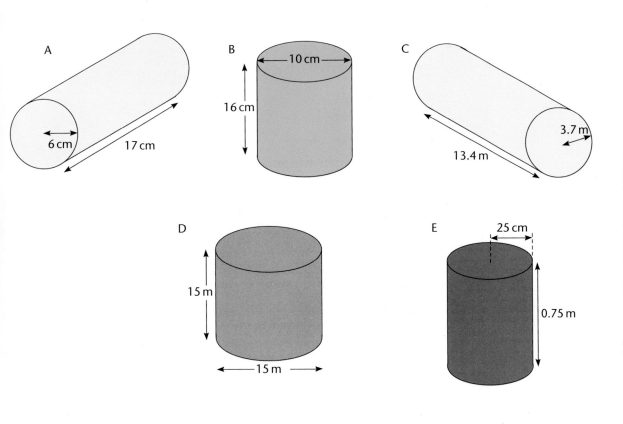

Think of a typical basket of shopping from the supermarket.

What shapes are the different containers in the shopping.

Are any of them prisms?

Find some containers which are prisms.

Measure them.

Put your results in a table like this.

Product	Prism type	Label	Measurements	Volume
bar of soap	cuboid	125 g	8 cm by 5 cm by 3 cm	120 cm³
bleach	cylinder	750 ml	diameter 7 cm height 22 cm	850 cm³

EXERCISE 7

1 Find the volume of each of these boxes.

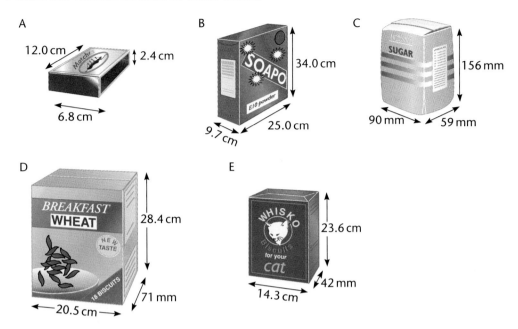

A
12.0 cm
2.4 cm
6.8 cm

B
34.0 cm
9.7 cm
25.0 cm
SOAPO
E10 powder

C
SUGAR
156 mm
90 mm
59 mm

D
BREAKFAST
WHEAT
NEW TASTE
18 BISCUITS
28.4 cm
71 mm
20.5 cm

E
WHISKO
biscuits
for your
cat
23.6 cm
42 mm
14.3 cm

2 Find the volume of each of these tins.

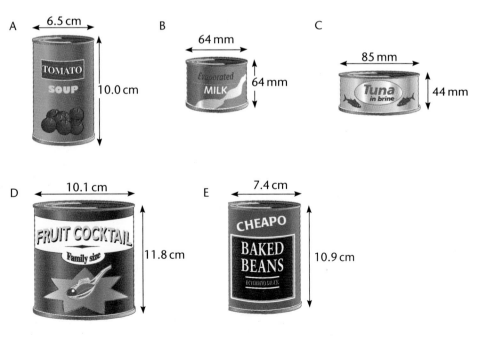

A
6.5 cm
TOMATO
SOUP
10.0 cm

B
64 mm
Evaporated
MILK
64 mm

C
85 mm
Tuna
in brine
44 mm

D
10.1 cm
FRUIT COCKTAIL
Family size
11.8 cm

E
7.4 cm
CHEAPO
BAKED
BEANS
IN TOMATO SAUCE
10.9 cm

3 A salt container is in the shape of a cylinder. The base of the cylinder has a radius of 3.0 cm.

(**a**) Calculate the area of the base.

(**b**) The volume of the cylinder is 568 cm³. Calculate the height of the container.

1000 mm³ = 1 cm³

4 A milk carton is shaped like a cuboid and measures 95 mm by 60 mm by 90 mm.

(**a**) Find the area of the largest side.

(**b**) Find the volume of the carton in cubic millimetres.

(**c**) Find the volume in cubic centimetres.

5 An orange juice carton measures 9.3 cm by 5.7 cm by 19.6 cm.

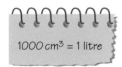

1000 cm³ = 1 litre

(**a**) Find the area of the largest side in square centimetres.

(**b**) Find the volume of the carton in cubic centimetres.

(**c**) Find the volume in millilitres.

(**d**) The label on the carton says '1 litre of orange juice'. Is this true?

1 gallon is approximately 4.5 litres.

6 This oil tank is a cuboid.

The gauge on the tank is used to measure the volume of the oil remaining in the tank. When the tank is full the height of oil in the gauge is 230 cm.

(a) When 600 gallons are delivered the oil in the gauge rises by 50 cm. Write down the volume of oil delivered in litres.

(b) Calculate the area of the base of the oil tank.

(c) Calculate the volume of oil in the tank when it is full. State clearly the units you use.

Surface area of prisms

DISCUSSION POINT

How would you find the surface area of this cuboid?

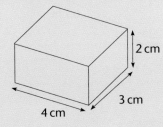

How would you find the area of the label on this tin?

How would you find the surface area of the tin?

1 Find the surface area of each of these cuboids.

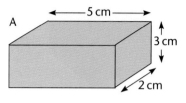

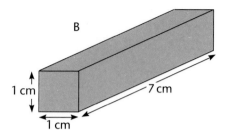

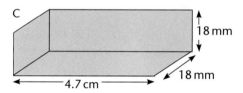

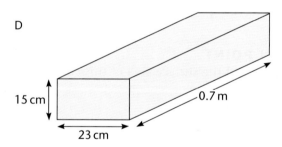

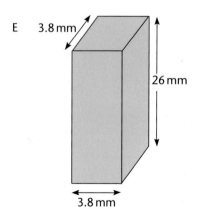

2 Find the surface area of each of these containers.

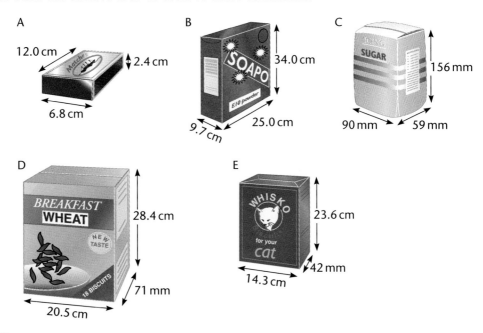

A
12.0 cm 2.4 cm
6.8 cm

B
34.0 cm
9.7 cm 25.0 cm
SOAPO
E10 powder

C
SUGAR
156 mm
90 mm 59 mm

D
BREAKFAST
WHEAT
NEW TASTE
28.4 cm
18 BISCUITS
71 mm
20.5 cm

E
WHISKO
for your
cat
23.6 cm
42 mm
14.3 cm

3 For each of these tins, answer the questions below.

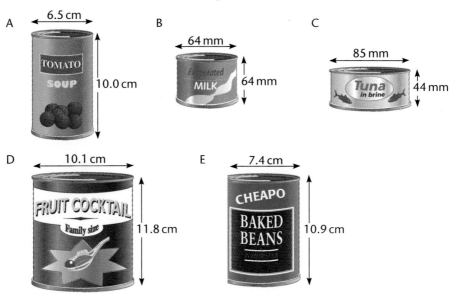

A
6.5 cm
TOMATO
SOUP
10.0 cm

B
64 mm
Evaporated
MILK
64 mm

C
85 mm
Tuna
in brine
44 mm

D
10.1 cm
FRUIT COCKTAIL
Family size
11.8 cm

E
7.4 cm
CHEAPO
BAKED
BEANS
10.9 cm

(a) Work out the length of the label round the tin.
(b) Sketch the label showing the approximate length and height on the sketch.
(c) Find the area of the label.
(d) Find the area of each end of the cylinder.
(e) Find the total surface area of the cylinder.

4 Find the total surface area of each of these cylinders.

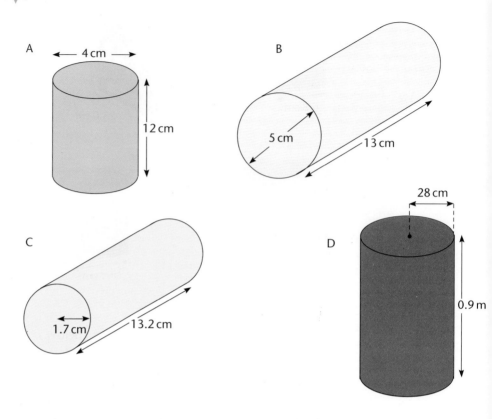

A   ← 4 cm →   12 cm

B   5 cm   13 cm

C   1.7 cm   13.2 cm

D   28 cm   0.9 m

5 All six faces of this cuboid are to be painted.

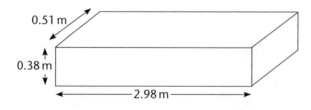

0.51 m

0.38 m

2.98 m

(a) The paint left in a pot is enough to cover 5 m². Estimate whether there is enough paint to cover the cuboid with one coat of paint.

(b) A new pot of paint covers 12 m². Calculate how many new pots of paint would be needed to paint the six faces of eight identical cuboids.

Water consumption

Investigate the water consumption in your home.

In the bathroom, how much water

- is there in the cistern for the toilet?
- would allow a comfortable bath?
- is used in the wash basin?
- is used each time in the shower?

In the kitchen, how much water is needed

- by the washing machine on a typical programme?
- in the washing-up bowl?
- for cooking?

You might consider how much water is used by one person

- in a day
- in a week
- in a month
- in a year.

You might want to find out the capacity of a typical cold water tank.
You could consider how you could store water if it was to be cut off for eight hours and how long the water you have stored would last.

Metric measures

Length

1 km = 1000 m
1 m = 100 cm = 1000 mm
1 cm = 10 mm

Capacity or volume

1 litre = 1000 ml
1 m³ = 1000 litres
1 cm³ = 1 ml

Mass or weight

1 tonne = 1000 kg
1 kg = 1000 g

Nelson GCSE Maths · MEASURES (INTERMEDIATE)

Imperial measures

Length

1 mile = 1760 yards
1 yard = 3 feet = 36 inches
1 foot = 12 inches

Mass or weight

1 pound (lb) = 16 ounces (oz)

Capacity or volume

1 gallon = 8 pints

Relationship between metric and Imperial units

Length

1 mile is about 1.6 km
1 foot is about 30 cm
1 metre is a bit more than a yard

Capacity or volume

1 litre is about $1\frac{3}{4}$ pints
1 gallon is about 4.5 litres

Mass or weight

1 kilogram is about 2.2 lb
1 ounce is about 30 g

Also remember

1 cm³ of water weighs 1 g

Circles

Circumference of a circle = π × diameter
Area of a circle = π × radius × radius = πr²

Prisms

A solid shape which has a constant cross-section is called a **prism**.
Volume of a prism = area of base × height

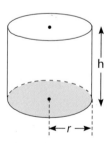

height

Base

Cylinders

A **cylinder** is a prism with a circular cross-section.

h

r

Volume of a cylinder = area of circular base × height = $\pi r^2 h$

The surface area of a cuboid

To find the surface area of a cuboid find the areas of the six rectangular faces and add them up.

Nelson GCSE Maths   MEASURES (INTERMEDIATE)

13 EQUATIONS

This chapter is about:

- manipulating algebraic expressions
- forming and solving linear equations using a variety of methods
- using linear equations to solve problems
- solving quadratic equations by trial and improvement.

Solving equations by doing and undoing

You have met flow diagrams before in Chapter 3.

This is the flow diagram for 'multiply by 7 and add 8'.

This is the flow diagram for 'divide by 5 and subtract 9'.

This is the flow diagram for 'square and add 9'.

This is the flow diagram for 'add 2 and multiply by 3'.

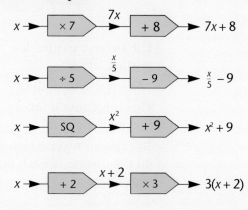

EXERCISE 1

1 Draw flow diagrams for each of these.

    (a) Multiply by 4 and add 6   **(b)** Divide by 2 and add 7

    (c) Multiply by 7 and subtract 4   **(d)** Divide by 3 and subtract 1

    (e) Multiply by 3 and add 6   **(f)** Multiply by 3 and add 9

    (g) Add 5 and multiply by 2   **(h)** Subtract 4 and multiply by 6

    (i) Square and subtract 7   **(j)** Add 4 and square

2 Draw flow diagrams for each of these expressions.

(a) $3x + 5$ (b) $6x + 1$ (c) $\frac{x}{7} - 2$ (d) $\frac{1}{2}x + 6$

(e) $5x - 8$ (f) $\frac{x}{9} + 11$ (g) $12x + 7$ (h) $\frac{x}{3} + 2$

(i) $4(x + 3)$ (j) $\frac{x - 4}{5}$ (k) $x^2 - 4$ (l) $(x + 3)^2$

3 Write the expressions for these flow diagrams.

A $x \rightarrow$ [× 3] [+ 6]   B $x \rightarrow$ [× 4] [− 8]

C $x \rightarrow$ [+ 3] [× 2]   D $x \rightarrow$ [− 5] [× 4]

E $x \rightarrow$ [÷ 2] [+ 3]   F $x \rightarrow$ [+ 3] [÷ 2]

G $x \rightarrow$ [÷ 7] [− 4]   H $x \rightarrow$ [− 4] [÷ 7]

I $x \rightarrow$ [SQ] [+ 3]   J $x \rightarrow$ [− 6] [SQ]

K $x \rightarrow$ [× 6] [SQ]   L $x \rightarrow$ [SQ] [× 6]

The **inverse expression** is what takes you back to the original number or starting letter.

The inverse of 'adding 7' is 'subtracting 7'.

This is because it takes you back to your starting point.

To draw an inverse flow diagram, you do the inverse of each box, in the reverse order.

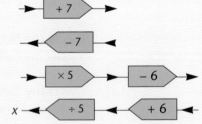

EXERCISE 2

1 Find the inverse of these expressions.

(a) Adding 9   (b) Subtracting 3   (c) Multiplying by 6   (d) Dividing by 4

2 What is the inverse of squaring a number?

3 Write down the inverse of these expressions.

(a) Multiplying by 6 and then adding 7

(b) Subtracting 5 and doubling the result

Check your answers to Question 3 by substituting numbers.

EXERCISE 3

Draw the flow diagrams and the inverse flow diagrams for these expressions.

1 (a) $2x + 5$ (b) $6y - 4$

2 (a) $3(x + 7)$ (b) $5(2y + 6)$

3 (a) $x^2 + 8$ (b) $(y - 3)^2$

4 (a) $\frac{2x + 6}{4}$ (b) $7x^2 - 3$ (c) $\frac{3y^2 + 2}{7}$

You can use flow diagrams to solve equations.

$6x + 4 = 22$

Draw the flow diagram.

Work out the inverse flow diagram and write it underneath.

Put 22 through the inverse flow diagram and calculate the result.

Check your answer by substituting $x = 3$ into the original equation.

EXERCISE 4

Once you have done a few of these questions, you might try to imagine the flow diagram instead of actually writing it all down every time.

Solve these equations.

1 (a) $x - 7 = 5$ (b) $x + 9 = 20$ (c) $x + 14 = 10$
   (d) $x - 5 = -2$ (e) $x + 7 = 0$ (f) $x - 7 = -15$

2 (a) $3x + 1 = 19$ (b) $5x - 4 = 26$ (c) $2x - 3 = 11$
   (d) $7x + 6 = 6$ (e) $9x - 4 = 2$ (f) $6x - 4 = 14$
   (g) $5x - 7 = 0$ (h) $6x + 3 = -4$ (i) $9x - 13 = -1$

3 (a) $2(2x + 5) = 26$ (b) $3(x - 2) = -3$ (c) $4(x - 6) = -16$
   (d) $3(2x - 8) = -21$ (e) $-7(4x - 11) = -28$

4 (a) $\frac{x}{7} = 2$ (b) $\frac{x}{8} - 3 = 0$

5 (a) $\frac{x}{5} + 7 = 10$ (b) $\frac{x + 6}{4} = -6$ (c) $\frac{3x + 4}{2} = -4$

Solving equations by balancing

DISCUSSION POINT

You can solve equations by using the idea of balancing.

Think of the equation as a balance.

Try to work out what is happening in these diagrams.

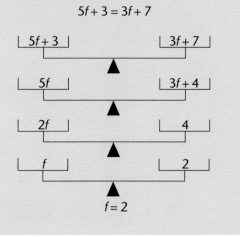

$5f + 3 = 3f + 7$

The unknown is on both sides in the questions in this exercise.

EXERCISE 5

1 Solve these equations.

(a) $7y + 4 = 3y + 8$

(b) $5f + 3 = 3f + 7$

(c) $7y + 1 = 2y + 15$

(d) $7g = g + 10$

2 Solve these equations.

(a) $8t + 2 = 6t - 4$

(b) $7x + 7 = 4x + 1$

(c) $8y - 8 = 3y - 2$

3 What value of f solves this equation? $13f + 5 = 7f + 5$

4 Solve these equations.

(a) $3p + 5 = 8 + p$

(b) $4 + 6z = z + 3$

(c) $6y - 8 = 4 - 3y$

(d) $5c + 1 = 9 - 2c$

5 Solve these equations.

(a) $7g - 3 = 1 - g$

(b) $4r - 10 = 2r - 3$

(c) $6d + 1 = 6 - 8d$

(d) $8r + 9 = 7r + 6$

6 Solve these equations.

(a) $12 + x = 9 - 5x$

(b) $3g + 7 = g + 1$

(c) $7 + x = 5 - 13x$

(d) $3d + 11 = 2 - 3d$

Working with brackets

In each room, the *unshaded* area is going to be carpeted.

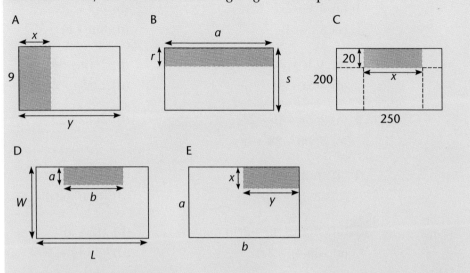

Divide each room into rectangles and find the total area of carpet that is needed. Work out the area in two different ways, write expressions for each way and check that your answers agree.

Diagrams can sometimes help to multiply out brackets.

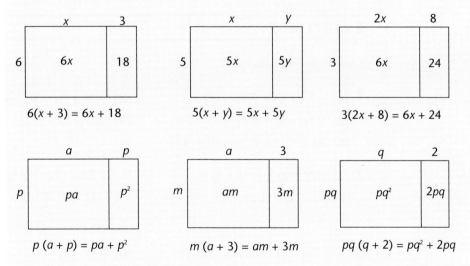

$6(x + 3) = 6x + 18$

$5(x + y) = 5x + 5y$

$3(2x + 8) = 6x + 24$

$p(a + p) = pa + p^2$

$m(a + 3) = am + 3m$

$pq(q + 2) = pq^2 + 2pq$

To multiply out brackets, each term inside the bracket must be multiplied by the term outside.

EXERCISE 6

In each of these questions, multiply out the brackets.

1 (a) $3(x + 2)$ (b) $6(y + 5)$

(c) $5(z + 2)$ (d) $8(a + b)$

2 (a) $4(3c + 2d)$ (b) $7(3a + 4b)$

(c) $3(5x + 4)$ (d) $12(3a - 2)$

3 (a) $2(3a + 4b - 2c)$ (b) $3(4p + 2q + 7r)$

(c) $5(4m - 2n + l)$

4 (a) $-6(2x - 5)$ (b) $-5(2d + 7)$

(c) $-8(3p - 2q)$ (d) $-3(4f - 2g)$

5 (a) $-9(3p - 4q + 2r)$ (b) $x(2 - a)$

(c) $-3a(4y - 3z)$ (d) $-3f(4g + 2)$

6 (a) $3z(2x - 9y)$ (b) $p(p - 2q)$

(c) $ab(2a - b + 4)$

7 (a) $4s(2s - 4 + 6st)$ (b) $2ab(3ab - 5b + a)$

(c) $-3xy(2y - 4x - 5xy + y^2)$

EXERCISE 7

Solve these equations.

1 (a) $3(2a + 1) + 2(4a + 2) = 21$ (b) $5(2b + 3) - 3(2b + 4) = 15$

(c) $3(3y + 4) - 2(2y + 1) = 30$ (d) $6(2t - 2) + 3(2t + 5) = 30$

(e) $3(6d + 1) - 2(7d - 4) = 43$

2 (a) $4(7f + 2) = 5(5f + 6)$ (b) $3(2a - 1) + 7 = 5a + 9$

(c) $9(y - 1) = 4(2y - 3)$ (d) $5(4k - 3) = 14k + 9$

(e) $3(3z + 5) - 7 = 5(z + 3)$

3 (a) $8(2a - 1) - 2(7a - 5) = 10$ (b) $4(5y - 1) - 3(5y + 2) = 3y - 2$

(c) $5(4 - y) = 4(5 - y)$ (d) $8 - 2(a + 4) = 3(2 - a)$

(e) $3d - 2(2d + 3) + 2d = -8$

Thinking with letters

Often, before you can solve a problem you need to translate it into an expression.

Words	Expression
How many days are there in *n* weeks?	There are 7*n* days in *n* weeks
The sum of 3 consecutive numbers is 21	*n* + *n* + 1 + *n* + 2 = 21

EXERCISE 8

1 Write down an expression for each of these statements.

(a) *x* more than 5   (b) 9 less than *d*

(c) 2 times *y*   (d) 6 less than *a*

(e) *t* divided by 6   (f) *h* more than 2

(g) 4 more than *u*   (h) 3 times *x*

(i) *a* taken away from *b*   (j) *p* divided by *q*

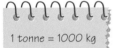

1 tonne = 1000 kg

2 Write as expressions, the number of:

(a) metres in *x* kilometres   (b) grams in *y* tonnes

(c) seconds in *p* hours   (d) days in *k* years

(e) pence in *d* pounds

3 Write expression for these.

(a) The sum of four consecutive numbers

(b) The product of two consecutive numbers

4 Write expressions for these.

(a) An even number   (b) An odd number

(c) An even number multiplied by an odd number

5 A woman has *m* CDs. She sells *n* CDs. How many does she have left?

6 The cost of a computer disc is *l* pence. How much do 12 discs cost?

7 A piece of string is *g*cm long. It has a piece *k*cm cut off.
How much string is left?

8 There are 1275 people on a train. *a* people get off. How many are left?

9 A woman earns £*b* an hour. How much does she earn in 18 hours?

1 You have two numbers: a and b. Write down equations for these statements.

A: a is the same as b.

B: a is 5 more than b.

C: b is 5 more than a.

D: a is 9 less than b.

E: b is 15 less than a.

F: a is 3 times as many as b.

G: a and b together make 92.

2 You have two numbers: x and y. Write down equations for these statements.

A: y is twice x.

B: y take away 7 is the same as x added to 36.

C: The difference between x and y is 15.

D: The sum of x and y is 51.

3 A man has x pence and a woman has y pence. Write down equations for these statements.

A: The woman has twice as many pence as the man.

B: The man and the woman have 45 pence altogether.

C: The man has 30 pence less than the woman.

D: If the woman gives the man 15 pence, they will have the same.

4 A man has a CDs and a woman has b CDs. Write equations for these statements.

A: The man and the woman have 200 CDs altogether.

B: The woman has four times as many CDs as the man.

C: If the woman gave 40 CDs away, she would have three times as many as the man.

D: If the woman gave 60 CDs to the man, they would both have the same.

5 A woman has a 1p coins and b 2p coins.

(a) If $a = 15$ and $b = 30$, what would be the total value of the coins?

(b) If $a = 2b$, what does that mean?

(c) If the total value of the coins is 30p, write that as an equation.

(d) What does $a + b$ mean?

Forming and solving linear equations

E X E R C I S E 10

1 Write down an equation for each of these diagrams and solve it to find the value of *a*.

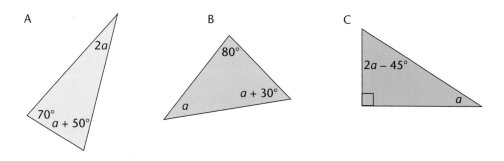

2 Write down an equation for each of these diagrams and solve it to find the value of *y*.

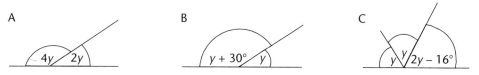

3 The area of each rectangle is given in cm². The lengths of the sides are in centimetres. Find the value of *b* in each rectangle.

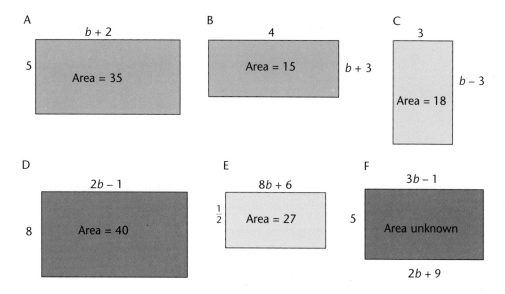

4 The perimeter of each shape is given in centimetres.
The lengths of the sides are also in centimetres.
Find the value of *d* in each shape.

A

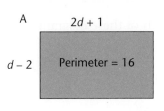

2*d* + 1

d – 2

Perimeter = 16

B

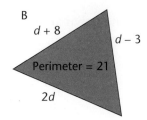

d + 8

d – 3

Perimeter = 21

2*d*

C

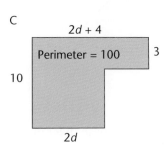

2*d* + 4

Perimeter = 100

3

10

2*d*

5 For each of these statements, form and solve an equation to find the number.

A: When a number is doubled and 7 is taken away, the result is 13.

B: When a number is divided by 3 and 17 is added, the result is 21.

C: When 3 is subtracted from a number and it is then multiplied by 8, the result is 16.

D: When 7 is subtracted from half of a number, the result is –5.

E: When a number is trebled and 8 taken away, the result is $-6\frac{1}{2}$.

6 For each of these statements, form and solve an equation to find the number.

A: Trebling a number and subtracting 2 gives the same result as doubling the number and adding 5.

B: Adding 3 to a number and then doubling it gives the same result as multiplying the number by 5 and subtracting 6.

C: Adding 4 to a number gives the same result as dividing the number by 3 and subtracting 4.

D: Subtracting 6 from a number and multiplying the result by 4 gives the same result as multiplying the number by –4.

E: Adding 11 to a number and dividing by 2 gives the same result as multiplying by –2 and subtracting 7.

7 This question is about three piles of stones. For each of these statements, find out how many stones there are in each pile by forming and solving an equation.

A: The first pile has 3 stones less than the third pile and the second pile has 17 stones more than the third pile.
There are 44 stones altogether.

B: The third pile has 3 more stones than the first pile and the second pile has twice as many stones as the third pile.
There are 105 stones altogether.

C: The second pile has 8 stones less than the first pile and the third pile has three times as many stones as the second pile.
There are 48 stones altogether.

D: The second pile has four times as many stones as in the first pile and the third pile has seven times as many stones as the first pile.
There are 168 stones altogether.

Check your answers by finding the numbers in each pile and making sure they give the correct total.

8 A tortoise is a years old. Her father is four times as old as she is.
Her mother is 7 years younger than her father.
Their ages add up to 101 years.
Find the age of each tortoise.

9 A boy spent x minutes playing computer games today.
Yesterday, he spent twice as long playing computer games.
Tomorrow, he will spend 20 minutes longer than he did today.
He spends 180 minutes over the three days.
Find out how long he spends playing computer games each day.

10 Two consecutive whole numbers have a sum of 29.
Find the value of the numbers.

11 Three consecutive whole numbers have a sum of 69.
What are the numbers?

12 (a) Write down expressions for five consecutive even numbers, the smallest of which is n.

(b) Five consecutive even numbers have a sum of 620.
What are the numbers?

13 A girl has b CDs.
If she buys 20 more, she will have three times as many as before.
Find the value of b.

14 A new car has t miles on the milometer.
When it has travelled another 72 miles the mileage recorded will have increased to $4t$ miles. What is t?

15 A class of 30 students contains x boys.

(a) Write an expression for the number of girls.

(b) The number of girls is twice the number of boys. Find the value of x.

Quadratic equations by trial and improvement

Sometimes exam questions tell you to use the **trial-and-improvement** method to solve an equation. Here is a typical question.

Find the positive solution to the equation $x^2 + x = 177$ by using your calculator and the trial-and-improvement method.

Give your answer correct to 1 decimal place.

Trials	Calculation	Size
Try $x = 12$	$12^2 + 12 = 156$	Too small
Try $x = 13$	$13^2 + 13 = 182$	Too big
Try $x = 12.8$	$12.8^2 + 12.8 = 176.64$	Too small
Try $x = 12.9$	$12.9^2 + 12.9 = 179.31$	Too big

You know the answer lies between 12.8 and 12.9 so try halfway, which is 12.85. This gives 177.9725 which is too big so 12.8 is the answer, correct to 1 decimal place.

EXERCISE 11

1 Find the positive solution to these equations by using your calculator and trial and improvement.

(a) $x^2 + x = 100$ (b) $x^2 + x = 65$

(c) $x^2 + 2x = 1$ (d) $x^2 + 6x = 9$

Give your answers correct to 1 decimal place.

2 Find the positive solution to this equation, using your calculator and trial and improvement.

$2x^2 + 6x = 5$

Give your answer correct to 1 decimal place.

3 Find the positive solution to these equations by using your calculator and trial and improvement.

(**a**) $3x^2 + 5x = 7$ (**b**) $x^2 - 3x = 11$ (**c**) $2x^2 - 2x = 1$

Give your answers correct to 1 decimal place.

4 In each of these shapes, the lengths of the sides are given in centimetres. The areas are shown within the shape.

A

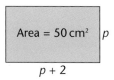

B

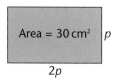

C

D

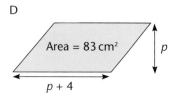

For each shape, form an equation and solve it using your calculator and trial and improvement.

Give your answers correct to 1 decimal place.

COURSEWORK OPPORTUNITY

Consecutive sums

The number 15 can be written as the sum of consecutive whole numbers in three different ways:

$$15 = 7 + 8$$
$$15 = 4 + 5 + 6$$
$$15 = 1 + 2 + 3 + 4 + 5$$

Look at other numbers.

Find out all you can about writing them as sums of consecutive whole numbers.

Solving equations by doing and undoing

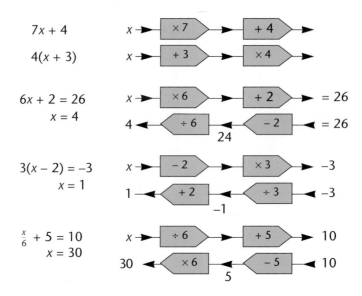

$7x + 4$

$4(x + 3)$

$6x + 2 = 26$
$x = 4$

$3(x - 2) = -3$
$x = 1$

$\frac{x}{6} + 5 = 10$
$x = 30$

Solving equations by balancing

$$3x + 7 = 5x + 3$$

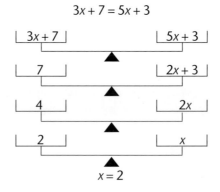

$x = 2$

Brackets

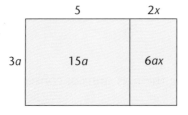

$$3a(5 + 2x) = 15a + 6ax$$

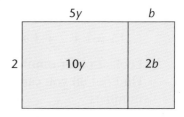

$$2(5y + b) = 10y + 2b$$

Thinking with letters

a is twice b: $a = 2b$
An odd number: $2a - 1$
x is 10 less than y: $x = y - 10$

Forming and solving linear equations

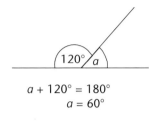

$a + 120° = 180°$
$a = 60°$

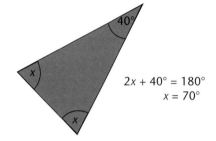

$2x + 40° = 180°$
$x = 70°$

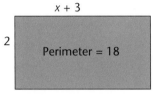

$2 + (x + 3) + 2 + (x + 3) = 18$
$2x + 10 = 18$
$x = 4$

A girl is y years old.
Her father is three times as old as she is.
Her mother is 2 years younger than her father.
The total of their ages is 103.
How old are they?

Father's age is $3y$.
So, mother's age is $3y - 2$.
$y + 3y + 3y - 2 = 103$
$\quad\quad 7y - 2 = 103$
$\quad\quad\quad\, 7y = 105$
$\quad\quad\quad\quad y = 15$
The girl is 15, the father is 45, and the mother is 43.

Quadratic equations by trial and improvement

Solve $x^2 + 3x = 57$ to 1 decimal place.

Trials	Calculation	Size
Try $x = 6$	$6^2 + 3 \times 6 = 54$	Too small
Try $x = 7$	$7^2 + 3 \times 7 = 70$	Too big
Try $x = 6.5$	$6.5^2 + 3 \times 6.5 = 61.75$	Too big
Try $x = 6.2$	$6.2^2 + 3 \times 6.2 = 57.04$	Too big
Try $x = 6.1$	$6.1^2 + 3 \times 6.1 = 55.51$	Too small

The answer is between 6.2 and 6.1, so try 6.15.
$6.15^2 + 3 \times 6.15 = 56.2725$ which is too small.
So, the answer is between 6.15 and 6.2.
So, the answer is 6.2, correct to 1 decimal place.

14

GEOMETRY

This chapter is about:

- accurate drawing
- solid shapes and nets, including symmetry
- triangles, including the exterior angle theorem
- congruence
- locus
- ruler and compass constructions.

Accurate drawing

DISCUSSION POINT

- Check that you know how to use a protractor to draw angles and to measure angles. Make sure that you know the difference between an angle of 70° and an angle of 110°, for example.
- How would you use a pair of compasses to construct a triangle with sides of length 10 cm, 7 cm and 6 cm?
- Can you construct a triangle ABC in which AB is 7 cm, ∠ABC is 50° and AC is 5.5 cm?
  There are two different triangles you can draw.
  Can you find them both?

EXERCISE 1

▷ Compasses
▷ Protractor

Drawing a rough sketch, before starting your accurate drawing, may help you.

1 Draw accurately a triangle in which one side is 6 cm, one side is 5 cm and one side is 7 cm. Measure the three angles of the triangle.

2 Draw accurately a triangle in which one side is 8 cm and the other two sides are 5 cm. Measure the three angles of the triangle.

3 Draw accurately a triangle ABC in which AB is 6.4 cm, ∠A is 50° and ∠B is 70°. Measure the length of side BC.

4 Draw a triangle DEF in which side DE is 8 cm, side EF is 6 cm and ∠E is 27°. Measure ∠D and ∠F.

5 Draw a triangle JKL in which side JK is 5 cm, ∠K is 110° and side JL is 9 cm. Measure the length of side KL.

6 In a triangle PQR, PQ is 10 cm, ∠PQR is 40° and PR is 8 cm.

This describes two different triangles. Draw both of them.
For each of your triangles measure ∠PRQ.

7 A parallelogram has two sides of length 6 cm and two sides of length 4.5 cm. The length of one of its diagonals is 7 cm. Draw the parallelogram accurately. Measure the length of its other diagonal.

8 In a trapezium WXYZ, side WX is parallel to side ZY. WX is 9 cm, XY is 7 cm and YZ is 6 cm. ∠WXY is 70°.

Draw the trapezium accurately. Measure the lengths of its diagonals.

Solid shapes and nets

Solid shapes can be made from nets.
Here are two possible nets of a cube.

This is *not* the net of a cube.

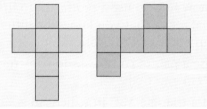
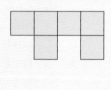

► Resource Sheet A: *Isometric dot*

A shape made of squares joined exactly edge to edge is called a **polyomino.**

EXERCISE 2

1 Here are two different pentominoes.

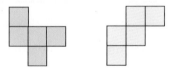

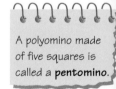

A polyomino made of five squares is called a **pentomino.**

(a) Draw all the different pentominoes (including the ones shown). Be sure that you have found them all.

(b) Describe the symmetry of each of the pentominoes.
Mark any lines of symmetry on your drawings.
State the order of rotational symmetry for each pentomino.

2 Which pentominoes are nets of a square box (a cube with one of its faces removed)?

3 Which of these hexominoes is a net of a cube?

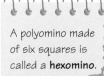

A polyomino made of six squares is called a **hexomino**.

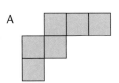

A

B

4 (a) Draw *all* the hexominoes which are nets of a cube.
Explain how you know you have found them all.

(b) Describe the symmetry of each of your nets.
Mark any lines of symmetry on your drawings.
State the order of rotational symmetry for each hexomino.

5 Here are three nets for a cube.

A

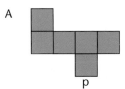

p

B

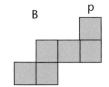

p

C

p

(a) Copy each of these diagrams.

(b) Imagine each net being made up into a cube.
Which edge does the edge labelled *p* join to?
Label this edge *q* on each of the nets you have drawn.

6 (a) Describe in words what a regular tetrahedron is.

(b) Which of these are nets of a regular tetrahedron?

A

B

C

A regular tetrahedron

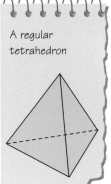

7 A cuboid has sides of length 2 cm, 3 cm and 4 cm.
Draw a net for this cuboid.

8 Which of these statements are possible for a cuboid?

A: None of its faces is a square.

B: One of its faces is a square.

C: Two of its faces are squares.

D: Three of its faces are squares.

E: Four of its faces are squares.

F: Five of its faces are squares.

G: Six of its faces are squares.

9 Some of the faces of a cuboid are squares with area 1 cm². Some of the faces are rectangles with area 2 cm².

(a) Draw a rough sketch of the cuboid.

(b) Draw two different nets of this cuboid.

10 Which of these is the net of a cuboid?

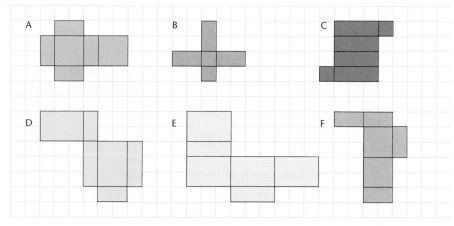

Nelson GCSE Maths   GEOMETRY (INTERMEDIATE)

11 (a) Describe in words what a regular octahedron is.

(b) Which of these is a net of a regular octahedron?

A shape made of equilateral triangles joined exactly edge to edge is called a **polyiamond**.

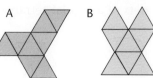

A regular octahedron

12 Draw all the octiamonds which are nets of a regular octahedron.

An **octiamond** is a polyiamond made from eight triangles.

Models with symmetry

These pictures show a net and an isometric drawing of a cube model made of five cubes.

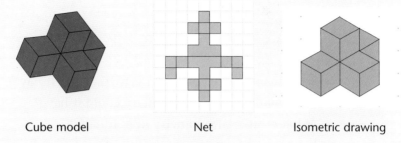

Cube model	Net	Isometric drawing

Some cube models have **mirror symmetry**.

The blue half of this model is the mirror image of the red half.

Some cube models have **rotational symmetry** about an **axis of symmetry**.

The **order** of rotational symmetry is the number of positions in which the solid looks the same when you rotate it.

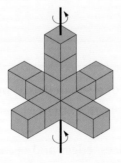

This model has rotational symmetry of order 4 about its axis of symmetry.

DISCUSSION POINT

Discuss what a triangular prism is.

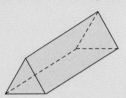 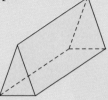 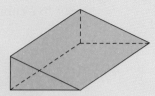

- How many faces, edges and vertices could it have?
- How many planes of symmetry could it have?
- What rotational symmetry does it have?

What is a regular hexagonal pyramid?

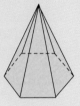

- How many faces, edges and vertices does it have?
- How many planes of symmetry does it have?
- What rotational symmetry does it have?

None of the faces of this cuboid is square.

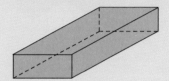

- How many faces, edges and vertices does this cuboid have?
- How many planes of symmetry does it have?
- What rotational symmetry does it have?

EXERCISE 3

1 Here is a picture of a square-based pyramid.

(a) Draw accurately *two* different nets for this pyramid.

(b) How many faces, edges and vertices does this pyramid have?

(c) How many planes of symmetry does it have?

(d) Where is its axis of symmetry?
What is the order of its rotational symmetry?

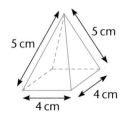

Resource Sheet A:
Isometric dot
Resource Sheet M:
Nets of halves
Cubes
Scissors

2 Here is a net for a solid.

   (a) Draw a rough sketch of the solid. Name the solid.
   (b) How many faces, edges and vertices does this solid have?
   (c) How many planes of symmetry does it have?
   (d) Where is its axis of symmetry?
       What is the order of its rotational symmetry?

3 Here is a net for a solid.

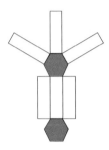

   (a) Draw a rough sketch of the solid. Name the solid.
   (b) How many faces, edges and vertices does this solid have?
   (c) How many planes of symmetry does it have?
   (d) How many axes of symmetry does it have? Where are these axes?
       What is the order of its rotational symmetry about each of these axes?

4 A solid has six faces.
   Four are rectangles and two are trapeziums.
   (a) Draw a rough sketch of what this solid might look like.
   (b) Draw a sketch of a possible net for this solid.
   (c) How many faces, edges and vertices does this solid have?

5 A solid has seven faces.
   Five of the faces are isosceles trapeziums and two faces are regular
   pentagons.
   (a) Draw a rough sketch of what this solid might look like.
   (b) Draw a sketch of a possible net for this solid.
   (c) How many faces, edges and vertices does this solid have?

6 In Questions 1 to 5, you were asked to find the number of faces, edges and vertices of different solids.

(a) Copy and complete this table to summarise your results.

Question number	Number of faces (F)	Number of edges (E)	Number of vertices (V)	V + F − E
1	5	8	5	2
2	6			
3				
4				
5				

(b) What do you notice about the numbers in the last column? Is this true for a cylinder?

7 Here is a picture of a triangular prism.
All the faces of this prism are regular polygons.

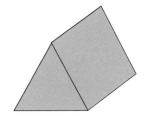

(a) How many square faces are there?

(b) How many equilateral triangular faces are there?

(c) Draw three different nets for this shape.

For Questions 8–11, you may find it helpful to cut out your nets to see if they are correct.

8 Here is a picture of a cube model.

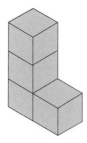

(a) How many cubes are there in the model?

(b) Make the model from cubes.

(c) Describe the symmetry of the model.

(d) Make an isometric drawing of the model.

(e) Draw a net for the model using squared paper.

9 (a) Use four cubes to make a model (not a cuboid), different from the one in Question 8.

(b) Draw a rough sketch of your model.

(c) Make an isometric drawing of your model.

(d) Draw a net for your model.

10 Here is an isometric drawing of a cube model made from five cubes.

(**a**) Make the model from cubes.

(**b**) Describe the symmetry of the model.

(**c**) Draw a net for the model.

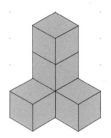

11 Here is an isometric drawing of a cube model.

(**a**) What is the smallest number of cubes the model could have?

(**b**) What is the largest number of cubes the model could have?

(**c**) Make the model with the smallest number of cubes.

(**d**) Draw a net of the model you have made.

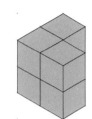

12 Here is the net of a cube model.

(**a**) Make the model from cubes.

(**b**) Make an isometric drawing of the model.

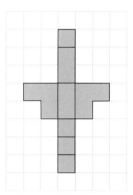

13 Here are the nets of three solids.

A 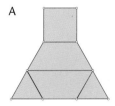   B 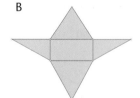   C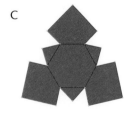

One of the solids is half of a regular tetrahedron, one is half of a cube and one is half of a square-based pyramid.

(**a**) Without making the solids, try to decide which net gives half of which solid.

(**b**) Use the Resource Sheet M: *'Nets of halves'* to make the solids and check your answers to part (a).

Explore some of the ideas introduced in Exercises 2 and 3.
Here are some starting points.

♦ **Hexominoes**: You could look at all the possible hexominoes and describe their symmetries.

♦ **Four-cube models**: You could look at all the cube models which can be made with four cubes. Describe their symmetries. Draw their nets.

♦ **Nets of cuboids**: You could choose a cuboid of a particular shape and size and find *all* its nets.

Triangles, including the exterior angle theorem

An **exterior angle** of a triangle is an angle made outside the triangle by extending one of the sides.

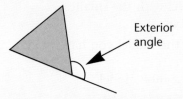

In this tessellation of triangles, all the red angles are equal, all the blue angles are equal, and all the green angles are equal.

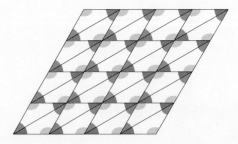

Here is a small part of the tessellation.

From this, you can see that the exterior angle at one vertex of a triangle is equal to the sum of the interior angles at the other two vertices.
This is called the **exterior angle theorem**.

EXERCISE 4

1 Sketch each of these drawings and find the size of the angle labelled *x*.

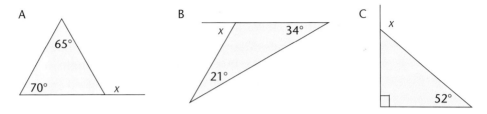

2 Sketch each of these drawings and find the size of the angle labelled *y*.

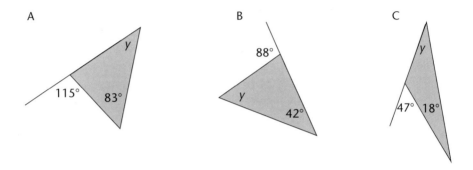

3 Sketch each of these drawings and find the size of the angle labelled *z*. In drawings C and E, AB = BC. In drawing D, ABC is an equilateral triangle.

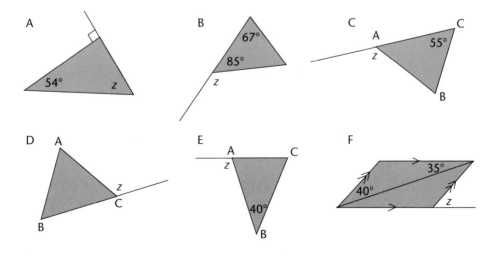

4 A right-angled triangle has an exterior angle of 125°.
What is the size of the smallest angle of the triangle?

5 The exterior angles at two vertices of a triangle are 120° and 140°.
Find the interior angle at the other vertex.

6 (a) An isosceles triangle has an exterior angle of 70°.
Find the equal interior angles of the triangle.
Is there only one answer?

(b) An isosceles triangle has an exterior angle of 140°.
Find the equal interior angles of the triangle.
Is there only one answer?

Congruence

Two triangles are congruent if one fits exactly on to the other.
These two triangles are congruent.

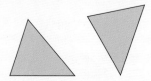

So are these two triangles (you would need to turn one over before it would
fit on to the other).

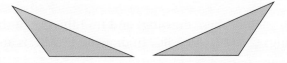

Two **polygons are congruent** if one fits exactly on to the other (after
turning over if necessary).

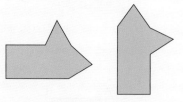

Two **shapes of any kind are congruent** if one fits exactly on to the other
(after turning over if necessary).

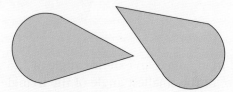

EXERCISE 5

1 Find all pairs of triangles which are congruent.

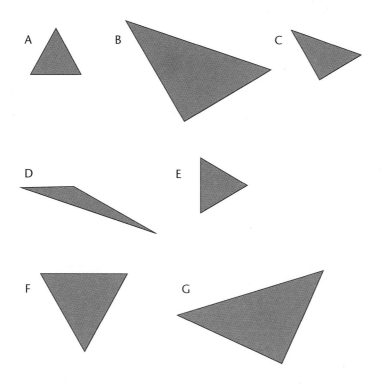

2 Find all pairs of rectangles which are congruent.

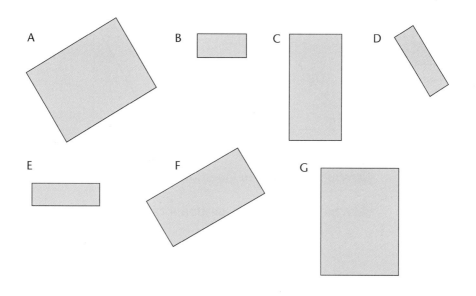

3 Find all pairs of quadrilaterals which are congruent.

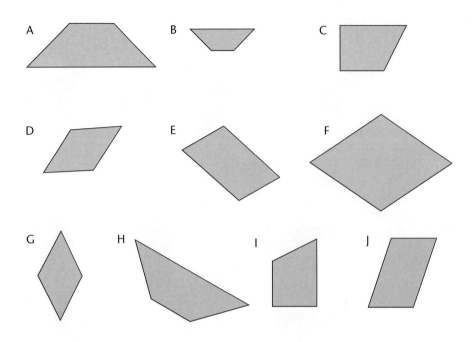

4 Which of these triangles can be cut into two congruent pieces?

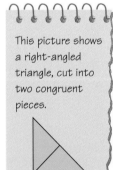

This picture shows a right-angled triangle, cut into two congruent pieces.

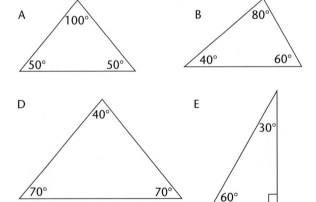

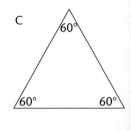

Drawing triangles C and E, on isometric paper, may help.

5 Which triangles in Question 4 can be cut into *three* congruent pieces?

6 Which triangles in Question 4 can be cut into *four* congruent pieces?

7 Which of these shapes can be cut into two congruent pieces?

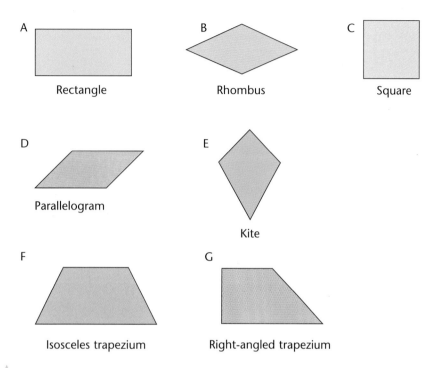

A
Rectangle

B
Rhombus

C
Square

D
Parallelogram

E
Kite

F
Isosceles trapezium

G
Right-angled trapezium

8 Which of the shapes in Question 7 can be cut into *four* congruent pieces?

9 Which of these statements are true?

A: Any shape with line symmetry can be cut into two congruent pieces.

B: Any shape with rotational symmetry of order 2 can be cut into two congruent pieces.

C: Any shape with rotational symmetry can be cut into two congruent pieces.

D: Any shape with rotational symmetry of order 3 can be cut into three congruent pieces.

E: Any shape with two lines of symmetry can be cut into four congruent pieces.

F: Any shape with two lines of symmetry can be cut into eight congruent pieces.

If a statement is true, give several examples and explain how you know where to cut the shape.
If it is not true, give one example to disprove it.

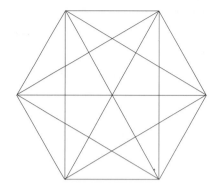

A mystic hexagon is a regular hexagon with all its diagonals drawn.

10 This is a copy of the diagram on Resource Sheet N: *Mystic hexagons*.

(**a**) Into how many pieces is a mystic hexagon divided?

(**b**) Name each of the different pieces using *one* of these:

EQUILATERAL TRIANGLE   ISOSCELES TRIANGLE

RIGHT-ANGLED   TRIANGLE   RHOMBUS   RECTANGLE

SQUARE   KITE   PARALLELOGRAM   TRAPEZIUM

(**c**) Find all the angles of each of the different pieces. Try to do this *without* using a protractor.

(**d**) On your copy of Resource Sheet N: *Mystic hexagons*, draw extra lines on one of the mystic hexagons so that it is divided into pieces, *all* of which are congruent.

(**e**) Use your answer to part (d) to find what fraction of the mystic hexagon each of the pieces you named in part (b) is.

(**f**) Use your answer to part (d) to find what fraction of the mystic hexagon the hexagon in the middle is (the one coloured red in the diagram here).

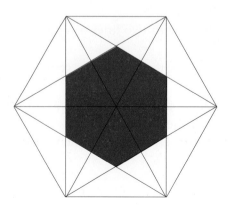

Loci

► Compasses
► Resource Sheet O:
  Loci
► Resource Sheet P:
  Goats

For Questions 1 to
8, you need to use
Resource Sheet O:
Loci

Exercise 6

1 (a) Mark on your copy of Resource Sheet O: *Loci,* two points which are the same distance from point A as from point B.

(b) Draw a line to show *all* the points which are the same distance from A as from B.
This line is called the **locus** of points which are the same distance from A as from B.

2 Draw the locus of points which are 4 cm from C on the resource sheet.

3 Draw the locus of points which are 2 cm from the line *d*.

4 Draw the locus of points which are 1 cm from the circumference of circle E.

5 Draw the locus of points which are 1 cm from the perimeter of square F.

6 Draw the points which are:

(a) 4 cm from point G and 5 cm from point H

(b) 4 cm from point J and 5 cm from point K

(c) 4 cm from point L and 5 cm from point M.

7 Draw the locus of points which are the same distance from line *p* and line *q*.

8 Draw the locus of points which are:

(a) the same distance from line *s* and line *t*

(b) the same distance from point U and point V.

For Question 9,
you will need
squared paper.

9 (a) Copy this design and shade all the points in the square which are nearer to A than to B.

(b) Copy the design again and shade all the points in the square which are nearer to D than to B.

(c) Copy the design again and shade all the points in the square which are nearer to line AB than to line BC.

(d) Copy the design again and shade all the points in the square which are nearer to line AC than to line BD.

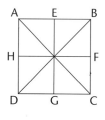

(e) Copy the design again and shade all the points in the square which are closer to H than to F and closer to D than to B.

(f) Copy the design again and shade all the points in the square which are closer to B than to D and closer to E than to G.

For Question 10, you will need Resource Sheet P: Goats.

10 Resource Sheet P: *Goats*, shows a large field in which five goats are tied up.

Goats A, B, C and D are each tied to a different post.

Goat A is tethered to post A, goat B to post B, and so on.

The posts are not shown on the diagram.

The grass each of these goats can reach is shaded.

(**a**) Mark on the diagram, the position of the posts to which goats A, B, C, and D are tethered.

(**b**) A straight footpath runs across the field.

All the points on the path are the same distance from post B as they are from post C.

Draw the path.

(**c**) Goat A becomes aggressive and so the owner needs to shorten the tether so it cannot reach any of the other goats.

By how much should the tether be shortened?

(**d**) Goat E has a tether which is 4m long.

One end of the tether is attached to the goat's collar.

The other end of the tether is a ring which is free to slide up and down a bar fixed between points X and Y.

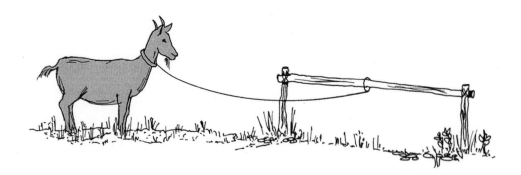

Shade the area of grass which goat E can reach.

COURSEWORK OPPORTUNITY

Goats

You have a field or a garden in which you keep goats.
All the goats are tethered in some way.

Make up a story about the goats which will give you some problems to solve.
Here are some of the decisions you can make in your story.

♦ What is the shape of the field or garden?

♦ How are the goats tethered?
  These pictures show two possibilities.

♦ Are there buildings in the field around which the goats can move?
  These will affect the region of the field which the goats can reach.

♦ Are the goats replacing a lawn mower?
  In other words, is it important that *all* the grass can be reached by at least
  one goat?

The decisions you make will set you problems to solve.

♦ How many goats do you need?

♦ How should they be tethered?

Ruler and compass constructions

DISCUSSION POINT

It is often possible to **construct** lines, points and shapes accurately *without* doing any measuring with a ruler or a protractor.

- You are given two points. Imagine a point which is the same distance from each of these points. Now imagine another.

  Discuss how to use a ruler and compasses to construct the locus of all points which are the same distance from each of these points.

  What is the angle between the locus and the line joining the two points?

- You are given two lines which intersect. Imagine a point which is the same distance from each of these lines. Now imagine another.

  Discuss how to use a ruler and compasses to construct the locus of all points which are the same distance from each of these lines.

  What does this locus do to the angle between the two lines?

- How can you use a ruler and compasses, but no protractor, to draw an angle of 60°?

- How can you use a ruler and compasses, but no protractor, to draw an angle of 90°?

EXERCISE 7

Do not use a protractor for this exercise. Use only a ruler and compasses.

1 (a) Draw two points P and Q, 8 cm apart.

(b) Construct the locus of points which are equidistant from P and Q.

2 Construct a triangle RST in which side RS is 5 cm, side ST is 8 cm and ∠S is 90°. Measure the length of RT.

3 (a) Draw any pair of intersecting lines.

(b) Bisect the acute angles.

(c) Bisect the obtuse angles.

(d) What do you notice?

(e) What is the locus of points which are the same distance from each of two lines?

4 (a) Construct a 60° angle.

(b) Construct a 30° angle by bisecting the 60° angle.

5 (a) Construct a 90° angle.

(b) Construct a 45° angle by bisecting the 90° angle.

6 These sketches of triangles have *not* been drawn accurately.

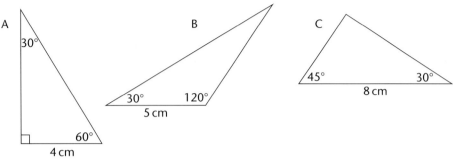

(a) Construct all the triangles accurately.

(b) Measure the lengths of all the sides of the triangles and mark them on your drawings.

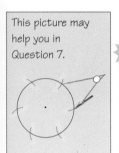

This picture may help you in Question 7.

7 Using a ruler and compasses only, construct a regular hexagon.

8 Using a ruler and compasses only, construct a regular octagon.

Regular octagon

9 (a) Draw this triangle accurately.

    (i) Construct the locus of points which are the same distance from X as from Y.

    (ii) Construct the locus of points which are the same distance from X as from Z.

    (iii) Construct a circle which passes through the points X, Y and Z.

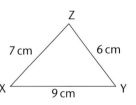

(b) Draw the triangle XYZ again.

    (i) Construct the locus of points which are inside triangle XYZ and the same distance from side XY and from side XZ.

    (ii) Construct the locus of points which are inside triangle XYZ and the same distance from side XZ and from side YZ.

    (iii) Construct a circle which touches (but does not cross) each of the sides of triangle XYZ.

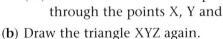

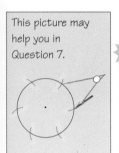

Nelson GCSE Maths   GEOMETRY (INTERMEDIATE)

Solid shapes and nets

This square-based pyramid has 5 faces, 8 edges, and 5 vertices.

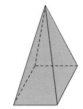

A square-based pyramid

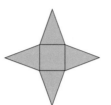

Net of a square-based pyramid

Exterior angle theorem

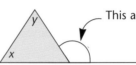

This angle is equal to $x + y$

Congruence: Two shapes are **congruent** if one fits exactly on the other (after turning over if necessary).

Loci

The **locus** of a point that is a constant distance away from a fixed point is a **circle**.

This is the locus of a point that is a constant distance from a line of fixed length.

The locus of a point which is equidistant from two fixed points A and B is the **perpendicular bisector** of the line joining A and B.

The locus of a point which is equidistant from two fixed lines is made up of both **angle bisectors** of the two lines.

REVISION EXERCISES

Do not use a calculator for this exercise, except in Question 29.

1 In the number 372, 3 stands for 300. What does 3 stand for in each of these numbers?
(a) 63 (b) 308 (c) 235 (d) 3475
(e) 30782

2 Find all the factors of each of these numbers.
(a) 40 (b) 41

3 Look at these numbers.
58 49 51 52 37 34 21 55 27 28
Pick out a number which is
(a) even (b) a multiple of 4
(c) a square number (d) a multiple of 9
(e) a prime number (f) a multiple of 13

4 Write down answers for these multiplications.
(a) 2.3×10 (b) 4.731×100 (c) 0.62×1000

5 Write down answers for these divisions.
(a) $56 \div 10$ (b) $3.4 \div 100$ (c) $850 \div 1000$

6 Write down answers for these divisions.
(a) $3400 \div 10$ (b) $0.61 \div 100$ (c) $3.6 \div 1000$

7 Copy and complete these, replacing the ? by a number.
(a) $? \times 1000 = 32.6$ (b) $420 \div ? = 0.42$

8 Arrange these numbers in order of size starting with the smallest.
2.7 0.274 2.69 0.27 2.07 0.265

9 Write down answers for these multiplications.
(a) 0.1×30 (b) 0.3×30 (c) 0.8×30

10 Write down answers for these multiplications.
(a) 0.1×0.3 (b) 0.2×0.3 (c) 0.6×0.3

11 $5 \times 19 = 95$ is correct. Write down answers for
(a) 0.5×19 (b) 0.5×1.9 (c) 0.05×0.19

12 Calculate
(a) $\frac{1}{5}$ of 125 (b) $\frac{3}{5}$ of 125 (c) $\frac{1}{3}$ of 0.48
(d) $\frac{2}{3}$ of 0.48

13 Copy and complete these equivalent fraction pairs, replacing the ? by a number.
(a) $\frac{3}{5} = \frac{?}{15}$ (b) $\frac{3}{4} = \frac{36}{?}$ (c) $\frac{2}{3} = \frac{?}{45}$

14 (a) Write these percentages as decimals.
(i) 20% (ii) 12% (iii) 5%
(b) Now write them as fractions, in their lowest form.

15 Work out 20% of these amounts.
(a) 400 (b) 45 (c) 3.5

16 Work out 15% of these amounts.
(a) 350 (b) 26 (c) 3.8

17 Work out 11% of these amounts.
(a) 630 (b) 49 (c) 3.4

18 (a) Write these fractions as decimals.
(i) $\frac{4}{5}$ (ii) $\frac{5}{8}$ (iii) $\frac{3}{25}$
(b) Now write them as percentages.

19 Write the number that comes halfway between each of these pairs of numbers.
(a) 4.3 and 4.4 (b) 8.6 and 8.7
(c) 18.61 and 18.62 (d) 34.24 and 34.25

20 Round these numbers to two decimal places.
(a) 6.3478 (b) 0.43293

21 Write 634000 and 0.04703 in standard form.

22 Write 3.6×10^6 and 2.71×10^{-3} as ordinary numbers.

23 Calculate these amounts.
(a) 8% of 700 (b) 0.6 of 12
(c) 7% of 84 (d) 0.3 of 8.2

24 Convert these fractions to decimals.
(a) $\frac{6}{25}$ (b) $\frac{7}{8}$ (c) $\frac{3}{20}$

25 Calculate these amounts.
(a) 9% of 6000 (b) 0.4 of 17
(c) 11% of 260 (d) 0.7 of 0.4

26 Round 473.24898 to
(a) the nearest hundred
(b) 3 s.f. (c) 3 d.p.

27 In each of these, replace each star by one of the digits 2, 3 or 5. You can only use each digit once in each sum. Try to make your answers as small as possible.
(a) $** + *$ (b) $** - *$ (c) $** \times *$
(d) $* \times * + *$ (e) $* \times * - *$

28 One of these fractions is not equal to the others. Find the odd one out.
$\frac{8}{20}$ $\frac{400}{1000}$ $\frac{8}{50}$ $\frac{12}{30}$ $\frac{6}{15}$ $\frac{2}{5}$

CCEA 1996

29 A number n, expressed in terms of its prime factors, is $2^6 \times 3^4 \times 11$.
(a) Find the value of n.
(b) Express $8n$ as a product of prime factors.
(c) Find the value of $8n$, giving your answer in standard form.

SEG 1995

1 Find the size of the angle labelled *x* in each of these diagrams.

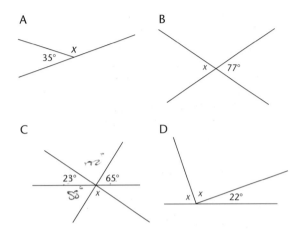

A

B

C

D

2 These isosceles triangles are not drawn accurately. Work out the size of each angle labelled *x*.

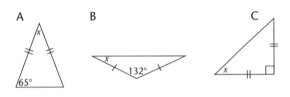

A

B

C

3 Richard is cutting out Christmas decorations. He folds a sheet of paper in half and cuts through both thicknesses.

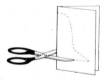

Two of the four Christmas decorations below were cut out by Richard in this way.

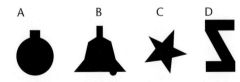

A   B   C   D

Which two shapes could not have been cut out in this way? Explain your answer.

MEG (MEI) 1996

4 (a) Work out the size of the angle marked *a*.

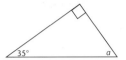

(b) The lines marked with the arrows are parallel. Work out the size of the angles marked *b*, *c* and *d*.

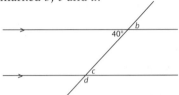

(c) Work out the size of the angle marked *e*.

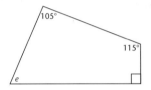

5 AB is a straight line.

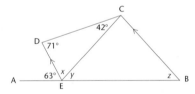

(a) Calculate
  (i) the size of angle *x*
  (ii) the size of angle *y*
(b) ED is parallel to line BC.
  Find the size of angle *z*.

6 Look at this diagram.

(a) Calculate the value of *x*. Explain your answer.
(b) Calculate the value of *y*. Explain your answer.
(c) Calculate the value of *z*. Explain your answer.

7 Sketch and name these shapes.
   (a) A quadrilateral which has exactly one line of symmetry
   (b) A quadrilateral which has four lines of symmetry and rotational symmetry of order 4
   (c) A quadrilateral which has no lines of symmetry and rotational symmetry of order 2

8 ABCDEF is a regular hexagon.

   (a) What type of triangle is FOA?
   (b) Write down the size of the four angles in quadrilateral FODE.
   (c) What type of quadrilateral is FODE?

9 These tiling patterns have been made using regular polygons.

   (i) Work out the size of the angles marked a and b.
   (ii) Explain why a tiling pattern *cannot* be made with only regular pentagons.

   SEG 1996

10 Copy and complete this table for regular polygons.

Number of sides	Exterior angle	Interior angle
15		
	20°	
24		
		170°
	9°	

3: FUNCTIONS AND FORMULAE

1 The rule is 'add 254'. Copy and complete these, using the rule.
   (a) $168 \rightarrow ?$ (b) $382 \rightarrow ?$ (c) $? \rightarrow 1000$
   (d) $? \rightarrow 508$

2 The rule is 'multiply by 23'. Copy and complete these, using the rule.
   (a) $7 \rightarrow ?$ (b) $16 \rightarrow ?$ (c) $37 \rightarrow ?$
   (d) $? \rightarrow 690$ (e) $? \rightarrow 1334$

 3 The rule is 'multiply by 4 and add 7'. Copy and complete these, using the rule.
   (a) $18 \rightarrow ?$ (b) $37 \rightarrow ?$ (c) $? \rightarrow 39$
   (d) $? \rightarrow 343$

 4 Work out these.
   (a) $3 - 6$ (b) $5 - (-4)$ (c) $-7 + 5$
   (d) $-8 + (-4)$ (e) $-13 - (-5)$ (f) $-5 - (-13)$

5 (a) The function is 'multiply by 5'. Write this function using n.
   (b) The function is 'subtract 7'. Write this function using n.
   (c) The function is 'multiply by 4 and then add 3'. Write this function using n.

 6 The function is $n \rightarrow 3n - 5$. Copy and complete these.
   (a) $8 \rightarrow ?$ (b) $27 \rightarrow ?$ (c) $? \rightarrow 100$
   (d) $? \rightarrow 4$

 7 The function is $n \rightarrow 2n^2 - n$. Copy and complete these.
   (a) $7 \rightarrow ?$ (b) $20 \rightarrow ?$ (c) $? \rightarrow 66$
   (d) $? \rightarrow 190$

8 Simplify these expressions.
   (a) $x + x + x$
   (b) $3a + 4b + 5a - 2b$
   (c) $3n - 4 - 2n - 3$
   (d) $x^2 + x + 2x^2 + 3x$
   (e) $5p^2 + 3q^2 - 3p^2 - 2q^2$
   (f) $5a^2 + a + 5 + 3a^3 - 2a^2 - a$

9 (a) The function is $n \rightarrow 4(n - 3)$. Describe this function in words.
   (b) The function is $n \rightarrow 4n - 3$. Describe this function in words.

10 If $x = 4$, $y = 3$ and $z = 2$, find the value of a in each of these equations.
   (a) $a = x + 4y$ (b) $a = 3(x - z)$
   (c) $a = 6(xy - 4z)$ (d) $a = 5xyz^2$
   (e) $a = (x + y)^2$ (f) $a = x^2 + y^2$
   (g) $a = 3y^2 - 2z^2$ (h) $a = (\frac{x}{2z})^2$

11 The temperature inside a fridge is 3°C. The temperature inside a freezer is −18°C.
   (a) How much colder is it inside the freezer than inside the fridge?
   (b) The formula
   $$F = \frac{9c}{5} + 32$$
   is used to convert °C to °F.

   Calculate the temperature inside the freezer in °F.

   SEG 1996

12 The cost of hiring a car can be calculated by using the formula

Cost (£) = $25d + \frac{12(m - 50d)}{100}$

where d is the number of days the car is hired and m is the number of miles the car is driven.

A car is hired for 7 days and driven 476 miles.

Calculate the total cost of the car hire.

SEG 1996

4: WORKING WITH DATA

1 A survey is carried out about two local supermarkets.
  (a) State why this question is not suitable for use in a questionnaire:
   "Do you agree that Toscas is cheaper for shopping than Sensways?"
  (b) Rewrite the question in a suitable form.

2 This table shows the times taken for some students to travel to school.

Minutes	Year 7	Year 8	Year 9	Year 10
20	4	4	4	
25	2	5	3	
30		3	5	4
35		2	1	6

  (a) How many Year 8 students took part in the survey?
  (b) Which time was the mode?
  (c) How many students took longer than 25 minutes to get to school?

3 The number of customers buying drinks in the canteen was recorded on a Wednesday.

Type of drink	Number of customers
Coffee	90
Tea	86
Chocolate	62
Orange juice	78

Draw a bar chart to show this information.

4 Here are the results of a survey of the number of peas in a pod for variety A.

9	5	8	9	10	7	6	8	8
10	8	8	8	9	8	7	8	9
6	7	9	7	9	9	8		

  (a) (i) What is the mode of the number of peas in a pod?
   (ii) What is the median number of peas in a pod?
  (b) This frequency diagram shows the results of a similar survey for another variety of pea plant, variety B.

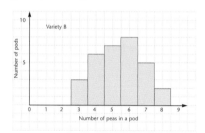

Make two different comparisons between the number of peas in the pods of the two varieties.

5 This table gives times (in seconds) for some men's running events, and the country that they represented.

	USA	Canada	UK	Germany	Italy
100m	9.85	9.84	10.20	10.00	10.30
200m	19.32	20.37	20.50	20.60	20.50
400m	43.29	45.17	44.73	44.91	46.50

  (a) Which country has the fastest time for 100 m?
  (b) Which country has the slowest time for 400 m?
  (c) Copy and complete this bar chart for the times taken to run 200 m.

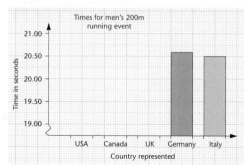

6 Fourteen women work in a local supermarket. This graph shows the distribution of their heights.

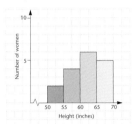

(a) Copy and complete this table for the data.

Height y inches	Number of women
$50 \leq y < 55$	
$55 \leq y < 60$	
$60 \leq y < 65$	
$65 \leq y < 70$	

(b) Calculate an estimate for the mean height of these women.

7 Thirty–seven girls were asked how much time they spent at a computer in one week. The results are shown in this grouped frequency table.

Time t hours	Frequency
$0 \leq t < 5$	4
$5 \leq t < 10$	6
$10 \leq t < 15$	11
$15 \leq t < 20$	12
$20 \leq t < 25$	4

(a) Calculate an estimate for the mean of these times.
(b) What is the modal group?
(c) Copy these axes and draw a histogram to illustrate the information.

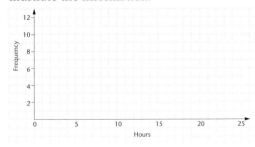

(d) A group of 40 boys were asked the same question.
Their mean was 10.6 hours.
Their range was 34 hours.
Describe two differences in the use of computers between the girls and the boys.

8 Elizabeth timed how long it took each member of three technology groups from Year 9 to solve her maze puzzle.
The results are shown in this grouped frequency table.

Time (secs)	Number of pupils
145–149	0
150–154	2
155–159	11
160–164	10
165–169	19
170–174	5
175–179	0

(a) Calculate an estimate of the mean time taken by the Year 9 students.
(b) Elizabeth timed three groups from Year 11 and the results are shown in this frequency polygon.

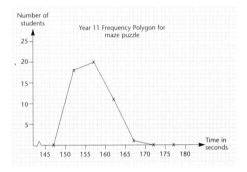

Copy the polygon and, on the same grid, draw a frequency polygon for Year 9.
(c) Write a brief comment comparing the two sets of results.

5: AREA AND PYTHAGORAS' THEOREM

1 Find the areas of these triangles.

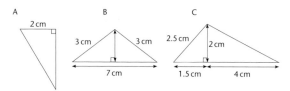

2 Copy and complete this table for four triangles A–D.

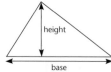

	Base of triangle (cm)	Height of triangle (cm)	Area of triangle (cm²)
A	5		20
B		6	42
C	6		15
D		8	36

3 Find the length of the third side in each of these triangles.

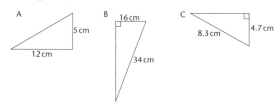

4 (a) Plot the points (–2, 3) and (4, 0).
   (b) Calculate the distance between these two points.

5 One side of a rectangle joins the points (1, 1) and (1, –3).
   The area of the rectangle is 12 squares.
   (a) Draw the two possible positions for the rectangle.
   (b) For each position of the rectangle, write down the coordinates of the other two corners.
   (c) Calculate the length of one of the diagonals of each rectangle.

6 Find the area of an equilateral triangle with sides of length 10 cm.

7 The diagonals of a square are of length 16 cm. Find the length of one side of the square.

8 This diagram shows two shapes, a parallelogram and a trapezium.
Both have the same area.

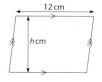 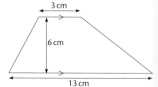

Find the height of the parallelogram marked h on the diagram.

9 The framework of a toy kite consists of two thin rods AB and CD which cross at X. AB bisects CD and is perpendicular to CD.
CD = 120 cm and AX = 11 cm.

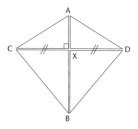

   (a) Calculate the distance AC.
      ACBD, the perimeter of the kite, is a taut string whose length is 296 cm.
   (b) Calculate the length of the rod AB.

CCEA 1996

6: PERCENTAGES

 1 (a) Write $\frac{2}{5}$ as a decimal.
   (b) Write $\frac{1}{8}$ as a percentage.
   (c) Write 2% as a decimal.

 2 Work out these.
   (a) 50% of 38   (b) 20% of 40
   (c) 75% of 60   (d) $33\frac{1}{3}$% of 75

3 Draw a rectangle 5 cm long and 4 cm wide.
   (a) Shade 60% of your rectangle.
   (b) What is the size of the shaded area?
   (c) What is 60% of £20?

 4 Write 80%
   (a) as a fraction   (b) as a decimal

5 Xanthe invests £50 in a building society for one year. The interest rate is 8% per year.
  (a) How much interest, in pounds, does Xanthe earn?
  (b) Kara invest £40 in a different building society. She get £2 interest after one year. Work out the percentage interest rate that Kara earns.

6 Increase £350 by 40%.

7 Decrease 70 by 25%.

8 In 1993, a 'CHOCO EASTER EGG' cost £1.60.
  (a) In 1994, a 'CHOCO EASTER EGG' cost 10% more. How much more did one of these eggs cost in 1994?
  (b) In 1995, a 'CHOCO EASTER EGG' cost £1.90. Calculate the percentage increase in the price of one of these eggs from 1993 to 1995.

SEG 1996

9 In 1990, a charity sold $2\frac{1}{4}$ million lottery tickets at 25p each.

  80% of the money obtained was kept by the charity.
  (a) Calculate the amount of money kept by the charity.

  In 1991, the price of a lottery ticket fell by 20%. Sales of lottery tickets increased by 20%. 80% of the money obtained was kept by the charity.
  (b) Calculate the percentage change in the amount of money kept by the charity.

ULEAC KMP 1996

10 A saleswoman earned £8500 for the year ending December 1995. Each year, she was given a wage rise of 4%. How much did she earn for the year ending December 1998?

7: CUBES AND SEQUENCES

1 The rule to work out the next term of a sequence is to add the previous two terms together. The first five terms of this sequence are 3, 3, 6, 9, and 15.

  Write down the next three terms in this sequence.

2 For each of these sequences, work out the next term and the nth term.
  (a) 7, 14, 21, 28, 35, ... (b) $\frac{1}{2}, \frac{1}{3}, \frac{1}{4}, \frac{1}{5}, \frac{1}{6}$, ...

  (c) 1, 4, 9, 16, 25, ... (d) 4, 7, 12, 19, 28, ...

  (e) 1, 8, 27, 64, 125, ... (f) $\frac{1}{2}, \frac{2}{3}, \frac{3}{4}, \frac{4}{5}, \frac{5}{6}$, ...

3 On this piece of bunting, there are three light flags between every pair of dark flags. All flags are numbered in order.

The first dark flag is number 1, the second dark flag is number 5 and so on.

  (a) Copy and complete this table by filling in the numbers of the dark flags.

Dark flag	1st	2nd	3rd	4th	5th	10th
Flag number	1	5				

  (b) Find an expression for the number of the nth dark flag.

NEAB 1995

4 The rule for a sequence is 'add the digits and square the result'. The first three terms in this sequence are 38, 121 and 16.

  $38 \Rightarrow 3 + 8 = 11 \Rightarrow 11^2 = 121$

  $121 \Rightarrow 1 + 2 + 1 = 4 \Rightarrow 4^2 = 16$

  (a) What are the next five terms in this sequence?
  (b) What happens if you start with 100?
  (c) What happens if you start with 9?

5 Patterns of hexagons are made using matchsticks.
The first three patterns are drawn.

Pattern 1   Pattern 2   Pattern 3

  (a) Copy and complete this table.

Pattern (p)	1	2	3	4
Number of sticks (n)	6			

  (b) A pattern has 36 sticks. What is the number of this pattern?
  (c) (i) How many sticks are needed to make Pattern 100?
    (ii) Write down a rule for finding the number of sticks used in Pattern p.

SEG 1996

6 Look at this flowchart.

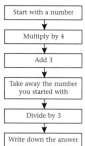

(a) What number do you finish with if you start with 8?
(b) Use algebra to show that the end number is always 1 more than the starting number.

7 Here is a sequence of shapes made from matchsticks.

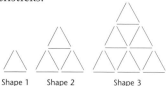

Shape 1   Shape 2   Shape 3

(a) Draw the next pattern in this sequence.
(b) How many matchsticks are there in the third shape?
(c) How many small triangles are there in each of the first four shapes?
(d) How many small triangles are there in the nth shape?
(e) How many small triangles will there be in the tenth shape?

8 This diagram shows the first three pictures in a sequence.

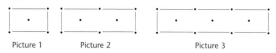

Picture 1   Picture 2   Picture 3

(a) Copy and complete this table.

Picture (n)	1	2	3	4	5
Number of dots (d)	5	8	11		
Number of lines (l)	4	6	8		

(b) Write down a formula which can be used to calculate the number of lines (l) in terms of the picture number (n).
(c) Write down a formula which can be used to calculate the number of dots in terms of the picture number.

9 To investigate the sequence 5, 6, 9, 14, 21, ... you need to find two rows of differences. Copy this difference table and fill in the three missing gaps.

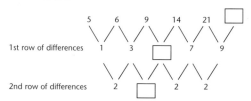

8: RATE AND RATIO

1 Simplify these ratios as much as possible.

(a) 4:8   (b) 9:12   (c) 15:9   (d) 18:30

2 Write these as ratios in their simplest form.
(a) 25p, 80p   (b) 600 g, 225 g   (c) £1, 40p
(d) 30 cm, 1.5 m   (e) 2.5 kg, 250 g

3 A car travels at an average speed of 30 m.p.h.

(a) How far would it travel in
(i) 4 hours?   (ii) $2\frac{1}{2}$ hours?
(iii) 20 mins?   (iv) 5 mins?
(b) How long would it take to travel
(i) 150 miles?   (ii) 45 miles?
(iii) 1 mile?

4 A recipe for a cake includes:

400 g self-raising flour
200 g soft brown sugar
360 g mixed dried fruit
240 g soft margarine.

(a) When I make a larger cake, I use 300 g brown sugar. How many grams of flour do I need?
(b) When I make a smaller cake, I use 100 g margarine. How many grams of dried fruit do I need?

5 Mortar is made by mixing 4 parts by weight of sand with 1 part by weight of cement.

How much sand is needed to make 800kg of mortar?

6 To make an orange drink, orange squash is mixed with water in the ratio 2:7.
  (**a**) How much water is mixed with 80 ml of orange squash?
  (**b**) How much orange drink can you make with 1 litre of orange squash?
  (**c**) How much orange squash do you need to make up 450 ml of orange drink?

7 These are the ingredients for a recipe for a marshmallow cake to serve 12 people:

300 g marshmallow
240 g biscuit crumbs
80 g butter
120 g cocoa powder
100 g castor sugar

  (**a**) Calculate the amount of biscuit crumbs required to make a cake for 8 people.
  (**b**) Calculate the amount of marshmallow needed to make a cake for 30 people.
  (**c**) Write the ratio of weight of marshmallow to biscuit crumbs in its simplest terms.

8 Two teachers are talking about a school visit.

  Teacher A: My group went to the Tower of London.
  We had 40 people and the total cost was £70.

  Teacher B: There are 45 in my group.
  I wonder how much that will cost?

  Calculate the cost of the visit for B's group.

9 A bag contains five black counters and three white counters.

  (**a**) A second bag contains 40 counters, and has the same ratio of black counters to white counters.
  How many white counters are there in this second bag?
  (**b**) A third bag contains black counters and white counters in the same ratio.
  This time there are 20 black counters.
  How many counters are there altogether in the bag?
  (**c**) What is the percentage of white counters in these bags?

1 Use your calculator to find the sine of each of these angles. Give your answers correct to 4 d.p.
  (**a**) 37°   (**b**) 54.8°   (**c**) 8.2°   (**d**) 78.3°

2 Use your calculator to find the angles whose cosines have these values.
  Give your answers correct to 1 d.p.
  (**a**) 0.4493 (**b**) 0.7125   (**c**) 0.6293   (**d**) 0.0872

3 Use your calculator to find the angles whose tangents have these values.
  Give your answers correct to 1 d.p.
  (**a**) 0.6235 (**b**) 1.4926   (**c**) 1.8807   (**d**) 0.3249

4 Look at this diagram.

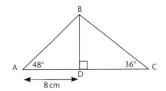

Calculate
  (**a**) the length of BD   (**b**) the length of BC

5 When an aeroplane takes off, its ascent is in two stages. These two stages are shown in the diagram below as AB and BC.

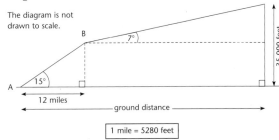

The diagram is not drawn to scale.

1 mile = 5280 feet

  (**a**) In the first stage, the aeroplane climbs at an angle of 15º to the horizontal.
  Calculate the height it has reached when it has covered a ground distance of 12 miles.
  Give your answer correct to the nearest thousand feet.
  (**b**) In the second stage, the aeroplane climbs at an angle of 7° to the horizontal.
  At the end of its ascent, it has reached a height of 35 000 feet above the ground.
  Calculate the total ground distance it has covered.
  Give your answer in miles, to a reasonable degree of accuracy.

NEAB 1995

Nelson GCSE Maths Revision

6 This diagram shows the roof of a small house.

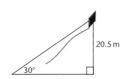

Find the height of R above the tops of the walls A and C.

7 A kite flies at a height of 20.5 m. The string makes an angle of 30° with the ground.

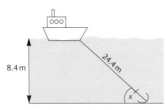

How long is the string?

8 Calculate angle x.

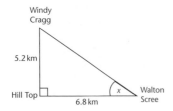

9 The diagram shows three places, which are on the same horizontal plane.

Windy Cragg is 5.2 km due North of Hill Top. Walton Scree is 6.8 km due East of Hill Top.
(a) Calculate the distance from Walton Scree to Windy Cragg. Give your answer correct to 1 decimal place.
(b) Calculate the size of the angle marked *x* in the diagram. Give your answer correct to 1 decimal place.

ULEAC 1995

10 Calculate the bearing of C from A.

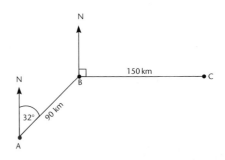

10: PROBABILITY

1 Work out these.
(a) $\frac{1}{2} + \frac{1}{4}$ (b) $\frac{1}{5} + \frac{3}{5}$ (c) $\frac{1}{4} + \frac{3}{8}$

(d) $\frac{5}{12} + \frac{1}{3}$ (e) $\frac{4}{9} + \frac{1}{12}$

2 Work out these.
(a) $1 - \frac{1}{4}$ (b) $\frac{1}{2} - \frac{1}{4}$ (c) $\frac{3}{10} - \frac{1}{5}$

(d) $\frac{5}{12} - \frac{1}{4}$ (e) $\frac{5}{9} - \frac{5}{12}$

3 Work out these.
(a) $\frac{3}{4} \times \frac{1}{2}$ (b) $\frac{2}{3} \times \frac{1}{2}$ (c) $\frac{1}{6} \times \frac{3}{4}$

(d) $\frac{1}{6} \times \frac{2}{9}$ (e) $\frac{5}{6} \times \frac{4}{5} \times \frac{3}{4}$

4 Connor and Georgia are brother and sister. Say whether you agree or do not agree with each of the following things they say. Give a reason for your answer each time.
(a) Georgia has bought a box of chocolates for her mother. There are 3 white chocolates and 5 milk chocolates in the box.
Georgia: "If Mother chooses a chocolate at random, the probability that it will be white is $\frac{3}{5}$."
(b) Storm clouds grew overhead.
Connor: "The probability that it will rain in the next five minutes is $\frac{7}{6}$."
(c) Every evening Connor and Georgia spin a coin to see who does the washing up. Georgia has won on the last four evenings.
Georgia: "The probability that I will win tonight is $\frac{1}{32}$."
(d) There is a biscuit tin on the table. It contains only chocolate biscuits, shortbread biscuits and ginger biscuits.
Connor: "If one biscuit is taken out at random, the probability that it will be a chocolate biscuit is $\frac{1}{3}$."

NEAB 1996

5 Martina is conducting a series of tests on a biased coin. She does five tests.
In each test, she throws the coin ten times and counts the number of heads.
This table shows the results of the five tests.

1st 10 throws	2nd 10 throws	3rd 10 throws	4th 10 throws	5th 10 throws
6 heads	7 heads	9 heads	8 heads	6 heads

Martina then calculates the proportion of heads throughout her tests.
She sets out her calculations like this.

	Number of heads	Proportion of heads
1st 10 throws	6	$\frac{6}{10} = 0.6$
1st 20 throws	6 + 7 = 13	$\frac{13}{20} = 0.65$
1st 30 throws	6 + 7 + 9 =	
1st 40 throws		
1st 50 throws		

(a) Copy and complete this table.
(b) Explain what happens to the proportion of heads as the number of throws increases.

6 This table shows the possible outcomes and their probabilities for a game at a fete.

Outcome	Lose	Win 20p	Win 40p	Win 50p
Probability	0.88	0.09	0.02	0.01

(a) A man plays the game once.
What is the probability that he will win 20p or more?
(b) At the fete, the game is played 300 times. Approximately how many times would you expect the player to lose?

7 (a) Bag X contains square counters: 1 red, 3 blue and 5 green.

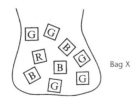

One counter is chosen at random from bag X.
What is the probability that it is
(i) a red counter?
(ii) not a green counter?

(b) Bag Y contains triangular counters: 1 red, 1 blue and 1 green.
Bag Z contains circular counters: 1 red, 1 blue and 1 green.

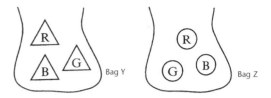

Show all the possible outcomes when two counters are chosen at random, one from bag Y and one from bag Z.

CCEA 1995

8 Mr Evans drives to school each morning.
The probability that he parks his car in the top car park is 0.7.
The probability that he parks his car on the drive is 0.2.
(a) What is the probability that he will park either in the top car park or on the drive tomorrow morning?
(b) In the next 200 school mornings, approximately how many times will Mr Evans *not* park either in the top car park or on the drive?

9 A bag contains 50 balls.
They are coloured red, blue, green or yellow.
They are labelled 1, 2, 3 or 4.

Colour of balls	Labels on balls
25 are red	10 are labelled 1
5 are blue	15 are labelled 2
10 are green	15 are labelled 3
10 are yellow	10 are labelled 4

A ball is chosen at random.
(a) Find, where possible, the probability that
(i) the ball is red or green
(ii) the ball is blue or labelled 2
(iii) the ball is labelled 2 or 3
(b) If you have answered 'not possible' to any of part (a), explain why it is not possible.

10 (a) Helen and Alex play a game using two fair dice.

The first dice has four faces.
The second dice has eight faces.
(i) Copy and complete this table to show the totals they can score.

+	1	2	3	4
1				
2				
3				
4				
5				
6				
7				
8				

(ii) You can start the game if you get
either   the same number on both dice
or   a total score of 9.

What is the probability of Helen starting the game on her first throw?

In a game with different dice, to start the game you need to score a total of either 5 or 8.

The probability of scoring a total of 5 is 0.35.

The probability of scoring a total of 8 is 0.1.

(b) What is the probability that you will start the game on your first throw?
You must show your working.

SEG 1996

11 A garden centre sells large numbers of house plants. Some have flowers and the others do not.
(a) The probability that a plant chosen at random has flowers is 0.7.
Find the probability that the plant does not have flowers.
(b) The probability that any plant costs more than £3 is 0.4.
(i) Copy and complete this probability tree diagram.

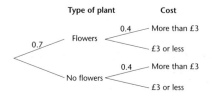

(ii) A plant is chosen at random from the garden centre. Find the probability that it has flowers and costs more than £3.

The garden centre also sells trees.
The probability that any tree is more than 2 metres tall is $\frac{1}{4}$.

(c) Two trees are chosen at random.
(i) Find the probability that they are both more than 2 metres tall.
(ii) Find the probability than one is more than 2 metres tall and the other is 2 metres tall or less.

MEG 1996

11: GRAPHS

1 (a) Find an equation for the straight line on which these points lie.

x	−3	−2	3	4
y	−6	−5	0	1

(b) Find an equation for the straight line on which these points lie.

x	−2	−1	0	3
y	4	2	0	−6

2 Find an equation for the straight line on which these points lie.

x	−2	0	3
y	−1	3	9

3 Find an equation for the straight line on which the points lie for these two graphs.

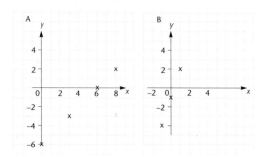

4 Write down the gradient of these lines.
   (a) $y = 4x - 3$ **(b)** $y = -3x + 2$

5 Write down the y intercept for these lines.
   (a) $y = 5x - 1$ **(b)** $y = 5 - 4x$

6 (a) Copy and complete this table for points
   on the line $y = 3x + 8$.

x	-3	-1	2	3
y		5		

   (b) Draw the graph of $y = 3x + 8$ for x
   between -3 and 3.
   (c) Find the gradient of this line.

7 (a) Write the equation $5x + y = 15$ in the form
   $y = ...$
   (b) Write down the gradient of this line.
   (c) Write down the y intercept for this line.

8 Find an equation for the line with gradient 3
   which goes through the point (0, 2).

9 Write down the equation of a line parallel to
   the line $y = 4x - 3$.

10 The equations $x = -2$, $x = 3$ and $y = -1$ fit three
   sides of a square.
   Draw these three lines.
   What are possible equations for the fourth
   side?

11 (a) Draw the graphs of $y = 2x - 4$ and $y = -x^2$
   for values of x from -4 to 4.

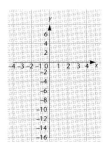

   (b) Use the graphs to find the smallest value of
   x which gives the same value of y in both
   equations.

                                        SEG 1996

12 Look at this graph.

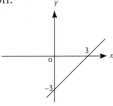

   Which of the following equations could
   represent the graph above?
   (a) $y = 3x$ (b) $y = x - 3$ (c) $y = x + 3$
   (d) $y = -3x$ (e) $y = -x + 3$

                                        CCEA 1996

12: MEASURES

1 Find the circumference and area of each of these
   circles.

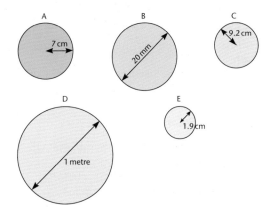

2 Find the volume of these cylinders.

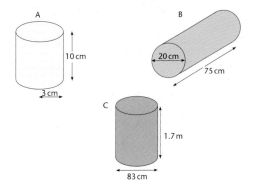

3 James has a scooter. Each wheel has a radius of
   12.5 centimetres.
   (a) What is the circumference of each wheel?
   (b) James travels 50 metres. How many
        complete revolutions does each wheel make?

4 A circular slab is made from concrete and has a thin metal strip around the circumference. The diameter of the circle is 1.7 metres.
   (a) What is the area of the concrete?
   (b) How long is the metal strip?

5 This diagram shows a running track.

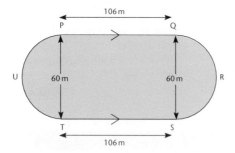

   PQ and TS are parallel and straight.
   PUT and QRS are semi-circular.
   (a) Calculate the perimeter of the track.
   (b) Calculate the total area inside the track.

6 Geoff has some wire netting, 30 metres in length.
   He wants to use the netting to make a run for his rabbits.
   (a) Geoff bends the wire netting into the shape of a square.
      What is the area of the square?
   (b) Instead of a square, Geoff bends the wire netting into a circle.
      (i) What is the radius of this circle?
      (ii) What is the area of this circle?

7 These three shapes are made from mauve card.

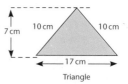

Triangle

Square

Circle

All three shapes have the same *perimeter*.
   (a) **(i)** Write down the perimeter of the triangle.
      (ii) Calculate the area of the triangle.
   (b) Calculate the area of the square.
   (c) **(i)** Show that the radius of the circle is 5.9 cm correct to one decimal place.
      (ii) Calculate the area of the circle.
   (d) Which shape uses the least amount of card?

8 **(a)** A circle has a radius of 28 cm. Calculate its circumference.
   (b) The diagram shows four touching circles.
      Each circle has a radius of 28 cm.
      P, Q, R and S are the centres of the circles.
      PQRS is a square.

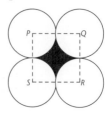

      (i) What is the perimeter of the shaded region?
      (ii) Calculate the area of the shaded region.

NEAB 1996

9 At Booth Outdoor Centre, the water storage tank is a cuboid of dimensions 2 m by 1 m by 1.5 m.

(a) Calculate the volume of the water storage tank.
(b) The mugs used at the Centre are all cylindrical with a radius of 4 cm and a height of 9 cm.

How much water does a full mug hold?
(c) The warden at the Centre claimed that from one full tank, you get over 6000 full mugs of water.
Is the warden correct?
Show all your working.

NEAB 1996

13: EQUATIONS

1 Solve these equations.
(a) $4x + 2 = 26$ (b) $18 + 4x = 8 - x$
(c) $4y - 7 = 20$ (d) $3(x + 5) = 42$

2 Solve these equations.
(a) $5d = 35$ (b) $3g - 4 = 20$
(c) $2y = 9$ (d) $3x + 2 = 11$
(e) $4z - 7 = z + 11$

3 Remove the brackets and simplify these expressions.
(a) $2(t + 3)$ (b) $3(y - 4)$
(c) $20 - 2(y - 3)$ (d) $2 + x(x - 2)$
(e) $2y(y + 3x)$

4 Write down an expression in terms of n and g for the total cost, in pence, of n packets of crisps at 18 pence each and 5 chocolate bars at g pence each.

5 Solve the equation $\frac{1}{2}y + 3 = 2y + 8$.

6 Ceri wants to plant a rectangular lawn with area 40m². The length of the lawn must be twice the width.

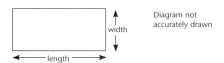

Diagram not accurately drawn

Ceri is trying to find the width by trial and improvement.

She records her results in a table.

Width (m)	Length = 2 x width (m)	Area = length x width (m²)
4	8	32
5		

(a) Copy the table and complete the second row.
(b) Complete the table in order to find two closer estimates of the required width.

ULEAC 1995

7 Use a trial and improvement method to find a solution to the equation $x^2 + x = 85$.
Find the solution correct to 1 decimal place.

8 A rectangle has an area of 30 cm².
One side is of length 4 cm.
The other side is of length $2(x - 3)$ cm.
Write down and solve an equation for x.

9 Trebling a number and then subtracting 4 gives the same result as doubling the number and then adding 10.
Form and solve an equation to find the number.

10 Bunting is used to decorate the sports field. It is made up of coloured flags attached to a rope.

Each flag is an equilateral triangle with sides 20 cm long.

This diagram shows a piece of bunting. It is 130 cm long.

There are gaps *g* cm long between the flags.

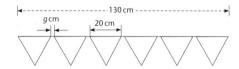

(a) (i) Copy and complete this equation using *g*.
... = 130
   (ii) Solve this equation to find the value of *g*.
(b) A piece of bunting consists of *p* flags with the same gaps as before.
   (i) Write down an expression, using *p*, for the length of the piece of bunting.
   (ii) Find the value of *p*, if the piece of bunting is 878 cm long.

NEAB 1995

14: GEOMETRY

1 Draw accurately a triangle with sides of length 5.5 cm, 4.5 cm and 7.5 cm. Measure the three angles of the triangle.

2 On centimetre-squared paper, draw a net for a cuboid measuring 1 cm by 2 cm by 3 cm.

3 (a) Copy this drawing of a model made from cubes.

(b) Add one cube to the drawing so that the model now has rotational symmetry of order 2.

4 Copy each of these sketches and, for each one, find the size of the angle labelled *x*. (The triangle in sketch E is equilateral.)

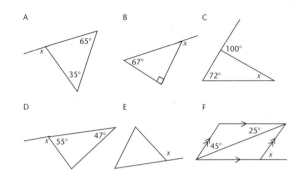

5 (a) Draw a sketch of a triangle that can be cut into two congruent pieces.
   Mark the cutting line on your diagram.
(b) Draw a sketch of a quadrilateral that can be cut into four congruent pieces.
   Mark the cutting lines on your diagram.
(c) Draw a sketch of a shape that cannot be cut into two congruent pieces.

6 These sketches show a square-based pyramid and its net. The sides of the square base and the height AB are all 4 cm.

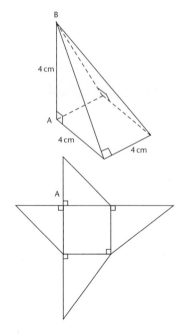

Use ruler and compasses to draw the net accurately.

7 (a) Which pairs of solids fit together to make a cuboid?

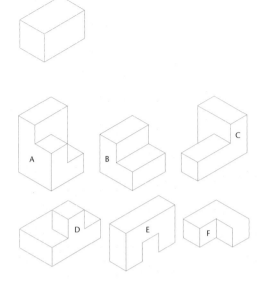

(b) One of the nets A, B or C makes this solid. Which is it?

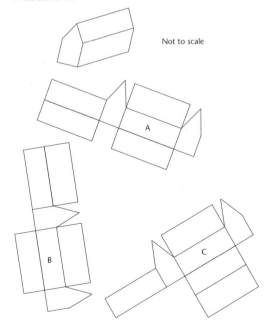

Not to scale

SEG 1996

8 On 1-cm isometric paper, taking 1 cm to represent 1 m, make a drawing of the 3-dimensional shape of the porch.
(Do not draw the plans.)

PLANS FOR A PORCH

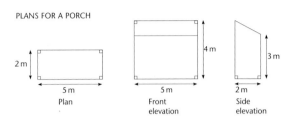

2 m — Plan — 5 m
Front elevation — 5 m — 4 m
Side elevation — 2 m — 3 m

CCEA 1995

9 (a) Draw accurately, a triangle ABC in which BC is 8 cm, AC is 4 cm and AB is 7 cm.

(b) On your triangle

   (i) draw the locus of a point which is the same distance from A as it is from B

   (ii) draw the locus of a point which is 6 cm from C.

(c) P is a point inside the triangle ABC.

   It is nearer to B than it is to A.

   It is less than 6 cm from C.

   Shade the region in which P can lie.

10 This diagram represents a rectangular car park.

There is a light in the corner at A.
The light shines on the car park up to a distance of 30 metres from A.

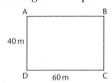

(a) (i) Make a scale drawing of the car park, using a scale of 1 cm to represent 10 m.

   (ii) Shade the part of the diagram which represents the region of the car park lit by the light.

A guard patrols the car park. He comes through a door at corner B. He then walks across the car park, keeping the same distance from the walls AB and BC.

The guard stops 5 metres from wall DC. He then walks to a door in wall AD. He keeps exactly 5 metres from wall DC.

(b) On your scale drawing, draw the path that the guard takes.

ULEAC 1995

SELECTED ANSWERS

1: NUMBERS

Exercise 11 — Page 15

1 $a = 3.43$, $b = 3.49$, $c = 3.56$, $d = 3.63$, $e = 4.71$, $f = 4.78$,
   $g = 4.84$, $h = 4.89$, $i = 13.02$, $j = 13.07$, $k = 13.13$

2 (a) 3.5   (b) 3.5   (c) 4.8   (d) 13.0

3 (a) 3.49, 3.51, 3.53, 3.55   (b) 3.50, 3.53, 3.56, 3.59
   (c) 4.86, 4.91, 4.96, 5.01   (d) 4.79, 4.76, 4.73, 4.70

4 (a) 3.5   (b) 3.5   (c) 3.6   (d) 4.8   (e) 13.1

5 (a) 3.45   (b) 4.75   (c) 4.85   (d) 13.05

6 (a) 4.4   (b) 5.8   (c) 6.7   (d) 9.0   (e) 0.6

7 (a) e.g. 3.48, 3.59, 3.52 ,3.54
   (b) e.g. 4.76, 4.79, 4.81, 4.84

8 (a) $a = 3.624$, $b = 3.629$, $c = 3.633$, $d = 3.641$, $e = 3.646$,
      $f = 3.655$, $g = 3.659$
   (b) (i) 3.62   (ii) 3.63   (iii) 3.64   (iv) 3.65   (v) 3.68
   (c) (i) 3.625   (ii) 3.655   (iii) 4.755

9 (a) 4.73   (b) 14.66 (c) 3.05   (d) 15.73

10 (a) 2.0   (b) 0.1   (c) 0.0   (d) 3.2

11 (a) 2.05   (b) 0.07   (c) 0.04   (d) 3.20

Exercise 12 — Page 16

1 (a) 29 000   (b) 471 000   (c) 4 036 000   (d) 6000   (e) 1000

2 (a) 2 000 000 (b) 2 000 000 (c) 3 000 000 (d) 3 000 000
   (e) 1 000 000

3 (a) 29 000   (b) 5700   (c) 56   (d) 0.041   (e) 0.080

4 (a) 28 600   (b) 5740   (c) 2 340 000   (d) 56.1
   (e) 0.0731   (f) 0.0406   (g) 0.0800

5 (c) and (e)

6 (b)

Exercise 17 — Page 22

1 (a) 5.4   (b) 210   (c) 3.48   (d) 340

2 (a) 303.8   (b) 2.8   (c) 64.5   (d) 1161

3 (a) 7   (b) 1.1375   (c) 16   (d) 11

Exercise 18 — Page 22

1 (a) $\frac{1}{4}$ (b) $\frac{2}{5}$ (c) $\frac{1}{10}$ (d) $\frac{1}{20}$ (e) $\frac{2}{25}$

2 (a) 60%   (b) 64%   (c) 90%   (d) 90%
   Notice that (c) and (d) are equivalent fractions.

3 5% = $\frac{1}{20}$ $\frac{4}{5}$ = 80% = 0.8 $0.28 = \frac{7}{25}$ = 28%

   20% = $\frac{1}{5}$ $0.35 = \frac{7}{20}$ = 35% $\frac{3}{10}$ = 0.3

   8%, 70% and 3% have no equivalents in the list.

4 (b)

Amount	Fraction	Decimal	Percentage	Answer
35	$\frac{2}{5}$	0.4	40%	14
84	$\frac{3}{4}$	0.75	75%	63
150	$\frac{7}{10}$	0.7	70%	105
60	$\frac{2}{3}$	0.666...	$66\frac{2}{3}$%	40
220	$\frac{1}{4}$	0.25	25%	55
200	$\frac{3}{5}$	0.6	60%	120
300	$\frac{7}{10}$	0.15	15%	45

4: WORKING WITH DATA

Exercise 3 — Page 75

1 (a) Cats, 7 million; dogs, 6.5 million; budgies, 1.5 million;
      rabbits, 1 million; hamsters 0.5 million;
      guinea pigs, 0.5 million
   (b) 48
   (c) 41 million

2 (a) 17
   (b) 58

3 (a) 12.5°C   (b) July   (c) January   (d) 13.6°C

5 (a) 5   (b) 20

Exercise 5 — Page 79

1 (a) 6.5
   (b) 6

2 (a) 55.8 kg
   (b) 26 kg

3 A: median 7, range 6
   B: median 23, range 65
   C: median 6, range 9

4 2.4

5 9

6 (a) 34   (b) 4.9   (c) 6

9 (a) 12.9   (b) 12   (c) 13

10 (c) Bands   (d) Films and Shows   (f) Films and Shows

Exercise 6 — Page 82

1 7.6 m

2 6.5 m

3 2.19 children

4 (a) 4 letters
   (b) 4.2 letters

5 (a) 1 person   (b) 1 person   (c) 1.8 people
   (d) Mean shows there is not *always* one person in a car!

6 (b) 249 ÷ 43 = 5.8

Exercise 7   Page 00

1 (b) 174 cm

2 (b) 167 cm

3 (b) 171 cm

  (c) Males' arm spans are significantly more than females: males mean is 3 cm above overall mean, females mean is 4 cm below.

4 (a) Male: 165–170 cm or 170–175 cm; female: 160–165 cm; all: 165–170 cm.

  (b) The modal classes for males, females and all give a lower value than the means, but still indicate the difference between males and females.

5 £101

6 (a) 3.25 kg; modal class is less than 3 kg

  (b) 2.9 kg

7 50

8 £29

9 16.4 secs.

10 (c) 21.1 cm

   (d) 19.0 cm

   (e) Males 21–23 cm; females 17–19 cm.

5: AREA AND PYTHAGORAS' THEOREM

Exercise 2   Page 93

1 A: 4 cm²   B: 4 cm²   C: 6 cm²   D: 8 cm²   E: 10 cm²

2 A: 15 cm²   B: 9 cm²   C: 20 cm²   D: 24.5 cm²

3 A: 1470 cm²   B: 60 cm²   C: 4200 cm²   D: 160 cm²

Exercise 6   Page 100

1 A: 28 cm²   B: 36.3 cm²   C: 26 cm²   D: 98.9 cm²

2 (a) 225 cm²   (b) 64 cm²   (c) 289 cm²   (d) 17 cm²

3 (a) 169 cm²   (b) 144 cm²   (c) 25 cm²   (d) 5 cm²

Exercise 7   Page 102

1 A: 15 cm   B: 21 cm   C: 200 mm   D: 27 cm   E: 76 mm

  F: 410 mm

2 A: 5.1 cm   B: 51 mm   C: 3.4 cm

3 A: 7.1 cm   B: 6.0 cm   C: 23 mm   D: 3.3 cm   E: 2.4 cm

4 (a) 7.8

  (b) 3.6

5 (a) 5.4

  (b) 5.7

6 (a) 5, 5, 4.5

  (b) Isosceles

7 (a) 4.5, 4.5, 3.2, 3.2

  (b) Kite

8 (a) 4.1 cm

  (b) 7.4 cm²

9 28 cm²

10 57 cm

Exercise 8   Page 104

1 5.6m

2 1.2m

3 7.8 miles

4 64m

5 23 cm

6 (a) 8.9 miles or 9 miles

  (b) 12 miles

  (c) Yes, 2 miles (or 2.3 miles)

7 23cm

8 (a) 36 cm²   (b) 90 cm²   (c) 12 cm   (d) 27 cm²

  (e) 10 cm   (f) 16 cm

6: PERCENTAGES

Exercise 5   Page 113

1 A: £8.40   B: £350   C: £66.50   D: £0.98

  E: £1.31   F: £7.88

2 A: £56.40   B: £2350   C: £446.50   D: £6.58

  E: £8.81   F: £52.88

Exercise 6   Page 113

1 330ml

2 (a) 50g   (b) 200g

3 It is fair because you get slightly more than an extra 10%.

4 £25.50

5 The £15 discount is better.

6 (a) 67.8%   (b) 45 g   (c) It is correct to 3 sig.fig.

Exercise 7   Page 115

1 35%

2 47%

3 7%

4 22.2%

5 39%

6 34.6%

7 67%

8 (a) 27%

  (b) £3800

9 12%

10 (a) (i) £4.35   (ii) 33% ($\frac{1}{3}$ reduction)

   (b) (i) 33% ($\frac{1}{3}$ reduction)   (ii) 33%   (iii) 33%

Exercise 8   Page 117

1 95% is more than $\frac{9}{10}$

2 (a) 87%   (b) 87.5%   (c) $\frac{7}{8}$

3 (a) 60%, 67%, 57%, 38%, 64%

  (b) $\frac{3}{8}$, $\frac{4}{7}$, $\frac{3}{5}$, $\frac{7}{11}$, $\frac{2}{3}$

4 Girls are more likely to smoke, with 26% compared with 25% of boys.

5 Skilled = 5.9% unskilled = 7.5%.
Unskilled worker receives highest percentage rise.

6 Women 2%; men 4%.
More men think they should be paid more.

7 (a) 1996
  (b) 1996
  (c) 1995 15.5%; 1996 15.9%.
    Higher percentage in 1996

Exercise 9 Page 119

1 (a) 40, 20. Some students presume if you reduce something by half twice you would have nothing left.
  (b) 10, 5, 2$\frac{1}{2}$, ... You will never reach zero, but you will keep drawing closer to it.

2 (a) £432 (b) £503.88 (c) £103.88

3 About £4690

4 £304.16

5 £79235

6 (a) £610
  (b) Total paid to this bank = £619.36; 22% p.a. is better.

7 4 years

8 (a) £34560
  (b) The manager is unfair.
    An increase of 8% followed by another increase of 6.5% is the same as an increase of 15.02% (1.08×1.065 = 1.1502), and so the salesman should have received his bonus.

9 Increase by 4.72%

10 (a) It gives an overall decrease of 1%
  (b) It makes no difference

Exercise 10 Page 121

1 12

2 60

3 £60

4 400

5 (a) £297.87
  (b) £52.13

6 £26

7 (a) £48
  (b) Swimsuit £18.67, sweatshirt £16, fishing rod £29.33, badminton racket £24, roller skates £45.33, skateboard £32.33

8 (a) 27
  (b) It is quite accurate; the customer has a little more than 33% extra.

9 130

10 (a) 20%
  (b) 16.7%

Exercise 1 Page 142

1 (a)

Margarine	1 kg
Granulated sugar	1 kg
Flour	1 kg
Baking powder	20 g
Cocoa powder	100 g
Coconut	320 g
Oats	320 g
Buttercream	

(b)

Margarine	50g
Granulated sugar	50g
Flour	50g
Baking powder	1g
Cocoa powder	5g
Coconut	16g
Oats	16g
Buttercream	

  (c) (i) 2 kg (ii) 640g (iii) 400
  (d) (i) 15g (ii) 240g (iii) 150
  (e) 5:16
  (f) You do not double the cooking time.
    It takes about the same time to cook any number of biscuits that will fit into the oven.

2 (a) 3:8
  (b) 5:4
  (c)

Margarine	675g
Lard	675g
Flour	1.8kg
Water	600ml
Vinegar	$\frac{3}{4}$ tablespoon
Jam	750g
Roselle cream	750ml

3 (a) 3:2
  (b) 3:2:1
  (c) 12 pink and 6 brown

4 (a) 20:1
  (b) 40

5 7:6

6 (a) 2:3 (b) 7:5 (c) 3:2:5 (d) 4:25
  (e) 12:1 (f) 1:2 (g) 1:100000 (h) 1:3:8

7 A: 8 and 2 B: 34 and 8
  C: 377 and 13 D: 610 and 55

Exercise 2 Page 144

1 250 g jar

2 (a) e.g. In the large box, 50 g cost 13.5p.
    In the small box, 50 g cost 30p.
  (b) If they cannot afford the large box or they may not be able to use all of the large box while the food is still fresh.

3 Both work out to be the same cost per window.

4 The box of 144 is better value.

5 The packet of 40 is the best value.

6 Trick! It depends on whether you prefer Mammoth Bars or Monster Bars.

Exercise 3 — Page 145

1 (a) 1000   (b) 800   (c) 900

2 400

3 28000

4 (a) 882

  (b) This level of accuracy is unreasonable.
Perhaps 900 would be a better estimate, but even this level
of accuracy might not be justified, because relatively few fish
are involved in the sample.

Exercise 4 — Page 147

1 £17.50 and £2.50

2 £12, £4 and £20

3 (a) 12

  (b) $\frac{3}{7}$

  (c) $\frac{4}{7}$

4 (a) 1 litre

  (b) (i) 15 litres   (ii) 5 litres

  (c) $\frac{1}{2}$

  (d) $\frac{1}{3}$

5 (a) Bricklayer = £1950; carpenter = £1560;
plasterer = £780

  (b) $\frac{2}{11}$

6 (a) 2:1   (b) £200   (c) $\frac{2}{3}$

7 (a) 31.5 cm   (b) 110 cm

Exercise 6 — Page 149

1 (a) About 5 miles

  (b) 1:50 000

2 (a) 4 to $4\frac{1}{2}$ miles

  (b) 1:33 333

3 1:2000 000

4 (a) 1:25000   (b) 480 cm   (c) 4 km

5 (a) 1:1000 000   (b) 1:300 000

6 23 cm

7 7320 km

Exercise 8 — Page 154

1 45 miles

2 1.5hrs

3 73.3 m.p.h.

4 2hrs 50mins

5 (a) 90 miles   (b) 225 miles   (c) 22.5 miles

  (d) 15 miles   (e) 75 miles   (f) 142.5 miles

6 (a) 105 miles   (b) 35 miles   (c) 1435 miles

7 (a) 4.2m (b) 0.0042 k.p.h.   (c) 14mins 17secs

8 40 320 k.p.h.

9 3000 000 km

10 (a) 30.6 metres per second

  (b) 13 seconds

  (c) The cheetah would win, 6.6 seconds or 66.8m ahead of
Christie.

11 (a) 25 years   (b) 25 000 years   (c) 0.000 000 005 k.p.h.

12 (a) 48 m.p.h.   (b) 20mins   (c) 26mins 40secs

  (d) 1 hour   (e) 53mins 20secs   (f) 32 m.p.h.

  (g) 38.4 m.p.h., a decrease of 20%

  (h) 64 m.p.h., an increase of $33\frac{1}{3}$ %

9: TRIGONOMETRY

Exercise 8 — Page 164

1 A: 2.9 cm   B: 11.3 cm   C: 16.0 cm

2 A: 19.1 cm   B: 16.0 cm   C: 11.3 cm

3 A: 11.3 cm   B: 64.3 cm   C: 12.6 cm   D: 12.0 cm

Exercise 10 — Page 166

1 A: 10.6 cm   B: 28.3 cm   C: 9.8 cm   D: 5.8 cm   E: 19.2 cm

2 A: 87.1 cm   B: 19.2 cm   C: 9.3 cm   D: 106 cm   E: 16.8 cm

3 A: 10.0 cm   B: 5.8 cm   C: 20.7 cm   D: 70 cm   E: 5.8 cm

Exercise 12 — Page 169

1 A: 66.4°   B: 63.4°   C: 43.2°   D: 44.4°   E: 34.8°

2 A: 82.4°   B: 47.6°   C: 66.3°   D: 44.2°   E: 30°

Exercise 13 — Page 171

1 2.3 m

2 65.2°

3 31.7°

4 6.5°

5 84.6m

Exercise 14 — Page 72

1 (a) 53°

  (b) 37°

2 31.4 m

3 767 m

4 35.5°

5 2.7 m

6 16.6°

7 4.4 m

8 Wire A: 61°; wire B: 51°; wire C: 39.5°; wire D: 30°

9 75 m

10 17.5 m

11 29 m

12 30.2°

13 31°

14 24.6°

15 4.9 m

16 2.7 km

17 36.6 m

18 66.4°

10: PROBABILITY

Exercise 1
Page 176

1 (a) $\frac{3}{4}$ (b) $\frac{1}{4}$

2 (a) $\frac{1}{8}$ (b) $\frac{1}{2}$

3 (a) $\frac{3}{20}$ (b) $\frac{3}{10}$ (c) $\frac{11}{20}$ (d) $\frac{1}{4}$

4 (a) 3 (b) 9 (c) 3 (d) 21

5 (a) 0.06
  (b) E
  (c) (i) 0.42 (ii) 0.39 (iii) 0.52

6 Still $\frac{1}{2}$ (cubes have no memory)

Exercise 4
Page 181

1 (a) 30
  (b) Yes, bound to have variation

2 (a) 2, 0.21 or 21%
  (b) 6, 0.12 or 12%
  (c) $\frac{1}{6}$, 0.167 or 16.7%
  (d) No clear evidence that it is biased

3 (a) 0.4 (b) 0.6 (c) 60
  (d) No; no equally likely outcomes to consider

4 (a) 50% (b) 60%
  (c)

Drops	10	20	30	40	50	60
%	50	60	63	60	56	57

  (e) 57%
  (f) Less variation

5 (a) 11%
  (b) 27 500

6 (a) 0.12, 0.14, 0.17, 0.15, 0.19, 0.23
  (b) Biased dice, about 35 sixes; unbiased dice, about 25 sixes

Exercise 7
Page 186

1 (b) 16
  (c) (i) $\frac{1}{4}$ (ii) $\frac{1}{4}$ (iii) $\frac{1}{2}$

2 (b) 16
  (c) (i) $\frac{1}{8}$ (ii) $\frac{1}{16}$ (iii) $\frac{9}{16}$ (iv) $\frac{1}{4}$

     (v) $\frac{1}{2}$ (vi) $\frac{7}{16}$ (vii) $\frac{3}{8}$ (viii) $\frac{9}{16}$

3 (a) HH, TH, HT, TT

  (b) $\frac{1}{4}$

  (c) $\frac{1}{2}$

4 (b) 36

  (c) (i) $\frac{1}{36}$ (ii) $\frac{3}{36} = \frac{1}{12}$ (iii) $\frac{9}{36} = \frac{1}{4}$ (iv) $\frac{12}{36} = \frac{1}{3}$

     (v) $\frac{6}{36} = \frac{1}{6}$ (vi) $\frac{8}{36} = \frac{2}{9}$ (vii) $\frac{16}{36} = \frac{4}{9}$

5 (b) $\frac{4}{36} = \frac{1}{9}$ (c) 7; $\frac{6}{36} = \frac{1}{6}$

  (d) (i) $\frac{1}{36}$ (ii) 0 (iii) $\frac{6}{36} = \frac{1}{6}$ (iv) $\frac{18}{36} = \frac{1}{2}$

Exercise 8
Page 189

1 (a) $\frac{4}{5}$ (b) $\frac{1}{5}$ (c) $\frac{4}{25}$

2 (a) $\frac{3}{8}$ (b) $\frac{1}{2}$ (c) $\frac{3}{16}$

3 (a) (i) $\frac{4}{5}$ (ii) $\frac{1}{5}$ (iii) $\frac{4}{25}$

  (b) (i) $\frac{3}{20}$ (ii) $\frac{1}{4}$ (iii) $\frac{3}{80}$

  (c) (iii) $\frac{3}{100}$

4 (a) $\frac{1}{2}$ (b) $\frac{1}{4}$ (c) $\frac{1}{8}$

Exercise 9
Page 191

1 (a) (i) $\frac{4}{25}$ (ii) $\frac{4}{25}$ (iii) $\frac{8}{25}$

  (b) (i) $\frac{16}{25}$ (ii) $\frac{1}{25}$ (iii) $\frac{17}{25}$

2 (a) (i) $\frac{6}{100} = \frac{3}{50}$ (ii) $\frac{3}{50}$ (iii) $\frac{3}{25}$

  (b) $\frac{1}{4}$

3 (a) $\frac{1}{2}$ (b) $\frac{1}{4}$ (c) $\frac{1}{8}$ (d) $\frac{1}{4}$ (e) $\frac{1}{4} + \frac{1}{16} = \frac{5}{16}$

4 (a) 0.36
  (b) 0.48

5 (a) $0.4 \times 0.3 + 0.6 \times 0.7 = 0.54$
  (b) $1 - 0.54 = 0.46$ A is more likely to win.

Exercise 10
Page 192

1 (a) $\frac{1}{4}, \frac{1}{4}, \frac{1}{4}, \frac{1}{4}$ (b) $\frac{1}{4}$ (c) $\frac{1}{2}$

2 (a) $\frac{1}{6}, \frac{2}{6}, \frac{1}{6}, \frac{2}{6}$ (b) $\frac{1}{6}$

3 (a) $\frac{1}{36}, \frac{5}{36}, \frac{5}{36}, \frac{25}{36}$ (b) $\frac{1}{36}$ (c) $\frac{5}{36}$

4 $0.7 \times 0.3 + 0.3 \times 0.7 = 0.42$

5 (a) $\frac{6}{25}$ (b) $\frac{17}{25}$

6 (a) $\frac{3}{13}$ (b) $\frac{9}{169}$ (c) $\frac{69}{169}$

7 (a) $\frac{1}{216}, \frac{5}{216}, \frac{5}{216}, \frac{25}{216}, \frac{5}{216}, \frac{25}{216}, \frac{25}{216}, \frac{125}{216}$

  (b) $\frac{15}{216} = \frac{5}{72}$

8 Probability of winning is $\frac{1}{6} \times \frac{2}{6} + \frac{1}{6} \times \frac{5}{6} = \frac{7}{36}$

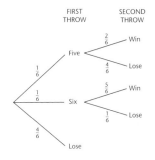

9 (a) $\frac{1}{6} + \frac{5}{36} = \frac{11}{36}$ **(b)** $\frac{1}{6} + \frac{5}{36} + \frac{25}{216} = \frac{91}{216}$

11: GRAPHS

Exercise 5   Page 207

NB These answers are calculated from the appropriate formulae. Students' answers may vary according to the accuracy of their graphs.

1 (b) (i) $64   **(ii)** $136   **(iii)** £40
   (c) 1.6; the number of $ per £
   (d) $p = 1.6d$

2 (a) 25, 100, 125, 150   **(c)** 87.5 m
   (d) 1.6hrs or 1hr 36 mins   **(e)** 50; speed in m.p.h.

3 (a) The same!   **(b)** 95°F
   (e) (0, 32); the temperature of the freezing point of water on the two scales
   (f) 1.8; multiple of e in the equation
   (g) (i) 41°F   **(ii)** 68°F   **(iii)** 23°F   **(iv)** −4°F
   (h) (i) 8.9°C   **(ii)** 15°C   **(iii)** 1.1°C   **(iv)** −20.6°C

4 (a) £120 + 50 × £3 = £270
   (b) $C = 120 + 3n$. Each extra T-shirt costs the same amount.
   (d) £840   **(e)** 176 or 177

5 (b) 53 mm   **(c)** 0.87 mm per g
   (d) $L = 0.87 + 53$

6 (b) 22 g to 24 g   **(c)** 3 g   **(d)** $m = 1.15s − 3.5$

12: MEASURES

Exercise 3   Page 219

1 A: 47.1 cm   B: 69.1 cm   C: 53.4 cm   D: 31.4 cm
2 3.4 cm
3 2.5 cm
4 A: 41 cm   B: 64 cm   C: 139 cm   D: 75 cm

Exercise 4   Page 221

1 A: 314 cm²   B: 661 cm²   C: 113 cm²   D: 573 cm²
2 7850 cm²
3 786 000 m²
4 A: 353 cm²   B: 2060 cm²   C: 124 cm²   D: 79 cm²
5 (b) 24 cm   **(d)** 25.1 cm
6 (a) 9.55 cm   **(b)** 72 cm²
7 676 cm²
8 (a) 625 cm²   **(b)** 525 cm²   **(c)** 796 cm²   **(d)** 600 cm²
   (e) 594cm²

Exercise 6   Page 225

1 A: 60 cm³   B: 84 cm³   C: 48 cm³   D: 84 cm³   E: 48 cm³
2 A: 29 cm³
   B: 340 000 cm³ or 0.34 m³
   C: 78 750 cm³
3 A: 105 cm²   B: 66 cm³   C: 150 cm³   D: 2930 mm³
   E: 76.1 cm³
4 A: 1920 cm³   B: 1260 cm³   C: 576 cm³   D: 2650 cm³
   E: 147 000 cm³ or 0.147 m³

Exercise 7   Page 00

1 A: 200 cm³   B: 8200 cm³   C: 828 000 mm³ or 828 cm³
   D: 4100 cm³   E: 1400 cm³
2 A: 330 cm³   B: 210 cm³   C: 250 cm³   D: 945 cm³   E: 470 cm³
3 (a) 28 cm²   **(b)** 20 cm
4 (a) 8600 mm²   **(b)** 510 000 mm³   **(c)** 510 cm³
5 (a) 180 cm²   **(b)** 1040 cm³   **(c)** 1040 ml
   (d) About right, dimensions inside the container will be smaller.
6 (a) 2700 litres   **(b)** 54 000 cm² or 5.4 m²
   (c) 2760 gallons or 12420 litres

Exercise 8   Page 232

1 A: 62 cm²   B: 30 cm²   C: 40 cm²   D: 6000 cm²
   E: 420 mm²
2 A: 250 cm²   B: 2800 cm²   C: 570 cm²   D: 1900 cm²
   E: 990 cm²
3 A: tomato soup
   (a) 20 cm   **(c)** 200 cm²   **(d)** 33 cm²   **(e)** 270 cm²
   B: evaporated milk
   (a) 20 cm   **(c)** 130 cm²   **(d)** 32 cm²   **(e)** 190 cm²
   C: tuna fish
   (a) 27 cm   **(c)** 120 cm²   **(d)** 57 cm²   **(e)** 230 cm²
   D: fruit cocktail
   (a) 31.7 cm   **(c)** 374 cm²   **(d)** 80.1 cm²   **(e)** 534 cm²
   E: baked beans
   (a) 23 cm   **(c)** 250 cm²   **(d)** 43 cm²   **(e)** 340 cm²
4 A: 180 cm²   B: 240 cm²   C: 160 cm²   D: 21 000 cm² or 2.1 m²
5 (a) Surface area 5.69 m². So not enough paint in the pot.
   (b) 4 pots

INDEX